REAL ANALYSIS

H. L. Royden

Professor of Mathematics

Stanford University

REAL

ANALYSIS

The Macmillan Company, New York

Collier-Macmillan Limited, London

Sixth Printing, 1966

Library of Congress catalog card number: 63–12707

The Macmillan Company, New York
Collier-Macmillan Canada, Ltd., Toronto, Ontario

Printed in the United States of America

To
John Slavens

Preface

This book is the outgrowth of a course at Stanford entitled Theory of Functions of a Real Variable which I have given from time to time during the last ten years. It was designed for first-year graduate students in mathematics and statistics. It presupposes not only a general background in undergraduate mathematics but also specific acquaintance with the material in an undergraduate course in the fundamental concepts of analysis. I have attempted to cover the basic material that every graduate student should know in the classical theory of functions of a real variable and in measure and integration theory, as well as some of the more important and elementary topics in general topology and in normed linear space theory. The treatment of material given here is quite standard in graduate courses of this sort, although Lebesgue measure and Lebesgue integration are done in this book before the general theory of measure and integration. I have found this a happy pedagogical practice, the student first becoming familiar with an important concrete case and then seeing that much of what he has learned can be applied in very general situations.

There is considerable independence among chapters, the chart on page xii giving the essential dependencies. The instructor thus has considerable freedom in arranging the material here into a course according to his taste. Sections which are peripheral to the principal line of argument have been starred. The Prologue to the Student lists some of the notations and conventions and makes some suggestions.

I wish to acknowledge here my indebtedness for helpful suggestions and criticism from numerous students and colleagues. Of the former I should like to mention in particular Peter Loeb, who read the manuscript and whose helpful suggestions improved the clarity of a number of arguments. Of my colleagues particular thanks are due to Herman Rubin, who provided counter examples to many of the theorems the first time I taught the course, and to John Kelley, who read the manuscript, giving helpful advice and making me omit my polemical remarks. (A few have reappeared as footnotes, however.) Finally, my thanks go to Margaret Cline for her patience and skill in transforming illegible copy into a finished typescript and to the editors at Macmillan for their forbearance and encouragement during the ten years in which this book was written.

H. L. R.

Stanford University

Prologue to the Student

This book covers a portion of the material that every graduate student in mathematics must know. For want of a better name I denote the material here by real analysis, by which I mean those parts of modern mathematics which have their roots in the classical theory of functions of a real variable. These include the classical theory of functions of a real variable itself, measure and integration, point-set topology, and the theory of normed linear spaces. This book is accordingly divided into three parts. The first part contains the classical theory of functions, including the classical Banach spaces. The second is devoted to general topology and to the theory of general Banach spaces, and the third to abstract treatments of measure and integration.

Prerequisites. It is assumed that the reader already has some acquaintance with the principal theorems on continuous functions of a real variable and with Riemann integration. No formal use of this knowledge is made here, and Chapter 2 provides (formally) all of the basic theorems required. The material in Chapter 2 is, however, presented in a rather brief fashion and is intended for review and as introduction to the succeeding chapters. The reader to whom this material is not already familiar will find it difficult to follow the presentation here. We also presuppose some acquaintance with the elements of modern algebra as taught in the usual undergraduate course. The definitions and elementary properties of groups and rings are used in some of the peripheral sections, and the basic notions of linear vector spaces are used in Chapter 10. The theory of sets underlies all of the material in this book, and I have sketched in Chapter 1 some of the basic facts from set theory. Since the remainder of the book is full of applications of set theory, the student should become adept at set theoretical arguments as he progresses through the book. I recommend that he first read Chapter 1 lightly and then refer back to it as needed. The books by Halmos [5] [1] and Suppes [17] contain a more thorough treatment of set theory and can be profitably read by the student while he reads this book.

Logical notation. We shall find it convenient to use some abbreviations for logical expressions. We use '&' to mean 'and' so that 'A & B' means 'A and B,' '$\vee$' means 'or' so that '$A \vee B$' means 'A or B (or both),' $\neg$ means 'not' or 'it is not the case that,' so that '$\neg A$' means 'it is not the case that A.' Another important notion is the one that we express by the symbol '$\Rightarrow$.' It has a number of synonyms in English, so that the statement '$A \Rightarrow B$' can be expressed by saying 'if A, then B,' 'A implies B,' 'A only if B,' 'A is sufficient for B,' or 'B is necessary for A.' The statement '$A \Rightarrow B$' is equivalent to each of the statements '$(\neg A) \vee B$' and '$\neg(A \,\&\, (\neg B))$.' We also use the notation '$A \Leftrightarrow B$' to mean '$(A \Rightarrow B) \,\&\, (B \Rightarrow A)$.' English synonyms for '$A \Leftrightarrow B$' are 'A if and only if B,' 'A iff B,' 'A is equivalent to B,' and 'A is necessary and sufficient for B.'

In addition to the preceding symbols we use two further abbreviations: '(x)' to mean 'for all x' or 'for every x,' and '$(\exists x)$' to mean 'there is an x' or 'for some x.' Thus the statement $(x)(\exists y)(x < y)$ says that for every x there is a y which is larger than x. Similarly $(\exists y)(x)(x < y)$ says that there is a y which is larger than every x. Note that these two statements are different: As applied to real numbers, the first is true and the second is false.

Since saying that there is an x such that $A(x)$ means that it is not the case that for every x we have $\neg A(x)$, we see that $(\exists x)\, A(x) \Leftrightarrow \neg (x) \neg A(x)$. Similarly $(x)\, A(x) \Leftrightarrow \neg(\exists x) \neg A(x)$. This rule is often convenient when we wish to express the negation of a complex statement. Thus

$$\begin{aligned} \neg \{(x)(\exists y)(x < y)\} &\Leftrightarrow \neg (x) \quad \neg (y) \quad \neg (x < y) \\ &\Leftrightarrow (\exists x)(y) \quad \neg (x < y) \\ &\Leftrightarrow (\exists x)(y)(y \leqq x) \end{aligned}$$

[1] Numbers in brackets refer to the bibliography, p. 279.

where we have used properties of the real numbers to infer that $\neg(x < y) \Leftrightarrow (y \leqq x)$.

We will sometimes modify the standard logical notation slightly and write $(\epsilon > 0)(\cdots)$, $(\exists\, \delta > 0)(\cdots)$, and $(\exists\, x \in A)(\cdots)$ to mean 'for every ϵ greater than 0 $(\cdots)$,' 'there is a δ greater than 0 such that $(\cdots)$', and 'there is an x in the set A such that $(\cdots)$'. This modification shortens our expressions. For example $(\epsilon > 0)(\cdots)$ would be written in standard notation $(\epsilon)\{(\epsilon > 0) \Rightarrow (\cdots)\}$.

For a thorough discussion of the formal use of this logical symbolism the student should refer to Suppes [16].

Statements and their proofs. Most of the principal statements (theorems, propositions, etc.) in mathematics have the standard form 'if A, then B' or in symbols '$A \Rightarrow B$.' The *contrapositive* of $A \Rightarrow B$ is the statement $(\neg B) \Rightarrow (\neg A)$. It is readily seen that a statement and its contrapositive are equivalent, i.e. if one is true then so is the other. The direct method of proving a theorem of the form '$A \Rightarrow B$' is to start with A, deduce various consequences from it, and end with B. It is sometimes easier to prove a theorem by contraposition, i.e. by starting with $\neg B$ and deriving $\neg A$. A third method of proof is proof by contradiction or *reductio ad absurdum*. we begin with A and $\neg B$ and derive a contradiction. All graduate students should be enjoined in the strongest possible terms to eschew proofs by contradiction for two reasons: First, they are very often fallacious, the contradiction on the final page arising from an erroneous deduction on an earlier page, rather than from the incompatibility of A with $\neg B$. Secondly, even when correct such a proof sheds little, if any, insight into the connection between A and B, whereas both the direct proof and the proof by contraposition construct a chain of argument connecting A with B.

The principal statements in this book are numbered consecutively in each chapter and are variously labeled lemma, proposition, theorem, or corollary. A theorem is a statement of such importance that it should be remembered since it will be used frequently. A proposition is a statement of some interest in its own right but which has less frequent application. A lemma is usually used only for proving propositions and theorems in the same section. References to statements in the same chapter are made by giving the statement number, as Theorem 17. References to statements in another chapter take the form Proposition 3.21, meaning Proposition 21 of Chapter 3. A similar convention is followed with respect to problems. I have tried to restrict the essential use of inter-chapter references to named theorems such as 'the Lebesgue convergence theorem'; the references to numbered statements are mostly auxiliary references which the student should find it unnecessary to consult.

The proof of a theorem, proposition, etc., in this book begins with the word 'proof' and ends with the symbol '❙' which has the meaning of 'this completes the proof.' If a theorem has the form '$A \Leftrightarrow B$', the proof is usually divided into two parts, one, the 'only if' part, proving $A \Rightarrow B$, the other, the 'if' part, proving $B \Rightarrow A$.

Interdependence of the chapters. The dependence of one chapter on the various preceding ones is indicated by the following chart (except for a few peripheral references). Chapter 14 depends on most of the preceding chapters. Chapter 10a indicates Sections 1–4 and 7 of Chapter 10, Chapter 10b denotes Sections 5 and 6 of that chapter.

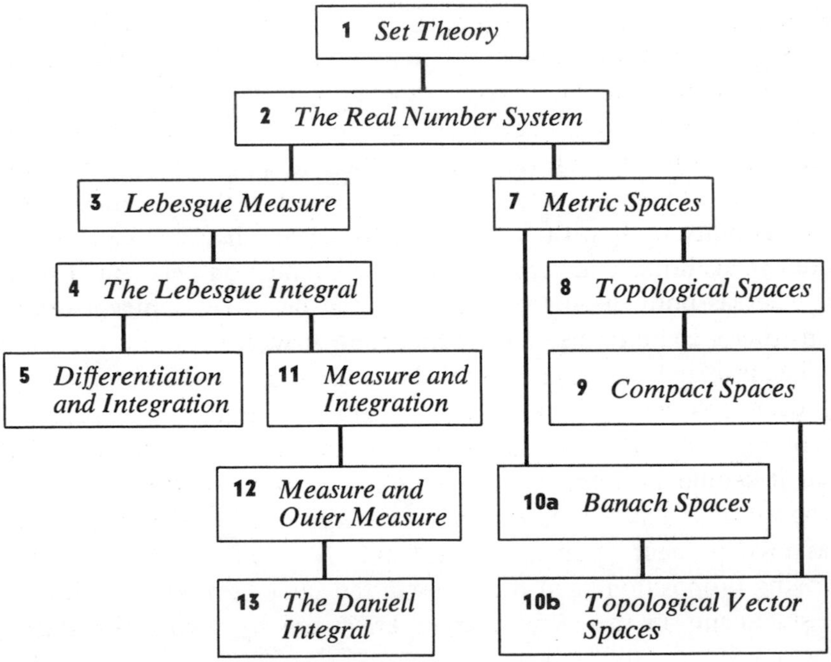

Contents

1 *Set Theory*

1 INTRODUCTION

One of the most important tools in modern mathematics is the theory of sets. The study of sets and their use in the foundations of mathematics was begun just before the turn of the century by Cantor, Frege, Russell, and others, and it appeared that all of mathematics could be based on set theory alone. It is in fact possible to base most of mathematics on set theory, but unfortunately this set theory is not quite as simple and natural as Frege and Russell supposed, since it was soon discovered that a free and uncritical use of set theory leads to contradictions and that set theory had to have a careful development with various devices used to exclude the contradictions. Roughly speaking, the contradictions appear when one uses sets that are "too big," such as trying to speak of a set which contains everything. In our mathematical discussions in this course we shall keep away from these contradictions by always having some set or space X fixed for a given discussion and considering only sets whose elements are elements of X, or sets (collections) whose elements are subsets of X, or sets (families) whose elements are collections of subsets of X, and so forth. In the first few chapters X will usually be the set of real numbers.

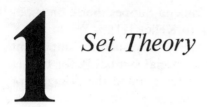

In the present chapter we shall describe some of the notions from set theory which will be useful later. Our purpose is descriptive and the arguments given are directed toward plausibility and (I hope) understanding rather than toward rigorous proof in some fixed basis for set theory. The descriptions and notations given here are for the most part consistent with the set theory described by Halmos in his book *Naive Set Theory* [5], although we assume as known, or primitive, a number of notions such as the natural numbers, the rational numbers, the notion of a function, and so forth, which can be defined (as in Halmos) in terms of the more primitive notions of set theory.

For an axiomatic treatment, I recommend Suppes' book on *Axiomatic Set Theory* [17] or the appendix to Kelley [11].

The natural numbers (positive integers) play such an important role in this book that we introduce the special symbol **N** for the set of natural numbers. We also shall take for granted the principle of mathematical induction and the well-ordering principle. The principle of mathematical induction states that if $P(n)$ is a proposition defined for each n in **N**, then $\{P(1) \,\&\, [P(n) \Rightarrow P(n + 1)]\} \Rightarrow (n)P(n)$. The well-ordering principle asserts that each nonempty subset of **N** has a smallest element.

The basic notions of set theory are those of set and the idea of membership in a set. We express this latter notion by ε, and write '$x \varepsilon A$' for the statement 'x is an element (or member) of A'. A set is completely determined by its members; that is, if two sets A and B have the property that $x \varepsilon A$ if and only if $x \varepsilon B$, then $A = B$. Suppose that each x in a set A is in the set B, that is, $x \varepsilon A \Rightarrow x \varepsilon B$; then we say that A is a subset of B or that A is contained in B and write $A \subset B$. Thus we always have $A \subset A$, and if $A \subset B$ and $B \subset A$ then $B = A$. It is perhaps unfortunate that the English phrase "contained in" is often used to represent both the notions ε and $\subset$, but we shall use it only in the latter context. We write '$x \notin A$' to mean 'not $(x \varepsilon A)$,' that is, that x is not an element of A.

Since a set is determined by its elements, one of the commonest ways of determining a set is by specifying its elements as in the definition: The set A is the set of all elements x in X which have the property P. We abbreviate this by writing

$$A = \{x \varepsilon X: P(x)\},$$

and where the set X is understood we sometimes write[1]

$$A = \{x: P(x)\}.$$

We usually think of a set as having some members, but it turns out to be convenient to consider also a set which has no members. Since a set is determined by its elements, there is only one such set, and

[1] The presence (explicit or implicit) of the qualifying set X is essential. Otherwise we are confronted with the Russell paradox. Cf. Suppes [17], p. 7.

we call it the **empty** set and denote it by $\varnothing$. If A is any set, then each member of $\varnothing$ (there are none) is a member of A, and so $\varnothing \subset A$. Thus the empty set is a subset of every set.

If x, y, z are elements of X, we define the set $\{x\}$ to be the set whose only element is x; the set $\{x, y\}$ to be the set whose elements are exactly x and y; the set $\{x, y, z\}$ to be the set whose elements are x, y, and z, and so forth. The set $\{x\}$ is called a **unit set,** or the **singleton** of x. One should distinguish carefully between x and $\{x\}$. For example, we always have $x \in \{x\}$, while we seldom have $x \in x$.

In $\{x, y\}$ there is no preference given to x over y; that is, $\{x, y\} = \{y, x\}$. For this reason we call $\{x, y\}$ an **unordered** pair. It is often useful to consider also the **ordered pair** $\langle x, y\rangle$ where we distinguish between the first element x and the second element y. Thus $\langle x, y\rangle = \langle a, b\rangle$ if and only if $x = a$ and $y = b$, so that $\langle x, y\rangle \neq \langle y, x\rangle$ if $x \neq y$. Similarly, we shall consider ordered triplets $\langle x, y, z\rangle$, quadruplets $\langle x, y, z, w\rangle$, and so forth, where we distinguish between the first, second, third, . . . , elements. Although it is possible to define ordered pairs, triplets, and so forth, in terms of unordered pairs (cf. Halmos), we shall not do so here.

If X and Y are two sets, we define the **Cartesian,** or **direct,** product $X \times Y$ to be the set $\{\langle x, y\rangle\}$ of all ordered pairs whose first element belongs to X and whose second element belongs to Y. Similarly, $X \times Y \times Z$ is the set $\{\langle x, y, z\rangle\}$ of all ordered triples such that $x \in X$, $y \in Y$, and $z \in Z$. If X is the set of real numbers, then $X \times X$ is the set of ordered pairs of real numbers and, as we know from analytic geometry, is equivalent to the set of points in the plane.

Problems

1. Show that $\{x: x \neq x\} = \varnothing$.

2. Show that if $x \in \varnothing$, then x is a green-eyed lion.

3. Show that in general the sets $X \times (Y \times Z)$ and $(X \times Y) \times Z$ are different but that there is a natural correspondence between each of them and $X \times Y \times Z$.

2 FUNCTIONS

By a function f from (or on) a set X to (or into) a set Y we mean a rule which assigns to each x in X a unique element $f(x)$ in Y. The collection G of pairs of the form $\langle x, f(x)\rangle$ in $X \times Y$ is called the **graph** of the function f. A subset G of $X \times Y$ is the graph of a function on X if and only if for each $x \in X$ there is a unique pair in G whose first element is x. Since a function is determined by its graph, many people like to define a function to be its graph. It is irrelevant for our purposes whether we do this or consider the notion of function as a primitive one.[2]

The word 'mapping' is often used as a synonym for 'function'. We often express the fact that f is a function on X into Y by writing

$$f: X \to Y.$$

The set X is called the *domain* (or domain of definition) of f. The set of values taken by f, that is, the set $\{y \in Y: (\exists x)\, [y = f(x)]\}$, is called the *range* of f. The range of a function f will in general be smaller than Y. If the range of f is Y, then we say that f is a function **onto** Y. (Another terminology for this case: f is *surjective*. We shall not use it here.)

If A is a subset of X, we define the *image* under f of A as the set of elements in Y such that $y = f(x)$ for some x in A. We denote this image by $f[A]$. Thus

$$f[A] = \{y \in Y: (\exists x)\, [x \in A \quad \text{and} \quad y = f(x)]\}.$$

Thus the range of f is $f[X]$, and f is onto Y if and only if $Y = f[X]$.

More important than the notion of image of a set under f is the notion of an inverse image. If B is a subset of Y, we define the **inverse image** $f^{-1}[B]$ of B to be the set of those x in X for which $f(x)$ is in B; that is

$$f^{-1}[B] = \{x \in X: f(x) \in B\}.$$

It should be noted that f is onto Y if and only if the inverse image of each nonempty subset of Y is nonempty.

A function $f: X \to Y$ is called **one-to-one** (or univalent, or injective) if $f(x_1) = f(x_2)$ only when $x_1 = x_2$. Functions which are one-to-one from X onto Y are often called one-to-one correspondences between

[2] The equivalence between functions and their graphs is valid only for functions from a given set X to a set Y. There are difficulties, for example, in defining the graph of the identity function i defined by $i(x) = x$ for all x. In a formal treatment which takes function as a primitive notion we must have axioms describing the properties of functions, such as $(f = g) \Leftrightarrow (x)[f(x) = g(x)]$, as well as axioms enabling us to construct functions.

X and Y. (They are also referred to as bijective.) In this case there is a function $g: Y \to X$ such that for all x and y we have $g(f(x)) = x$ and $f(g(y)) = y$. The function g is called the inverse of f and is sometimes denoted by f^{-1}.

If $f: X \to Y$ and $g: Y \to Z$, we define a new function $h: X \to Z$ by setting $h(x) = g(f(x))$. The function h is called the *composition* of g with f and denoted by $g \circ f$. If $f: X \to Y$ and A is a subset of X, we can define a new function $g: A \to Y$ by defining $g(x) = f(x)$ for $x \in A$. This new function g is called the *restriction* of f to A and sometimes written $f \mid A$. In many cases it is important to distinguish this function g carefully from f: It has a different range, and the inverse images under g are different from those under f.

Having mentioned the possibility of defining functions by means of ordered pairs, it is only fair that we point out that, conversely, ordered pairs may be defined in terms of the notion of a function: An ordered pair is a function whose domain is the set $\{1, 2\}$. Similarly, a **finite sequence,** or n-tuple, is a function whose domain is the first n natural numbers, that is the set $\{i \in \mathbf{N}: i \leq n\}$. (We call such a set a *segment* of $\mathbf{N}$.) Generalizing, an **infinite sequence** is a function whose domain is the set $\mathbf{N}$ of natural numbers. We use the term 'sequence' to mean a finite or infinite sequence. If the range of a sequence is in a set X, we speak of a sequence from (or in) X or of a sequence of elements of X. It is customary to depart somewhat from the usual functional notation when dealing with sequences and denote the value of the function at i by x_i and to call this value the ith element of the sequence. We shall often denote ordered n-tuples by $\langle x_i \rangle_{i=1}^{n}$ and infinite sequences by $\langle x_i \rangle_{i=1}^{\infty}$. When no misunderstanding is likely to arise we often write simply $\langle x_i \rangle$. The range of the sequence $\langle x_i \rangle$ will be denoted by $\{x_i\}$. Thus the range of an ordered n-tuple $\langle x_i \rangle_{i=1}^{n}$ is the unordered n-tuple $\{x_i\}_{i=1}^{n}$. This notation is reasonably consistent with our earlier notation concerning ordered and unordered pairs, triplets, and so forth.

A set A is called **countable** if it is the range of some sequence and **finite** if it is the range of some finite sequence. A set which is not finite is called infinite. (Many authors restrict the use of the word 'countable' to sets which are infinite and countable, but our definition includes the finite sets among the countable sets.) We use the term 'countably infinite' for infinite countable sets. We shall return to this notion again in Section 6.

One of the most useful ways of defining an infinite sequence is given by the following principle:

Principle of Recursive Definition. *Let f be a function from a set X to itself, and let a be an element of X. Then there is a unique infinite sequence $\langle x_i \rangle$ from X such that $x_1 = a$ and $x_{i+1} = f(x_i)$ for each i.*

The existence of such a sequence is intuitively clear: We define $x_1 = a$, $x_2 = f(a)$, $x_3 = f(f(a))$, and so on. If you want a formal proof, one can be given as follows: We first prove by induction on n that for each natural number n there is a unique finite sequence $x_1^{(n)}, x_2^{(n)}, \ldots, x_n^{(n)}$, such that

$$x_1^{(n)} = a \quad \text{and} \quad x_{i+1}^{(n)} = f(x_i^n) \qquad \text{for } 1 \leq i < n\,.$$

From the uniqueness, it follows that $x_i^{(n)} = x_i^{(m)}$ for $i \leq n \leq m$. Thus if we define x_n to be $x_n^{(n)}$, we have $x_i^{(n)} = x_i$, and we see that the sequence $\langle x_i \rangle$ satisfies the requirements of our principle.

A slight extension of this principle is the following: Let f be a function on $X \times \mathbf{N}$ to X (where $\mathbf{N}$ is the set of natural numbers) and let $a \in X$. Then there is a unique sequence $\langle x_i \rangle$ such that $x_1 = a$ and $x_{i+1} = f(x_i, i)$.

An important notion in connection with that of a sequence is the notion of a subsequence. We say that a mapping g of $\mathbf{N}$ into $\mathbf{N}$ is **monotone** if $(i > j) \Rightarrow (g(i) > g(j))$. If f is an infinite sequence (that is a function whose domain is $\mathbf{N}$), we say that h is an infinite **subsequence** of f if there is a monotone mapping g of $\mathbf{N}$ into $\mathbf{N}$ such that $h = f \circ g$. If we write f as $\langle f_i \rangle$ and g as $\langle g_i \rangle$, then we usually denote $f \circ g$ by $\langle f_{g_i} \rangle$.

3 UNIONS, INTERSECTIONS, AND COMPLEMENTS

Let us fix a given set X and consider the set $\mathscr{P}(X)$ consisting of all subsets of X. There are certain set-theoretic operations that we can perform on subsets of X. If A and B are subsets of X, we define their intersection $A \cap B$ to be the set of all elements which belong to both A and B. Thus

$$A \cap B = \{x : x \in A \;\&\; x \in B\}\,.$$

We note that the definition is symmetric in A and B; that is, $A \cap B = B \cap A$. Also $A \cap B \subset A$ and $A \cap B = A \Leftrightarrow A \subset B$. We have

$(A \cap B) \cap C = A \cap (B \cap C)$ and write this set as $A \cap B \cap C$. It is the set of all elements which belong to each of the sets A, B, and C.

We define the union $A \cup B$ of two sets A and B to be the set of elements that are in either A or B. Thus

$$A \cup B = \{x\colon x \in A \vee x \in B\}.$$

We have

$$A \cup B = B \cup A$$

$$A \cup (B \cup C) = (A \cup B) \cup C = A \cup B \cup C$$

$$A \subset A \cup B$$

$$A = A \cup B \Leftrightarrow B \subset A.$$

We also have relations between unions and intersections which are called distributive laws:

$$A \cap (B \cup C) = (A \cap B) \cup (A \cap C)$$

$$A \cup (B \cap C) = (A \cup B) \cap (A \cup C).$$

The empty set $\varnothing$ and the space X play special roles:

$$A \cup \varnothing = A, \qquad A \cap \varnothing = \varnothing$$

$$A \cup X = X, \qquad A \cap X = A.$$

If A is a subset of X, we define the complement $\tilde{A}$ of A (relative to X) as the set of elements not in A. Thus

$$\tilde{A} = \{x \in X\colon x \notin A\}.$$

We sometimes will write $\sim A$ instead of $\tilde{A}$. We have

$$\tilde{\varnothing} = X, \quad \tilde{X} = \varnothing$$

$$\tilde{\tilde{A}} = A, \quad A \cup \tilde{A} = X, \quad A \cap \tilde{A} = \varnothing$$

$$A \subset B \Leftrightarrow \tilde{B} \subset \tilde{A}.$$

Two special laws relating complements to unions and intersections are De Morgan's laws:

$$\sim(A \cup B) = \tilde{A} \cap \tilde{B}$$

$$\sim(A \cap B) = \tilde{A} \cup \tilde{B}.$$

If A and B are two subsets of X we define the difference $B \sim A$, or relative complement of A in B, as the set of elements in B which are not in A. Thus

$$B \sim A = \{x \colon x \in B \,\&\, x \notin A\}.$$

We have $B \sim A = B \cap \tilde{A}$.

If the intersection of two sets is empty we say the sets are disjoint. A collection $\mathcal{C}$ of sets is said to be a **disjoint** collection of sets or a collection of pairwise disjoint sets if any two sets in $\mathcal{C}$ are disjoint.

The process of taking unions (or intersections) of two sets can be extended by repetition to give unions (or intersections) of any finite collection of sets. However, we can give a definition of intersection for an arbitrary collection $\mathcal{C}$ of sets: The intersection of the collection $\mathcal{C}$ is the set of those elements of X which belong to each member of $\mathcal{C}$. We denote this intersection by $\bigcap_{A \in \mathcal{C}} A$ or $\bigcap\{A : A \in \mathcal{C}\}$. Thus

$$\bigcap_{A \in \mathcal{C}} A = \{x \in X \colon (A)(A \in \mathcal{C} \Rightarrow x \in A)\}.$$

Similarly, we define unions by

$$\bigcup_{A \in \mathcal{C}} A = \{x \in X \colon (\exists A)(A \in \mathcal{C} \,\&\, x \in A)\}.$$

De Morgan's laws hold for arbitrary unions and intersections:

$$\sim\left[\bigcup_{A \in \mathcal{C}} A\right] = \bigcap_{A \in \mathcal{C}} \tilde{A}$$

$$\sim\left[\bigcap_{A \in \mathcal{C}} A\right] = \bigcup_{A \in \mathcal{C}} \tilde{A}.$$

Also the distributive laws:

$$B \cap \left[\bigcup_{A \in \mathcal{C}} A\right] = \bigcup_{A \in \mathcal{C}} (B \cap A)$$

$$B \cup \left[\bigcap_{A \in \mathcal{C}} A\right] = \bigcap_{A \in \mathcal{C}} (B \cup A).$$

It follows from our definition that the union of an empty collection of sets is empty and that the intersection of the empty collection of sets is X.

By a sequence of subsets of X we mean a sequence from $\mathcal{P}(X)$, that is, a mapping of $\mathbf{N}$ or (a segment of $\mathbf{N}$) into $\mathcal{P}(X)$. If $\langle A_i \rangle$ is an infinite sequence of subsets of X, we write $\bigcup_{i=1}^{\infty} A_i$ for the union of the range of the sequence. Thus

$$\bigcup_{i=1}^{\infty} A_i = \{x: (\exists i)(x \in A_i)\}.$$

Similarly, if $\langle B_i \rangle_{i=1}^{n}$ is a finite sequence of subsets of X, we write $\bigcap_{i=1}^{n} B_i$ for the intersection of the range of the sequence so that

$$\bigcap_{i=1}^{n} B_i = B_1 \cap B_2 \cap \cdots \cap B_n .$$

This notation for sequences of sets is so convenient that we often generalize it to arbitrary collections of sets by using the notion of an indexed collection: An **indexed subset** of X (or collection of subsets of X) is a function on an index set Λ to X (or the set of subsets of X). If Λ is the set of natural numbers, then the notion of an indexed set coincides with the notion of a sequence.

In keeping with the notation for sequences, we shall often write x_λ instead of $x(\lambda)$, and denote the indexed set itself by $\{x_\lambda\}$ or $\{x_\lambda: \lambda \in \Lambda\}$. We say that $\{x_\lambda\}$ is indexed by Λ. We define the union and intersection of an indexed set to be the union and intersection of the range of the function defining the indexed set. Thus

$$\bigcup_{\lambda \in \Lambda} A_\lambda = \{x \in X: (\exists \lambda)(\lambda \in \Lambda \;\&\; x \in A_\lambda)\}$$

and

$$\bigcap_{\lambda \in \Lambda} A_\lambda = \{x \in X: (\lambda)(\lambda \in \Lambda \Rightarrow x \in A_\lambda)\}.$$

In the case when Λ is the set $\mathbf{N}$ of natural numbers we have

$$\bigcap_{i \in N} A_i = \bigcap_{i=1}^{\infty} A_i ,$$

and similarly for unions.

If f maps X into Y and $\{A_\lambda\}$ is a collection of subsets of X, then

$$f\left[\bigcup_{\lambda} A_\lambda\right] = \bigcup_{\lambda} f[A_\lambda]$$

but we can only conclude

$$f\left[\bigcap_{\lambda} A_\lambda\right] \subset \bigcap_{\lambda} f[A_\lambda] .$$

For inverse images we have, for $\{B_\lambda\}$ a collection of subsets of Y,

$$f^{-1}\Big[\bigcup_\lambda B_\lambda\Big] = \bigcup_\lambda f^{-1}[B_\lambda]$$

$$f^{-1}\Big[\bigcap_\lambda B_\lambda\Big] = \bigcap_\lambda f^{-1}[B_\lambda]$$

and

$$f^{-1}[\tilde{B}] = \sim f^{-1}[B]$$

for $B \subset Y$. Also

$$f[f^{-1}[B]] \subset B$$

and

$$f^{-1}[f[A]] \supset A$$

for $A \subset X$ and $B \subset Y$.

Problems

4. Show that $A \subset B \Leftrightarrow A \cap B = A \Leftrightarrow A \cup B = B$.

5. Prove the distributive laws.

6. Show that $A \subset B \Leftrightarrow \tilde{B} \subset \tilde{A}$.

7. Prove DeMorgan's laws (for arbitrary unions and intersections).

8. Show that

$$B \cap \Big[\bigcup_{A \varepsilon \mathcal{C}} A\Big] = \bigcup_{A \varepsilon \mathcal{C}} (B \cap A)\,.$$

9. a. Show $f[\bigcup A_\lambda] = \bigcup f[A_\lambda]$.

b. Show $f[\bigcap A_\lambda] \subset \bigcap f[A_\lambda]$.

c. Give an example where

$$f[\bigcap A_\lambda] \neq \bigcap f[A_\lambda]\,.$$

10. Show that

a. $f^{-1}[\bigcup B_\lambda] = \bigcup f^{-1}[B_\lambda]$.

b. $f^{-1}[\bigcap B_\lambda] = \bigcap f^{-1}[B_\lambda]$.

c. $f^{-1}[\tilde{B}] = \sim f^{-1}[B]$ for $B \subset Y$.

11. Show that if f maps X into Y and $A \subset X$, $B \subset Y$ then

$$f[f^{-1}[B]] \subset B$$

and

$$f^{-1}[f[A]] \supset A\,.$$

Give examples to show that we need not have equality.

4 ALGEBRAS OF SETS

A collection $\mathcal{A}$ of subsets of X is called an **algebra** of sets or a **Boolean algebra** if (i) $A \cup B$ is in $\mathcal{A}$ whenever A and B are, and (ii) $\tilde{A}$ is in $\mathcal{A}$ whenever A is. It follows from De Morgan's laws that (iii) $A \cap B$ is in $\mathcal{A}$ whenever A and B are. If a collection $\mathcal{A}$ of subsets of X satisfies (ii) and (iii), then by De Morgan's laws it also satisfies (i) and is therefore a Boolean algebra. By taking unions two at a time we see that if $A_1, \ldots, A_n$ are sets in $\mathcal{A}$ then $A_1 \cup A_2 \cup \cdots \cup A_n$ is again in $\mathcal{A}$. Similarly, $A_1 \cap A_2 \cap \cdots \cap A_n$ is in $\mathcal{A}$.

We shall find several propositions concerning algebras of sets useful. The first is the following:

1. Proposition: *Given any collection $\mathcal{C}$ of subsets of X, there is a smallest algebra $\mathcal{A}$ which contains $\mathcal{C}$; that is, there is an algebra $\mathcal{A}$ containing $\mathcal{C}$ and such that if $\mathcal{B}$ is any algebra containing $\mathcal{C}$ then $\mathcal{B}$ contains $\mathcal{A}$.*

Proof. Let $\mathcal{F}$ be the family of all algebras (of subsets of X) which contain $\mathcal{C}$. Let $\mathcal{A} = \bigcap \{\mathcal{B}: \mathcal{B} \in \mathcal{F}\}$. Then $\mathcal{C}$ is a subcollection of $\mathcal{A}$, for each $\mathcal{B}$ in $\mathcal{F}$ contains $\mathcal{C}$. Moreover, $\mathcal{A}$ is an algebra. For if A and B are in $\mathcal{A}$, then for each $\mathcal{B} \in \mathcal{F}$ we have $A \in \mathcal{B}$ and $B \in \mathcal{B}$. Since $\mathcal{B}$ is an algebra, $A \cup B$ belongs to $\mathcal{B}$. Since this is true for every $\mathcal{B} \in \mathcal{F}$, we have $A \cup B$ in $\bigcap \{\mathcal{B}: \mathcal{B} \in \mathcal{F}\}$. Similarly, we show that if $A \in \mathcal{A}$ then $\tilde{A} \in \mathcal{A}$. From the definition of $\mathcal{A}$, we see that if $\mathcal{B}$ is an algebra containing $\mathcal{C}$, then $\mathcal{B} \supset \mathcal{A}$. ▮

2. Proposition: *Let $\mathcal{A}$ be an algebra of subsets and $\langle A_i \rangle$ a sequence of sets in $\mathcal{A}$. Then we can find a sequence $\langle B_i \rangle$ of sets in $\mathcal{A}$ such that $B_n \cap B_m = \varnothing$ for $n \neq m$ and*

$$\bigcup_{i=1}^{\infty} B_i = \bigcup_{i=1}^{\infty} A_i .$$

Proof. Since the proposition is trivial when $\langle A_i \rangle$ is finite, we assume $\langle A_i \rangle$ to be an infinite sequence. Set $B_1 = A_1$, and for each natural number $n > 1$ define

$$\begin{aligned} B_n &= A_n \sim [A_1 \cup A_2 \cup \cdots \cup A_{n-1}] \\ &= A_n \cap \tilde{A}_1 \cap \tilde{A}_2 \cap \cdots \cap \tilde{A}_{n-1} . \end{aligned}$$

Since the complements and intersections of sets in $\mathcal{A}$ are in $\mathcal{A}$, we have each $B_n \in \mathcal{A}$. We also have $B_n \subset A_n$. Let B_n and B_m be two such sets, and suppose $m < n$. Then $B_m \subset A_m$, and so

$$\begin{aligned} B_m \cap B_n &\subset A_m \cap B_n \\ &= A_m \cap A_n \cap \cdots \cap \tilde{A}_m \cap \cdots \\ &= (A_m \cap \tilde{A}_m) \cap \cdots \\ &= \varnothing \cap \cdots \\ &= \varnothing\,. \end{aligned}$$

Since $B_i \subset A_i$, we have

$$\bigcup_{i=1}^{\infty} B_i \subset \bigcup_{i=1}^{\infty} A_i\,.$$

Let $x \in \bigcup_{i=1} A_i$. Then x must belong to at least one of the A_i's. Let n be the smallest value of i such that $x \in A_i$. Then $x \in B_n$, and so $x \in \bigcup_{n=1}^{\infty} B_n$. Thus

$$\bigcup_{n=1}^{\infty} B_n \supset \bigcup_{n=1}^{\infty} A_n\,,$$

and we have

$$\bigcup_{n=1}^{\infty} B_n = \bigcup_{n=1}^{\infty} A_n\,. \ \blacksquare$$

An algebra $\mathcal{A}$ of sets is called a **σ-algebra,** or a **Borel field,** if every union of a countable collection of sets in $\mathcal{A}$ is again in $\mathcal{A}$. That is, if $\langle A_i \rangle$ is a sequence of sets then $\bigcup_{i=1}^{\infty} A_i$ must again be in $\mathcal{A}$. From De Morgan's laws it follows that the intersection of a countable collection of sets in $\mathcal{A}$ is again in $\mathcal{A}$. A slight modification of the proof of Proposition 1 gives us the following proposition:

3. Proposition: *Given any collection $\mathcal{C}$ of subsets of X, there is a smallest σ-algebra which contains $\mathcal{C}$; that is, there is a σ-algebra $\mathcal{A}$ containing $\mathcal{C}$ such that if $\mathcal{B}$ is any σ-algebra containing $\mathcal{C}$ then $\mathcal{A} \subset \mathcal{B}$.*

Problem

12. Prove Proposition 3.

5 THE AXIOM OF CHOICE AND INFINITE DIRECT PRODUCTS

An important axiom in set theory is the so-called axiom of choice. It is somewhat less elementary than the other axioms used in axiomatic set theory and is known to be independent of them. Many mathematicians like to be very explicit about the use of the axiom of choice and its consequences, but we shall be rather informal about its use. The axiom is the following:

Axiom of Choice: *Let $\mathcal{C}$ be any collection of nonempty sets. Then there is a function F defined on $\mathcal{C}$ which assigns to each set $A \in \mathcal{C}$ an element $F(A)$ in A.*

The function F is called a 'choice function,' and its existence may be thought of as the result of choosing for each of the sets A in $\mathcal{C}$ an element in A. There is, of course, no difficulty in doing this if there are only a finite number of sets in $\mathcal{C}$, but we need the axiom of choice in case the collection $\mathcal{C}$ is infinite. If the sets in $\mathcal{C}$ are disjoint, we may think of the axiom of choice as asserting the possibility of selecting a 'parliament' consisting of one member from each of the sets in $\mathcal{C}$.

Let $\mathcal{C} = \{X_\lambda\}$ be a collection of sets indexed by an index set Λ. We define the **direct product**

$$\bigtimes_{\lambda} X_\lambda$$

to be the collection of all sets $\{x_\lambda\}$ indexed by Λ and having the property that $x_\lambda \in X_\lambda$. If $\Lambda = \{1, 2\}$, we have our earlier definition of the direct product $X_1 \times X_2$ of the two sets X_1 and X_2. If $z = \{x_\lambda\}$ is an element of $\bigtimes_\lambda X_\lambda$, we call x_λ the λth coordinate of z.

If one of the X_λ is empty, then $\bigtimes_\lambda X_\lambda$ is also empty. The axiom of choice is equivalent to the converse statement that if none of the X_λ are empty then $\bigtimes_\lambda X_\lambda$ is not empty. For this reason Bertrand Russell prefers to call the axiom of choice the 'multiplicative axiom'.

6 COUNTABLE SETS

In an earlier section we defined a set to be countable if it was the range of some sequence. If it is the range of a finite sequence, we have a finite set, but the range of an infinite sequence may also be finite. In fact every nonempty finite set is the range of an infinite sequence, for example the finite set $\{x_1, \ldots, x_n\}$ is the range of the infinite sequence defined by setting $x_i = x_n$ for $i > n$. Thus a set is countably infinite if it is the range of some infinite sequence but not the range of any finite sequence. The set **N** of natural numbers is an example of a countably infinite set.

Before proceeding further, we had better come to terms with the empty set. The empty set is not the range of any sequence (unless we admit sequences with zero terms). It is convenient, however, to define finite and countable sets so that the empty set is both finite and countable. Hence:

Definition: *A set is called* ***finite*** *if it is either empty or the range of a finite sequence. A set is called* ***countable*** *(or* ***denumerable****) if it is either empty or the range of a sequence.*

It follows at once from this definition that the image of any countable set is countable, that is, that the range of any function with a countable domain is itself countable, and similarly for finite sets.

It is usual in mathematics to give a slightly different but equivalent definition based on the notion of a one-to-one correspondence. We first note that any set that can be put in one-to-one correspondence with a finite set is finite and that any set that can be put in one-to-one correspondence with a countable set must be countable. Since the set **N** of natural numbers is countable but not finite, any set which can be put in one-to-one correspondence with **N** is countably infinite. It is customary to use this property to define the notion of countably infinite. Thus to show that our definition is equivalent to the customary one, we must show that, if an infinite set E is the range of a sequence $\langle x_n \rangle$, then E can be put in one-to-one correspondence with **N**. To do this we define a function φ from **N** into **N** by recursion as follows: Let $\varphi(1) = 1$, and define $\varphi(n + 1)$ to be the smallest value of m such that $x_m \neq x_i$ for all $i \leq \varphi(n)$. Since E is infinite, such an m always exists, and by the well-ordering principle for **N** there is always a least such m. The correspondence $n \to x_{\varphi(n)}$ is a one-to-one correspondence between **N** and E. Thus we have shown that a set is countably infinite if and only if it can be put into one-to-one correspondence with **N**. We are now in a position to prove some simple propositions about countable sets:

4. Proposition: *Every subset of a countable set is countable.*

Proof: Let $E = \{x_n\}$ be a countable set, and let A be a subset of E. If A is empty, A is countable by definition. If A is not empty, choose x in A. Define a new sequence $\langle y_n \rangle$ by setting $y_n = x_n$ if $x_n \in A$ and $y_n = x$ if $x_n \notin A$. Then A is the range of $\langle y_n \rangle$ and is therefore countable. ▎

5. Proposition: *Let A be a countable set. Then the set of all finite sequences from A is also countable.*

Proof: Since A is countable, it can be put into one-to-one correspondence with a subset of the set **N** of natural numbers. Thus it suffices to prove that the set S of all finite sequences of natural numbers is countable. Let $\langle 2, 3, 5, 7, 11, \ldots, p_k, \ldots \rangle$ be the sequence of prime numbers. Then each n in **N** has a unique factorization of the form[3] $n = 2^{x_1} 3^{x_2} \cdots p_k^{x_k}$ where $x_i \in \mathbf{N}_0 = \mathbf{N} \cup \{0\}$ and $x_k > 0$. Let f be the function on **N** which assigns to the natural number n the finite sequence $\langle x_1, \ldots, x_k \rangle$ from $\mathbf{N}_0$. Then S is a subset of the range f. Hence S is countable by Proposition 4. ▎

6. Proposition: *The set of all rational numbers is countable.*

7. Proposition: *The union of a countable collection of countable sets is countable.*

Proof: Let $\mathcal{C}$ be a countable collection of countable sets. If all the sets in $\mathcal{C}$ are empty, the union is empty and thus countable. Thus we may as well assume that $\mathcal{C}$ contains nonempty sets, and since the empty set contributes nothing to the union of $\mathcal{C}$, we can assume that the sets in $\mathcal{C}$ are nonempty. Thus $\mathcal{C}$ is the range of an infinite sequence $\langle A_n \rangle_{n=1}^{\infty}$, and each A_n is the range of an infinite sequence $\langle x_{nm} \rangle_{m=1}^{\infty}$. But the mapping of $\langle n, m \rangle$ to x_{nm} is a mapping of the set of ordered pairs of natural numbers onto the union of $\mathcal{C}$. Since the set of pairs of natural numbers is countable, the union of the collection $\mathcal{C}$ must also be countable. ▎

[3] Except 1; we agree to write $1 = 2^0$.

Problems

13. Show that every subset of a finite set is finite.

14. Prove Proposition 6 by using Propositions 4 and 5. (Hint: The mapping

$$\langle p, q, 1\rangle \to p/q$$
$$\langle p, q, 2\rangle \to -p/q$$
$$\langle 1, 1, 3\rangle \to 0$$

is a function whose range is the set of rational numbers and whose domain is a subset of the set of finite sequences from N.)

15. Show that the set E of infinite sequences from $\{0, 1\}$ is not countable. (Hint: Let f be a function from N to E. Then $f(\nu)$ is a sequence $\langle a_{\nu n}\rangle_{n=1}^{\infty}$. Let $b_\nu = 1 - a_{\nu\nu}$. Then $\langle b_n\rangle$ is again a sequence from $\{0, 1\}$, and for each $\nu \in$ N we have $\langle b_n\rangle \neq \langle a_{\nu n}\rangle$.)

7 RELATIONS AND EQUIVALENCES

Two given entities x and y may be "related" to each other in many ways, as in $x = y$, $x \in y$, $x \subset y$, or for numbers $x < y$. In general we say that R denotes a relation if, given x and y, either x stands in the relation R to y (written x R y) or x does not stand in the relation R to y. A relation R is said to be a relation on a set X if x R y implies $x \in X$ and $y \in X$. If R is a relation on a set X, we define the graph of R to be the set $\{\langle x, y\rangle: x \mathrel{R} y\}$. Since we consider two relations R and S to be the same if $(x \mathrel{R} y) \Leftrightarrow (x \mathrel{S} y)$, each relation on a set X is uniquely determined by its graph, and conversely each subset of $X \times X$ is the graph of some relation on X. Thus we may if we like identify a relation on X with its graph and define a relation to be a subset of $X \times X$. In many formalized treatments of set theory a relation is in general defined simply as a set of ordered pairs.[4]

A relation R is said to be *transitive* on a set X if x R y and y R z imply x R z for all x, y, and z in X. Thus $=$ and $<$ are transitive

[4] Cf. Suppes [17], p. 57 or Halmos [5], p. 26. It should be pointed out, however, that there is a difficulty in this approach in that $=$, $\in$, and $\subset$ are no longer relations. For this reason I prefer some treatment such as the one in Kelley [11], p. 56, where relations are not necessarily *sets* of ordered pairs.

relations on the set of real numbers. A relation R is said to be *symmetric* on X if $x \mathrel{R} y$ implies $y \mathrel{R} x$ for all x and y in X. It is said to be *reflexive* on X if for all $x \in X$ we have $x \mathrel{R} x$.

A relation which is transitive, reflexive, and symmetric on X is said to be an *equivalence* relation on X or simply an equivalence on X. Suppose that $\equiv$ is an equivalence relation on a set X. For a given $x \in X$, let E_x be the set of elements equivalent to x, that is $E_x = \{y: y \equiv x\}$. If y and z are both in E_x, then $y \equiv x$ and $z \equiv x$, and by symmetry and transitivity we have $z \equiv y$. Thus any two elements of E_x are equivalent. If $y \in E_x$ and $z \equiv y$, then $z \equiv y$ and $y \equiv x$, whence $z \equiv x$, and so $z \in E_x$. Thus any element of X which is equivalent to an element of E_x is itself an element of E_x. Consequently, for any two elements x and y of X the sets E_x and E_y are either identical (if $x \equiv y$) or disjoint (if $x \not\equiv y$). The sets in the collection $\{E_x: x \in X\}$ are called equivalence sets or classes of X under $\equiv$. Thus X is the disjoint union of the equivalence classes under $\equiv$. Note that $x \in E_x$, and so no equivalence class is empty.

The collection of equivalence classes under an equivalence $\equiv$ is called the *quotient* of X with respect to $\equiv$, and is sometimes denoted by $X/\equiv$. The mapping $x \to E_x$ is called the natural mapping of X onto $X/\equiv$.

A *binary operation* on a set X is a mapping from $X \times X$ to X. We say that an equivalence relation $\equiv$ is *compatible* with a binary operation $+$ if $x \equiv x'$ and $y \equiv y'$ imply that $(x + y) \equiv (x' + y')$. In this case $+$ defines an operation on the quotient $Q = X/\equiv$ as follows: If E and F belong to Q, choose $x \in E$, $y \in F$ and define $E + F$ to be $E_{(x+y)}$. Since $\equiv$ is an equivalence, $E + F$ is seen to depend only on E and F and not on the choice of x and y.

For further details the reader may consult Birkhoff and Maclane [1], pp. 155 f.

Problems

16. Prove that $F + G$ as defined above depends only on F and G.

17. Let X be an Abelian group under $+$. Then $\equiv$ is compatible with $+$ if and only if $x \equiv x'$ implies $x + y \equiv x' + y$. The induced relation then makes the quotient space into a group if and only if $\equiv$ is compatible with subtraction.

8 PARTIAL ORDERINGS AND THE MAXIMAL PRINCIPLE

A relation R is said to be *antisymmetric* on a set X if $x \mathrm{R} y$ and $y \mathrm{R} x$ imply $x = y$ for all x and y in X. A relation $\prec$ is said to be a **partial ordering** of a set X (or to partially order X) if it is transitive, reflexive, and antisymmetric on X. Thus $\leq$ is a partial ordering on the real numbers and $\subset$ is a partial ordering on $\mathscr{P}(X)$. A partial ordering $\prec$ on a set X is said to be a **linear ordering** (or simple ordering) of X if for any two elements x and y of X we have either $x \prec y$ or $y \prec x$. Thus $\leq$ linearly orders the set of real numbers, while $\subset$ is not a linear ordering on $\mathscr{P}(X)$.

The following principle is equivalent to the axiom of choice and is often more convenient to apply. For a proof of this equivalence and a discussion of related principles see Suppes [17], Chapter 8, or Kelley [11], pp. 31–36.

Hausdorff Maximal Principle: *Let $\prec$ be a partial ordering on a set X. Then there is a maximal linearly ordered subset S of X, that is, a subset S of X which is linearly ordered by $\prec$ and has the property that, if $S \subset T \subset X$ and T is linearly ordered by $\prec$, then $S = T$.*

Problem

18. A relation S is called a strict partial ordering on X if it is transitive and asymmetric [i.e. $x \mathrm{S} y$ implies not $(y \mathrm{S} x)$]. Show that to each partial ordering R on X there is a unique strict partial ordering S such that for $x \neq y$ we have $x \mathrm{S} y$ if and only if $x \mathrm{R} y$.

Part One

THEORY OF FUNCTIONS OF A REAL VARIABLE

2 The Real Number System

1 AXIOMS FOR THE REAL NUMBERS

We assume that the reader has a familiarity with the set **R** of real numbers and those basic properties of real numbers which are usually treated in an undergraduate course in analysis. The present chapter is devoted to a review and systematization of those results which will be useful later.

One approach to the subject of real numbers is to define them as Dedekind cuts of rational numbers, the rational numbers in turn being defined in terms of the natural numbers. Such a program gives an elegant construction of the real numbers out of more primitive concepts and set theory. We shall not concern ourselves here with the construction of the real numbers, but will think of them as already given, and list a set of axioms for them. All of the properties we need are consequences of these axioms, and in fact these axioms completely characterize the real numbers.

We thus assume as given the set **R** of real numbers, the set P of positive real numbers, and the functions '$+$' and '$\cdot$' on $\mathbf{R} \times \mathbf{R}$ to **R** and assume that these satisfy the following axioms, which we list in three groups. The first group describes the algebraic properties and the second the order properties. The third is comprised of the least upper bound axiom.

A. The Field Axioms: *For all real numbers x, y, and z we have*

A1 $x + y = y + x$.

A2 $(x + y) + z = x + (y + z)$.

A3 $\exists 0 \in R$ such that $x + 0 = x$ for all $x \in R$.

A4 For each $x \in R$ there is a $w \in R$ such that $x + w = 0$.

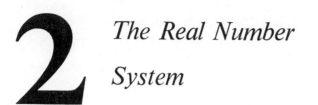

A5 $xy = yx$

A6 $(xy)z = x(yz)$

A7 $\exists 1 \in R$ such that $1 \neq 0$ and $x \cdot 1 = x$ for all $x \in R$.

A8 For each x in R different from 0 there is $w \in R$ such that $xw = 1$.

A9 $x(y + z) = xy + xz$.

Any set which satisfies these axioms is called a field (under $+$ and $\cdot$). It follows from A1 that the 0 in A3 is unique, a fact which we have assumed in the formulation of A4, A7, and A8. The w in A4 is unique and denoted by "$-x$". We define subtraction $x - y$ as $x + (-y)$. The 1 in A7 is unique. The w in A8 can be shown to be unique and is denoted by "x^{-1}". If we have a field, that is, any system satisfying A1 through A9, we can perform all the operations of elementary algebra including the solution of simultaneous linear equations. We shall use the various consequences of these axioms without explicit mention.

The second class of properties possessed by the real numbers have to do with the fact the real numbers are ordered. We could axiomatize the notion of a less than b, but it is somewhat more convenient to use the notions of a positive real number as the primitive one. When we do this our second group of axioms takes the following form:

B. Axioms of Order: *The subset P of positive real numbers satisfies the following:*

B1 $(x, y \in P) \Rightarrow x + y \in P$.

B2 $(x, y \in P) \Rightarrow xy \in P$.

B3 $(x \in P) \Rightarrow -x \notin P$.

B4 $(x \in R) \Rightarrow (x = 0)$ or $(x \in P)$ or $(-x \in P)$.

Any system satisfying the axioms of groups A and B is called an **ordered field.** Thus the real numbers are an ordered field. The rational numbers give another example of an ordered field.

In an ordered field we define the notion $x < y$ to mean $y - x \in P$. We write $x \leq y$ for "$x < y$ or $x = y$." In terms of "$<$" the axiom B1 is equivalent to

$$(x < y \,\&\, z < w) \Rightarrow x + z < y + w,$$

and B2 is equivalent to

$$(0 < x < y \,\&\, 0 < z < w) \Rightarrow xz < yw\,.$$

Axiom B3 asserts that a number cannot be both greater than and less than another, while B4 states that of any two different numbers one must be the larger. Since axiom B1 implies that the relation $<$ is transitive, we see that the real numbers are linearly ordered by $<$. Except for the discussion in the beginning of the next section we take all of the consequences of these two axiom groups for granted and use them without explicit mention. For further properties of ordered fields the reader should see Birkhoff and Maclane [1].

The third axiom group consists of a single axiom, and it is this axiom which distinguishes the real numbers from other ordered fields. In contrast to our cavalier policy about the consequences of the first two axiom groups we shall be explicit about the use of this last axiom. Before stating this final axiom, let us introduce some terminology: If S is a set of real numbers, we say that b is an **upper bound** for S if for each $x \in S$ we have $x \leq b$. We sometimes express this by writing $S \leq b$. A number c is called a **least upper bound** for S if it is an upper bound for S and if $c \leq b$ for each upper bound b of S. Clearly the least upper bound of a set S is unique if it exists. Our final axiom for real numbers simply guarantees its existence for sets with an upper bound.

C. Completeness Axiom: *Every nonempty set S of real numbers which has an upper bound has a least upper bound.*

As a consequence of axiom C we have the following proposition.

1. Proposition: *If $\mathbf{R} = L \cup U$ and if for each l in L and each u in U we have $l < u$, then either L has a greatest element or U has a least element.*

We shall often denote the least upper bound of S by sup S or by $\sup_{x \in S} x$ and occasionally by sup $\{x: x \in S\}$. We can define lower bounds and greatest lower bounds in a similar fashion, and it follows from axiom C that every set of real numbers with a lower bound has a greatest lower bound. We denote the greatest lower bound of a set S by inf S or by $\inf_{x \in S} x$. Note that $\inf_{x \in S} x = -\sup_{x \in S} -x$.

Problems

1. Show that $1 \varepsilon P$.

2. Use axiom C to show that every set of real numbers with a lower bound has a greatest lower bound.

3. Prove Proposition 1 using axiom C.

4. If x and y are two real numbers we define $\max(x, y)$ to be x if $x \geq y$ and y if $y \geq x$. We often denote $\max(x, y)$ by $x \vee y$. Similarly we define $\min(x, y)$ to be the smaller of x and y, and denote it by $x \wedge y$. Show that

- **a.** $(x \wedge y) \wedge z = x \wedge (y \wedge z)$
- **b.** $x \wedge y + x \vee y = x + y$
- **c.** $(-x) \wedge (-y) = -(x \vee y)$
- **d.** $x \vee y + z = (x + z) \vee (y + z)$
- **e.** $z(x \vee y) = (zx) \vee (zy)$ if $z \geq 0$

5. We define $|x|$ to be x if $x \geq 0$ and to be $-x$ if $x < 0$. Show that

- **a.** $|xy| = |x|\,|y|$;
- **b.** $|x + y| \leq |x| + |y|$;
- **c.** $|x| = x \vee (-x)$;
- **d.** $x \vee y = \frac{1}{2}(x + y + |x - y|)$;
- **e.** if $-y \leq x \leq y$, then $|x| \leq y$.

2 THE NATURAL AND RATIONAL NUMBERS AS SUBSETS OF R

We have adopted the procedure of taking the natural numbers for granted and of using them as counting numbers. Yet we all regard such a number as 3 not only as a natural number but also as a real number. In fact, we have used the symbol 1 not only to denote the first natural number but also the special real number given by axiom A7, and one is tempted to say that we define the real number 3 as $1 + 1 + 1$, and that in a 'similar' fashion we can define real numbers corresponding to any natural number. Actually we may use the tools we have at hand to do this in a more precise fashion.

By the principle of recursive definition there is a function φ from the natural numbers to the real numbers defined by $\varphi(1) = 1$ and $\varphi(n + 1) = \varphi(n) + 1$. (Here 1 denotes a real number on the right side and a natural number on the left.) We shall show that the mapping φ is a one-to-one mapping of $\mathbf{N}$ into $\mathbf{R}$. Let p and q be two different natural numbers, say $p < q$. Then $q = p + n$, and we shall show that $\varphi(p) < \varphi(q)$ by induction on n. For $n = 1$, we have $q = p + 1$ and $\varphi(q) = \varphi(p) + 1 > \varphi(p)$. For general n we have $\varphi(p + n + 1) = \varphi(p + n) + 1 > \varphi(p + n)$, and so $\varphi(p + n) > \varphi(p)$ implies $\varphi(p + n + 1) > \varphi(p)$. Thus by induction $\varphi(p + n) > \varphi(p)$ and we see that the mapping φ is one-to-one. We can also prove by induction that $\varphi(p + q) = \varphi(p) + \varphi(q)$ and $\varphi(pq) = \varphi(p)\varphi(q)$. Thus φ gives a one-to-one correspondence between the natural numbers and a subset of **R**, and φ preserves sums, products, and the relation $<$. Strictly speaking, we should distinguish between the natural number n and its image $\varphi(n)$ under φ, but we shall not make the distinction here; we shall consider the set **N** of integers to be a subset of **R**. By taking differences of natural numbers, we obtain the integers as a subset of **R**, and taking quotients of integers gives us the rationals. Since axiom C was not used in this discussion, the same results hold for any ordered field. Thus we have shown the following:

2. Proposition: *Every ordered field contains (sets isomorphic to) the natural numbers, the integers, and the rational numbers.*

If we make use of axiom C we can prove several further facts about the integers and rational numbers as subsets of the reals. One of the most important is the following theorem, which for historical reasons is called the Axiom of Archimedes:

3. Axiom of Archimedes: *Given any real number x, there is an integer n such that $x < n$.*

Proof: Let S be the set of integers k such that $k \leq x$. Since S has the upper bound x, it has a least upper bound y by axiom C. Since y is the least upper bound for S, $y - \frac{1}{2}$ cannot be an upper bound for S, and so there is a $k \in S$ such that $k > y - \frac{1}{2}$. But $k + 1 > y + \frac{1}{2} > y$, and so $(k + 1) \notin S$. Since $k + 1$ is an integer not in S, we must have $k + 1$ greater than x by the definition of S. ∎

4. Corollary: *Between any two real numbers is a rational; that is, if $x < y$, then there is a rational r with $x < r < y$.*

Proof: Let us first suppose $0 \leq x$. By the Axiom of Archimedes there is an integer $q > (y - x)^{-1}$. Then $(1/q) < y - x$. The set of integers n such that $y < (n/q)$ is a nonempty (by the Axiom of

Archimedes) set of positive integers, and so has a least element p. Then $(p - 1)/q < y < (p/q)$, and $x = y - (y - x) < (p/q) - (1/q) = (p - 1)/q$. Thus $r = (p - 1)/q$ lies between x and y. If $x < 0$, we can find an integer n such that $n > -x$. Then $n + x > 0$, and there is a rational r with $n + x < r < n + y$, and $r - n$ is a rational between x and y. ∎

3 THE EXTENDED REAL NUMBERS

It is often convenient to extend the system of real numbers by the addition of two elements $+\infty$ and $-\infty$. This enlarged set is called the set of **extended** real numbers. We extend the definition of $<$ to the extended real numbers by postulating $-\infty < x < \infty$, for each real number x. We define

$$x + \infty = \infty, \quad x - \infty = -\infty$$
$$x \cdot \infty = \infty, \qquad \text{if } x > 0$$
$$x \cdot -\infty = -\infty, \qquad \text{if } x > 0$$

for all real numbers x, and set

$$\infty + \infty = \infty, \quad -\infty - \infty = -\infty$$
$$\infty \cdot (\pm\infty) = \pm\infty, \quad -\infty(\pm\infty) = \mp\infty\,.$$

The operation $\infty - \infty$ is left undefined, but we shall adopt the arbitrary *convention* that $0 \cdot \infty = 0$.

One use of extended real numbers is in the expression "sup S." If S is a nonempty set of real numbers with an upper bound, we define sup S to be the least upper bound of S. If S has no upper bound, we write sup $S = \infty$. Then sup S is defined for all nonempty sets S, and if we define sup $\varnothing$ to be $-\infty$, then in all cases sup E is the smallest extended real number which is greater than or equal to each element of E. Similar conventions are adopted with respect to inf S.

4 SEQUENCES OF REAL NUMBERS

By a sequence[1] $\langle x_n \rangle$ of real numbers we mean a function which maps each natural number n into the real number x_n. We say that a real

[1] These are *infinite* sequences in the terminology of Chapter 1. Since we shall be mostly interested in infinite sequences in the remainder of this book, we drop the adjective "infinite" and assume all sequences infinite unless otherwise specified.

number l is a limit of the sequence $\langle x_n \rangle$ if for each positive ϵ there is an N such that for all $n \geq N$ we have $|x_n - l| < \epsilon$. It is easily verified that a sequence can have at most one limit, and we denote this limit by $\lim x_n$ when it exists. In symbols $l = \lim x_n$ if $(\epsilon > 0)(\exists N)(n \geq N)(|x_n - l| < \epsilon)$.

We extend this notion of limit of a sequence to include the value ∞ as follows: $\lim x_n = \infty$ if given Δ there is an N such that for all $n \geq N$ we have $x_n > \Delta$. A sequence is called convergent if it has a limit. This definition is ambiguous, and depends on whether or not we mean a limit which is a real number or an extended real number. In most of analysis it is more usual to use the restricted definition for convergence which requires a limit to be a real number, but we shall find it convenient in the next few chapters to allow $\pm\infty$ as limits in good standing. In those cases in which it is important to distinguish between the two concepts of a limit we shall try to be explicit by the use of such phrases as "converges to a real number" or "converges in the set of extended real numbers."

In the case of a real number we can paraphrase the definition of limit as follows: l is the limit of $\langle x_n \rangle$ if, given $\epsilon > 0$, all but a finite number of terms of the sequence $\langle x_n \rangle$ are within ϵ of l. A weaker requirement is to have infinitely many terms of the sequence within ϵ of l. In this case we say that l is a **cluster point** of the sequence $\langle x_n \rangle$. Thus l is a cluster point of $\langle x_n \rangle$ if, given $\epsilon > 0$, and given N, $\exists n \geq N$ such that $|x_n - l| < \epsilon$. We extend this definition to the case $l = \infty$, by saying that ∞ is a cluster point of $\langle x_n \rangle$ if given Δ, and given N, $\exists n \geq N$, such that $x_n \geq \Delta$. An obvious modification applies to $-\infty$. Thus, if a sequence has a limit l, then l is a cluster point, but the converse is not usually true. For example, the sequence $\langle x_n \rangle$ defined by $x_n = (-1)^n$ has $+1$ and -1 as cluster points but has no limit.

If $\langle x_n \rangle$ is a sequence, we define its limit superior by

$$\overline{\lim}\, x_n = \inf_n \sup_{k \geq n} x_k .$$

The symbols $\overline{\lim}$ and lim sup are both used for the limit superior. A real number l is the limit superior of the sequence $\langle x_n \rangle$ if and only if (i) given $\epsilon > 0$, $\exists n$ such that $x_k < l + \epsilon$ for all $k \geq n$, and (ii) given $\epsilon > 0$, and given n, $\exists k \geq n$ such that $x_k > l - \epsilon$. The extended real number ∞ is the limit superior of $\langle x_n \rangle$ if and only if, given Δ and n, there is a $k \geq n$ such that $x_k > \Delta$. The extended real number $-\infty$ is the limit superior of $\langle x_n \rangle$ if and only if $-\infty = \lim x_n$.

We define the limit inferior by

$$\underline{\lim}\, x_n = \sup_n \inf_{k \geq n} x_k .$$

We have $\overline{\lim} - x_n = -\underline{\lim}\, x_n$, and $\underline{\lim}\, x_n \leq \overline{\lim}\, x_n$. The sequence $\langle x_n \rangle$ converges to an extended real number l if and only if $l = \underline{\lim}\, x_n = \overline{\lim}\, x_n$. If $\langle x_n \rangle$ and $\langle y_n \rangle$ are two sequences, we have

$$\begin{aligned} \underline{\lim}\, x_n + \underline{\lim}\, y_n \leq \underline{\lim}\, (x_n + y_n) &\leq \overline{\lim}\, x_n + \underline{\lim}\, y_n \\ &\leq \overline{\lim}\, (x_n + y_n) \leq \overline{\lim}\, x_n + \overline{\lim}\, y_n. \end{aligned}$$

Problems

6. Show that a sequence can have at most one limit.

7. Show that l is a cluster point of $\langle x_n \rangle$ if and only if there is a subsequence $\langle x_{n_j} \rangle_{j=1}^{\infty}$ which converges to l.

8. a. Show that $\overline{\lim}\, x_n$ and $\underline{\lim}\, x_n$ are the largest and smallest cluster points of the sequence $\langle x_n \rangle$.

b. Show that every bounded infinite sequence has a subsequence which converges to a real number.

9. Show that a sequence $\langle x_n \rangle$ is convergent if and only if there is exactly one extended real number which is a cluster point of the sequence. Is this statement true if we omit the word "extended"?

10. Show that $x = \lim x_n$ if and only if every subsequence of $\langle x_n \rangle$ has in turn a subsequence which converges to x.

11. Show that the real number l is the limit superior of the sequence $\langle x_n \rangle$ if and only if (i) given $\epsilon > 0$, $\exists n$ such that $x_k < l + \epsilon$ for all $k \geq n$ and (ii) given $\epsilon > 0$, and n, $\exists k \geq n$ such that $x_k > l - \epsilon$.

12. Show that $\overline{\lim}\, x_n = \infty$ if and only if given Δ and n, $\exists k \geq n$ with $x_k > \Delta$.

13. Show that $\underline{\lim}\, x_n \leq \overline{\lim}\, x_n$ and that $\underline{\lim}\, x_n = \overline{\lim}\, x_n = l$ if and only if $l = \lim x_n$.

14. Prove that

$$\overline{\lim}\, x_n + \underline{\lim}\, y_n \leq \overline{\lim}\, (x_n + y_n) \leq \overline{\lim}\, x_n + \overline{\lim}\, y_n.$$

15. Prove that if $x_n \geq 0$ and $y_n \geq 0$, then

$$\overline{\lim}\, (x_n y_n) \leq (\overline{\lim}\, x_n)(\overline{\lim}\, y_n)$$

provided the product on the right is not of the form $0 \cdot \infty$.

16. We shall say that a sequence (or series) $\langle x_\nu \rangle$ is **summable** to s or has a sum s if the sequence $\langle s_n \rangle$ defined by $s_n = \sum_{\nu=1}^{n} x_\nu$ has s as a limit. In this case we write $s = \sum_{\nu=1}^{\infty} x_\nu$. Show that if each $x_\nu \geq 0$ then there is always an extended real number s such that

$$s = \sum_{\nu=1}^{\infty} x_\nu.$$

17. Show that the series $\langle x_\nu \rangle$ has a sum if

$$\sum_{\nu=1}^{\infty} |x_\nu| < \infty.$$

18. Let $\langle x_n \rangle$ be a sequence of real numbers. Show that $x = \lim_{n\to\infty} x_n$ if and only if

$$x = x_1 + \sum_{\nu=1}^{\infty} (x_{\nu+1} - x_\nu).$$

19. Let E be a set of positive real numbers. We define $\sum_{x\varepsilon E} x$ as $\sup_{F\varepsilon\mathcal{F}} s_F$ where $\mathcal{F}$ is the collection of finite subsets of E and s_F is the (finite) sum of the elements of F.

a. Show that $\sum_{x\varepsilon E} x < \infty$ only if E is countable.

b. Show that if E is countable and $\langle x_n \rangle$ is a one-to-one mapping of $\mathbf{N}$ onto E, then $\sum_{x\varepsilon E} x = \sum_{n=1}^{\infty} x_n$.

20. Let p be an integer greater than 1, and x a real number, $0 \leq x \leq 1$. Show that there is a sequence $\langle a_n \rangle$ of integers with $0 \leq a_n < p$ such that

$$x = \sum_{n=1}^{\infty} \frac{a_n}{p^n}$$

and that this sequence is unique except when x is of the form q/p^n, in which case there are exactly two such sequences. Show that, conversely, if $\langle a_n \rangle$ is any sequence of integers with $0 \leq a_n < p$, the series

$$\sum_{n=1}^{\infty} \frac{a_n}{p^n}$$

converges to a real number x with $0 \leq x \leq 1$.

If $p = 10$, this sequence is called the *decimal* expansion of x. For $p = 2$ it is called the *binary* expansion; and for $p = 3$, the *ternary* expansion.

5 OPEN AND CLOSED SETS OF REAL NUMBERS

The simplest sets of real numbers are the intervals. We define the open interval (a, b) to be the set $\{x: a < x < b\}$. We always take $a < b$ but we consider also the infinite intervals $(a, \infty) = \{x: a < x\}$ and $(-\infty, b) = \{x: x < b\}$. Sometimes we write $(-\infty, \infty)$ for the set of all real numbers. We define the closed interval $[a, b]$ to be the set $\{x: a \leq x \leq b\}$. For closed intervals we take a and b finite. The half-open interval $(a, b]$ is defined to be $\{x: a < x \leq b\}$, and $[a, b) = \{x: a \leq x < b\}$. A generalization of the notion of an open interval is given by that of an open set:

Definition: *A set O of real numbers is called* **open** *if for each $x \in O$ there is a $\delta > 0$ such that each y with $|x - y| < \delta$ belongs to O.*

Another way of phrasing this definition is to say that a set O is open if for every x in O there is an open interval I such that $x \in I \subset O$. The open intervals are examples of open sets, and both the empty set $\varnothing$ and the set $\mathbf{R}$ of real numbers are open. We establish some properties of open sets.

5. Proposition: *The intersection $O_1 \cap O_2$ of two open sets O_1 and O_2 is open.*

Proof: Let $x \in O_1 \cap O_2$. Since $x \in O_1$ and O_1 is open, there is a $\delta_1 > 0$ such that all y with $|x - y| < \delta_1$ belong to O_1. Similarly, there is a $\delta_2 > 0$ such that all y with $|x - y| < \delta_2$ belongs to O_2. Take δ to be the smaller of δ_1 and δ_2. Then $\delta > 0$, and if $|x - y| < \delta$, then y belongs to both O_1 and O_2, i.e. to $O_1 \cap O_2$. ▌

6. Corollary: *The intersection of any finite collection of open sets is open.*

7. Proposition: *The union of any collection $\mathcal{C}$ of open sets is open.*

Proof: Let U be the union of the collection $\mathcal{C}$, and $x \in U$. Then there is an $O \in \mathcal{C}$ with $x \in O$. Since O is open, there is an $\epsilon > 0$ such that all y with $|x - y| < \epsilon$ belong to O and hence to U, since $O \subset U$. Thus U is open. ▌

It follows from Proposition 5 that the intersection of any *finite* collection of open sets is open. It is not true, however, that the intersection of any collection of open sets is open. Take, for example, O_n to be the open interval $\left(-\frac{1}{n}, \frac{1}{n}\right)$. Then $\bigcap_{n=1}^{\infty} O_n = \{0\}$, and $\{0\}$ is not an open set.

Every union of open intervals is an open set by Proposition 7. A strong form of the converse of this is also true:

8. Proposition: *Every open set of real numbers is the union of a countable collection of disjoint open intervals.*

Proof: Since O is open, for each $x \in O$ there is a $y > x$ such that $(x, y) \subset O$. Let $b = \sup\{y: (x, y) \subset O\}$. Let $a = \inf\{z: (z, x) \subset O\}$. Then $a < x < b$, and $I_x = (a, b)$ is an open interval containing x. Now $I_x \subset O$, for if $w \in I_x$, say $x < w < b$, we have by the definition of b a number $y > w$ such that $(x, y) \subset O$, and so $w \in O$. Moreover, $b \notin O$, for if $b \in O$, then for some $\epsilon > 0$, we have $(b - \epsilon, b + \epsilon) \subset O$, whence $(x, b + \epsilon) \subset O$, contradicting the definition of b. Similarly $a \notin O$. Consider the collection of open intervals $\{I_x\}, x \in O$. Since each x in O is contained in I_x, and each I_x is contained in O, we have $O = \bigcup I_x$. Let (a, b) and (c, d) be two intervals in this collection with a point in common. Then we must have $c < b$ and $a < d$. Since c does not belong to O, it does not belong to (a, b) and we have $c \leq a$. Since a does not belong to O and hence not to (c, d), we have $a \leq c$. Thus $a = c$. Similarly $b = d$, and $(a, b) = (c, d)$. Thus two *different* intervals in the collection $\{I_x\}$ must be disjoint. Thus O is the union of the disjoint collection $\{I_x\}$ of open intervals, and it remains only to show that this collection is countable. But each open interval contains a rational number by the corollary to the Axiom of Archimedes. Since we have a collection of disjoint open intervals, each open interval contains a different rational number, and the collection can be put in one-to-one correspondence with a subset of the rationals. Thus it is a countable collection. ▌

9. Proposition (Lindelöf): *Let $\mathcal{C}$ be a collection of open sets of real numbers. Then there is a countable subcollection $\{O_i\}$ of $\mathcal{C}$ such that*

$$\bigcup_{O\varepsilon\mathcal{C}} O = \bigcup_{i=1}^{\infty} O_i .$$

Proof: Let $U = \bigcup\{O:O \varepsilon \mathcal{C}\}$, and $x \varepsilon U$. Then there is an $O \varepsilon \mathcal{C}$ with $x \varepsilon O$. Since O is open, there is an open interval I_x such that $x \varepsilon I_x \subset O$. It follows from Corollary 4 that we can find an open interval J_x with rational endpoints such that $x \varepsilon J_x \subset I_x$. Since the collection of all open intervals with rational endpoints is countable, the collection $\{J_x\}$, $x \varepsilon U$ is countable, and $U = \bigcup_{x\varepsilon U} J_x$. For each interval in $\{J_x\}$ choose a set O in $\mathcal{C}$ which contains it. This gives a countable subcollection $\{O_i\}_{i=1}^{\infty}$ of $\mathcal{C}$, and $U = \sum_{i=1}^{\infty} O_i$. ▎

We shall also study the notion of a closed set which generalizes the notion of a closed interval. We begin by defining a point of closure:

Definition: *A real number x is called a* ***point of closure*** *of a set E if for every $\delta > 0$ there is a y in E such that $|x - y| < \delta$.*

This is equivalent to saying that x is a point of closure of E if every open interval containing x also contains a point of E. Each point of E is trivially a point of closure of E. We denote the set of points of closure of E by $\bar{E}$. Thus $E \subset \bar{E}$.

10. Proposition: *If $A \subset B$, then $\bar{A} \subset \bar{B}$. Also $\overline{(A \cup B)} = \bar{A} \cup \bar{B}$.*

Proof: The first part follows immediately from the definition of points of closure. Since $A \subset A \cup B$, we have $\bar{A} \subset \overline{(A \cup B)}$. Similarly, $\bar{B} \subset \overline{(A \cup B)}$. Thus $\bar{A} \cup \bar{B} \subset \overline{(A \cup B)}$. Suppose that $x \not\varepsilon \bar{A} \cup \bar{B}$. Then there is a $\delta_1 > 0$ such that there is no $y \varepsilon A$ with $|x - y| < \delta_1$, and there is a $\delta_2 > 0$ such that there is no $y \varepsilon B$ with $|x - y| < \delta_2$. Thus if $\delta = \min(\delta_1, \delta_2)$, there is no $y \varepsilon A \cup B$ with $|x - y| < \delta$. Consequently $x \not\varepsilon \overline{(A \cup B)}$, and we have $\overline{(A \cup B)} \subset \bar{A} \cup \bar{B}$. ▎

Definition: *A set F is called* ***closed*** *if $F = \bar{F}$.*

Since we always have $F \subset \bar{F}$, a set F is closed if $\bar{F} \subset F$, that is, if F contains all of its points of closure. The empty set $\varnothing$ and the set **R** of all real numbers are closed. The closed intervals $[a, b]$ and

$[a, \infty)$ are closed. It is customary to use the letter F to denote closed sets (French, *fermé*).

11. Proposition: *For any set E the set $\bar{E}$ is closed; that is, $\bar{\bar{E}} = \bar{E}$.*

Proof: Let x be a point of closure of $\bar{E}$. Then, given $\delta > 0$, there is a point $y \in \bar{E}$ with $|x - y| < \delta/2$. Since $y \in \bar{E}$, there is a $z \in E$ with $|y - z| < \delta/2$. Thus $|x - z| < \delta$, and we see that x is a point of closure of E. ▌

12. Proposition: *The union $F_1 \cup F_2$ of two closed sets F_1 and F_2 is closed.*

Proof: By Proposition 10 we have

$$\overline{(F_1 \cup F_2)} = \bar{F}_1 \cup \bar{F}_2 = F_1 \cup F_2 . \ ▌$$

13. Proposition: *The intersection of any collection $\mathcal{C}$ of closed sets is closed.*

Proof: Let x be a point of closure of $\bigcap\{F : F \in \mathcal{C}\}$. Then given $\delta > 0$, there is a $y \in \bigcap\{F : F \in \mathcal{C}\}$ such that $|x - y| < \delta$. Since such a y belongs to each $F \in \mathcal{C}$, we see that x is a point of closure of each $F \in \mathcal{C}$. Since each F is closed, we have $x \in F$ for each F in $\mathcal{C}$. Hence $x \in \bigcap\{F : F \in \mathcal{C}\}$. ▌

14. Proposition: *The complement of an open set is closed and the complement of a closed set is open.*

Proof: Let O be open. If $x \in O$, there is a $\delta > 0$ such that if $|x - y| < \delta$ then $y \in O$. Hence x cannot be a point of closure of $\tilde{O}$, since there is no $y \in \tilde{O}$ with $|x - y| < \delta$. Thus $\tilde{O}$ contains all of its points of closure and is therefore closed.

On the other hand let F be closed and $x \in \tilde{F}$. Then, since x is not a point of closure of F, there is a $\delta > 0$ such that there is no $y \in F$ with $|x - y| < \delta$. Hence, if $|x - y| < \delta$, then $y \in \tilde{F}$. Thus $\tilde{F}$ is open. ▌

We say that a collection $\mathcal{C}$ of sets **covers** a set F if $F \subset \bigcup\{O : O \in \mathcal{C}\}$. In this case the collection $\mathcal{C}$ is called a covering of F. If each $O \in \mathcal{C}$ is open we call $\mathcal{C}$ an **open** covering of F. If $\mathcal{C}$ contains only a finite number of sets, we call $\mathcal{C}$ a **finite** covering. This terminology is inconsistent: In 'open covering' the adjective 'open' refers to the sets in the covering; in 'finite covering' the adjective 'finite' refers to the collection, and does not imply that the sets in the collection are finite sets. Thus the term 'open covering' is an abuse of language and should properly be 'covering by open sets'. Unfortunately, the former terminology is well established in mathematics. With this terminology we state the following theorem:

15. Theorem (Heine-Borel): *Let F be a closed and bounded set of real numbers. Then each open covering of F has a finite subcovering. That is, if $\mathcal{C}$ is a collection of open sets such that $F \subset \bigcup \{O: O \in \mathcal{C}\}$, then there is a finite collection $\{O_1, \ldots, O_n\}$ of sets in $\mathcal{C}$ such that $F \subset \bigcup_{i=1}^{n} O_i$.*

Proof: Let us first consider the case that F is the closed interval $[a, b]$, where $-\infty < a < b < \infty$. Let E be the set of numbers $x \leq b$ with the property that the interval $[a, x]$ can be covered by a finite number of the sets of $\mathcal{C}$. The set E is bounded by b and so has a least upper bound c. Since $c \in [a, b]$, there is an $O \in \mathcal{C}$ which contains c. Since O is open there is an $\epsilon > 0$, such that the interval $(c - \epsilon, c + \epsilon)$ is contained in O. Now $c - \epsilon$ cannot be an upper bound for E, and so there must be an $x \in E$ with $x > c - \epsilon$. Since $x \in E$, there is a finite collection $\{O_1, \ldots, O_k\}$ of sets in $\mathcal{C}$ which covers $[a, x]$. Consequently, the finite collection $\{O_1, \ldots, O_k, O\}$ covers $[a, c + \epsilon]$. Thus each point of $[c, c + \epsilon]$ would be in E if it were less than or equal to b. Since no point of $[c, c + \epsilon]$ except c can belong to E, we must have $c = b$ and $b \in E$. Thus $[a, b]$ can be covered by a finite number of sets from $\mathcal{C}$, proving our special case.

Let now F be any closed and bounded set and $\mathcal{C}$ an open covering of F. Since F is bounded it is contained in some closed bounded interval $[a, b]$. Let $\mathcal{C}^*$ be the collection obtained by adding $\tilde{F}$ to $\mathcal{C}$, that is, $\mathcal{C}^* = \mathcal{C} \cup \{\tilde{F}\}$. Since F is closed, $\tilde{F}$ is open, and $\mathcal{C}^*$ is a collection of open sets. By hypothesis $F \subset \bigcup\{O: O \in \mathcal{C}\}$, and so $\mathbf{R} = \tilde{F} \cup F \subset \tilde{F} \cup \bigcup\{O: O \in \mathcal{C}\} = \bigcup\{O: O \in \mathcal{C}^*\}$. Thus $\mathcal{C}^*$ is an open covering of $\mathbf{R}$ and therefore of $[a, b]$. By our previous case there is a finite subcollection of $\mathcal{C}^*$ which covers $[a, b]$ and hence F. If this finite subcollection does not contain $\tilde{F}$, it is a subcollection of $\mathcal{C}$ and the conclusion of our theorem holds. If the subcollection contains

$\tilde{F}$, denote it by $\{O_1, \ldots, O_n, \tilde{F}\}$. Then $F \subset \tilde{F} \cup O_1 \cup \cdots \cup O_n$. Since no point of F is contained in $\tilde{F}$, we have $F \subset O_1 \cup \cdots \cup O_n$ and the collection $\{O_1, \ldots, O_n\}$ is a finite subcollection of $\mathcal{C}$ which covers F. ▎

16. Proposition: *Let* $\mathcal{C}$ *be a collection of closed sets (of real numbers) with the property that every finite subcollection of* $\mathcal{C}$ *has a nonempty intersection, and suppose that one of the sets in* $\mathcal{C}$ *is bounded. Then*

$$\bigcap_{F \in \mathcal{C}} F \neq \varnothing .$$

Problems

21. Is the set of rational numbers open or closed?

22. What are the sets of real numbers that are both open and closed?

23. Find two sets A and B such that $A \cap B = \varnothing$ and $\bar{A} \cap \bar{B} \neq \varnothing$

24. Show that x is a point of closure of E if and only if there is a sequence $\langle y_n \rangle$ with $y_n \in E$ and $x = \lim y_n$.

25. A number x is called an **accumulation point** of a set E if it is a point of closure of $E \sim \{x\}$. Show that the set E' of accumulation points of E is a closed set.

26. Show that $\bar{E} = E \cup E'$.

27. A set is called **isolated** if $E \cap E' = \varnothing$. Show that every isolated set of real numbers is countable.

28. A set D is called **dense** in **R** if $\bar{D} = \mathbf{R}$. Show that the set of rational numbers is dense in **R**.

29. Prove Propositions 12 and 13 using Propositions 5, 7, and 14.

30. Prove Propositions 5 and 7 using Propositions 12, 13, and 14.

31. A point x is called an **interior** point of a set A if there is a $\delta > 0$ such that the interval $(x - \delta, x + \delta)$ is contained in A. The set of interior points of A is denoted by A°. Show

a. A is open if and only if $A = A^\circ$

b. $A^\circ = \sim(\bar{\tilde{A}})$.

32. Derive Proposition 16 from the Heine-Borel Theorem using DeMorgan's laws.

33. Let $\langle F_n \rangle$ be a sequence of nonempty closed sets of real numbers with $F_{n+1} \subset F_n$. Show that if one of the sets F_n is bounded, then $\bigcap_{i=1}^{\infty} F_i \neq \varnothing$. Give an example to show that this conclusion may be false if we do not require one of the sets to be bounded.

34. The **Cantor ternary set** C consists of all those real numbers in $[0, 1]$ which have ternary expansion (cf. Problem 20) $\langle a_n \rangle$ for which a_n is never 1. (If x has two ternary expansions, we put x in the Cantor set if *one* of the expansions has no term equal to one). Show that C is a closed set, and that C is obtained by first removing the middle third $(\frac{1}{3}, \frac{2}{3})$ from $[0, 1]$, then removing the middle thirds $(\frac{1}{9}, \frac{2}{9})$ and $(\frac{7}{9}, \frac{8}{9})$ of the remaining intervals and so on.

35. Show that the Cantor set can be put into a one-to-one correspondence with the interval $[0, 1]$.

36. Show that the set of accumulation points of the Cantor set is the Cantor set itself.

6 CONTINUOUS FUNCTIONS

Let f be a real-valued function whose domain of definition is a set E of real numbers. We say that f is **continuous at the point** x in E if, given $\epsilon > 0$, there is a $\delta > 0$ such that for all y in E with $|x - y| < \delta$ we have $|f(x) - f(y)| < \epsilon$. The function f is said to be **continuous** on a subset A of E if it is continuous at each point of A. If we merely say that f is continuous, we mean that f is continuous on its domain.

17. Proposition: *Let f be a real-valued function defined and continuous on a closed and bounded set F. Then f is bounded on F and assumes its maximum and minimum on F, i.e. there are points x_1 and x_2 in F such that $f(x_1) \leq f(x) \leq f(x_2)$ for all x in F.*

Proof: We shall first show that f is bounded on F. Since f is continuous on F, for each $x \in F$ there is an open interval I_x containing x such that $|f(y) - f(x)| < 1$ for $y \in I_x \cap F$. Thus for $y \in I_x \cap F$, we have $|f(y)| \leq |f(x)| + 1$ and so f is bounded in I_x. The collection $\{I_x \colon x \in F\}$ is a collection of open intervals which covers F, and by the Heine-Borel Theorem there is a finite subcollection $\{I_{x_1}, \ldots, I_{x_n}\}$ which covers F. Let $M = 1 + \max [\, |f(x_1)|, \ldots, |f(x_n)|\,]$. Then each y in F belongs to some interval I_{x_k} in the finite subcollection, and hence $|f(y)| < 1 + |f(x_k)| \leq M$. This shows that f is bounded (by M) on F.

To see that f assumes its maximum on F, let $m = \sup_{x \in F} f(x)$. Since f is bounded, m is finite, and our goal is to show that there is an

$x_1 \in F$ such that $f(x_1) = m$. Suppose not. Then $f(x) < m$ for each $x \in F$, and by continuity there is an open interval I_x containing x such that $f(y) < \frac{1}{2}(f(x) + m)$ for all $y \in I_x \cap F$. Again using the Heine-Borel Theorem, we can find a finite number of these intervals $\{I_{x_1}, \ldots, I_{x_n}\}$ which cover F. Set $a = \max [f(x_1), \ldots, f(x_n)]$. Then each $y \in F$ belongs to one such interval I_{x_k} and $f(y) < \frac{1}{2}[f(x_k) + m] \leq \frac{1}{2}(a + m)$. Thus $\frac{1}{2}(a + m)$ is a bound for f on F. But this is impossible, since $\frac{1}{2}(a + m) < m$. Consequently there must be an x_1, such that $f(x_1) = m$. Similarly, there is an x_2 at which f assumes its minimum. ▎

18. Proposition: *Let f be a real-valued function defined on $(-\infty, \infty)$. Then f is continuous if and only if for each open set O of real numbers $f^{-1}[O]$ is an open set.*

Proof: Suppose $f^{-1}[O]$ is open for each open set O, and let x be an arbitrary real number. Then, given $\epsilon > 0$, the interval $I = (f(x) - \epsilon, f(x) + \epsilon)$ is an open set, and so its inverse image $f^{-1}[I]$ must be open. Since $x \in f^{-1}[I]$, there must be some $\delta > 0$ such that $(x - \delta, x + \delta) \subset f^{-1}[I]$. But this implies that if $|y - x| < \delta$, then $f(y) \in (f(x) - \epsilon, f(x) + \epsilon)$; that is, $|f(x) - f(y)| < \epsilon$. Hence f is continuous at x. Since x was arbitrary, f is continuous.

Suppose now that f is continuous and that O is an open set. Let x be a point of $f^{-1}[O]$. Then $f(x) \in O$, and there is an $\epsilon > 0$ such that $(f(x) - \epsilon, f(x) + \epsilon) \subset O$. Since f is continuous at x, there is a $\delta > 0$ such that $|f(x) - f(y)| < \epsilon$ for $|x - y| < \delta$. Thus, if $y \in (x - \delta, x + \delta)$, we have $f(y) \in (f(x) - \epsilon, f(x) + \epsilon) \subset O$. Hence $(x - \delta, x + \delta) \subset f^{-1}[O]$, and so $f^{-1}[O]$ is open. ▎

Definition: *A real-valued function defined on a set E is said to be uniformly continuous (on E) if, given $\epsilon > 0$, there is a $\delta > 0$ such that for all x and y in E with $|x - y| < \delta$ we have $|f(x) - f(y)| < \epsilon$.*

19. Proposition: *If a real-valued function f is defined and continuous on a closed and bounded set F of real numbers, it is uniformly continuous on F.*

Proof: Given $\epsilon > 0$ and x in F, there is a $\delta_x > 0$ such that $|x - y| < \delta_x$ implies $|f(x) - f(y)| < \frac{1}{2}\epsilon$. Let O_x be the interval

$(x - \frac{1}{2}\delta_x, x + \frac{1}{2}\delta_x)$. Then $\{O_x : x \in F\}$ is an open covering of F. By the Heine-Borel Theorem there is a finite subcollection $\{O_{x_1}, \ldots, O_{x_n}\}$ which covers F. Let $\delta = \frac{1}{2}\min(\delta_{x_1}, \ldots, \delta_{x_n})$. Then δ is positive. Given two points y and z in F such that $|y - z| < \delta$, the point y must belong to some O_{x_i}, and hence there is an i such that $|y - x_i| < \frac{1}{2}\delta_{x_i}$. Consequently

$$|z - x_i| \le |z - y| + |y - x_i| < \tfrac{1}{2}\delta_{x_i} + \delta \le \delta_{x_i}$$

Hence

$$|f(y) - f(x_i)| < \frac{\epsilon}{2},$$

and

$$|f(z) - f(x_i)| < \frac{\epsilon}{2},$$

whence

$$|f(z) - f(y)| < \epsilon,$$

showing that f is uniformly continuous on F. ▌

Definition: *A sequence* $\langle f_n \rangle$ *of functions defined on a set* E *is said to converge* **pointwise** *on* E *to a function* f *if for every* x *in* E *we have* $f(x) = \lim f_n(x)$; *that is, if given* $x \in E$ *and* $\epsilon > 0$ *there is an* N *such that for all* $n \ge N$ *we have* $|f(x) - f_n(x)| < \epsilon$.

Definition: *A sequence* $\langle f_n \rangle$ *of functions defined on a set* E *is said to converge* **uniformly** *on* E *if, given* $\epsilon > 0$, *there is an* N *such that for all* $x \in E$ *and all* $n \ge N$ *we have* $|f_n(x) - f(x)| < \epsilon$.

Problems

37. Let F be a closed set of real numbers and f a real-valued function which is defined and continuous on F. Show that there is a function g defined and continuous on $(-\infty, \infty)$ such that $f(x) = g(x)$ for each $x \in F$. (Hint: Take g to be linear in each of the intervals of which $\tilde{F}$ is composed).

38. Let f be a real valued function with domain E. Prove that f is continuous if and only if for each open set O there is an open set U such that $f^{-1}[O] = E \cap U$.

39. Let $\langle f_n \rangle$ be a sequence of continuous functions defined on a set E. Prove that if $\langle f_n \rangle$ converges uniformly to f on E then f is continuous on E.

40. Let f be that function defined by setting

$$f(x) = \begin{cases} x & \text{if } x \text{ irrational} \\ p \sin \dfrac{1}{q} & \text{if } x = \dfrac{p}{q} \text{ in lowest terms.} \end{cases}$$

At what points is f continuous?

41. a. Show that if f and g are continuous functions, then the functions $f + g$ and fg are continuous.

b. Show that if f and g are continuous then so is $f \circ g$.

c. Let $f \vee g$ be the function defined by $(f \vee g)(x) = f(x) \vee g(x)$, and define $f \wedge g$ similarly. Show that if f and g are continuous so are $f \vee g$ and $f \wedge g$.

d. If f is continuous, then so is $|f|$.

42. Let x be a real number in $[0, 1]$ with the ternary expansion (cf. Problem 20) $\langle a_n \rangle$. Let $N = \infty$ if none of the a_n are 1, and otherwise let N be the smallest value of n such that $a_n = 1$. Let $b_n = \frac{1}{2}a_n$ for $n < N$, and $b_N = 1$. Show that

$$\sum_{n=1}^{N} \frac{b_n}{2^n}$$

is independent of the ternary expansion of x (if x has two expansions) and that the function f defined by setting

$$f(x) = \sum_{n=1}^{N} \frac{b_n}{2^n}$$

is a continuous, monotone function on the interval $[0, 1]$. Show that f is constant on each interval contained in the complement of the Cantor ternary set (Problem 34), and that f maps the Cantor ternary set *onto* the interval $[0, 1]$. (This function is called the *Cantor ternary function.*)

43. ***Limit superior of a function of a real variable.*** Let f be a real (or extended-real) valued function defined for all x in an interval containing y. We define

$$\overline{\lim_{x \to y}} f(x) = \inf_{\delta > 0} \sup_{0 < |x - y| < \delta} f(x)$$

$$\overline{\lim_{x \to y+}} f(x) = \inf_{\delta > 0} \sup_{0 < x - y < \delta} f(x)$$

with similar definitions for $\underline{\lim}$.

a. $\overline{\lim_{x\to y}} f(x) \le A$ if and only if, given $\epsilon > 0$, there is a $\delta > 0$ such that for all x with $0 < |x - y| < \delta$ we have $f(x) \le A + \epsilon$.

b. $\overline{\lim_{x\to y}} f(x) \ge A$ if and only if, given $\epsilon > 0$ and $\delta > 0$, there is an x such that $0 < |x - y| < \delta$ and $f(x) \ge A - \epsilon$.

c. $\underline{\lim_{x\to y}} f(x) \le \overline{\lim_{x\to y}} f(x)$ with equality (for $\overline{\lim} f \ne \pm\infty$) if and only if $\lim_{x\to y} f(x)$ exists.

d. If $\overline{\lim_{x\to y}} f(x) = A$ and $\langle x_n \rangle$ is a sequence with $x_n \ne x$ such that $y = \lim x_n$, then $\overline{\lim} f(x_n) \le A$.

e. If $\overline{\lim_{x\to y}} f(x) = A$, then there is a sequence $\langle x_n \rangle$ with $x_n \ne x$ such that $y = \lim x_n$ and $A = \lim f(x_n)$.

f. For a real number l we have $l = \lim_{x\to y} f(x)$ if and only if $l = \lim f(x_n)$ for every sequence $\langle x_n \rangle$ with $x_n \ne x$ and $y = \lim x_n$.

44. ***Semicontinuous functions.*** An extended real-valued function f is called *lower semicontinuous* at the point y if $f(y) \ne -\infty$ and $f(y) \le \underline{\lim_{x\to y}} f(x)$. Similarly f is called upper semicontinuous at y if $f(y) \ne +\infty$ and $f(y) \ge \overline{\lim_{x\to y}} f(x)$. We say that f is lower (upper) semicontinuous on an interval if it is lower (upper) semicontinuous at each point of the interval. The function f is upper semicontinuous if and only if the function $-f$ is lower semicontinuous.

a. Prove that f is lower semicontinuous at y if and only if given $\epsilon > 0$, $\exists \delta > 0$ such that $f(y) \le f(x) + \epsilon$ for all x with $|x - y| < \delta$.

b. A function f is continuous (at a point or in an interval) if and only if it is both upper and lower semicontinuous (at the point or in the interval).

c. Show that if f and g are lower semicontinuous functions so is $f \vee g$.

d. Let $\langle f_n \rangle$ be a sequence of lower semicontinuous functions. Show that the function f defined by $f(x) = \sup_n f_n(x)$ is also lower semicontinuous.

e. A real valued function φ defined on an interval $[a, b]$ is called a step function if there is a partition $a = x_0 < x_1 < \cdots < x_n = b$ such that for each i the function φ assumes only one value in the interval (x_i, x_{i+1}). Show that a step function φ is lower semicontinuous iff $\varphi(x_i)$ is less than or equal to the smaller of the two values assumed in (x_{i-1}, x_i) and (x_i, x_{i+1}).

f. A function f defined on an interval $[a, b]$ is lower semicontinuous if and only if there is a monotone increasing sequence $\langle\varphi_n\rangle$ of lower semicontinuous step functions on $[a, b]$ such that for each $x \in [a, b]$ we have $f(x) = \lim \varphi_n(x)$.

g. Show that the step functions in (f) can be replaced by continuous functions.

h. Prove that a function f which is defined and lower semicontinuous on a closed interval $[a, b]$ is bounded from below and assumes its minimum on $[a, b]$; that is, that there is a $y \in [a, b]$ such that $f(y) \leq f(x)$ for all $x \in [a, b]$.

45. ***Upper and lower envelopes of a function.*** Let f be a real-valued function defined on $[a, b]$. We define the *lower envelope* g of f to be the function g defined by

$$g(y) = \sup_{\delta>0} \inf_{|x-y|<\delta} f(x),$$

and the upper envelope h by

$$h(y) = \inf_{\delta>0} \sup_{|x-y|<\delta} f(x).$$

a. For each $x \in [a, b]$, $g(x) \leq f(x) \leq h(x)$, and $g(x) = f(x)$ if and only if f is lower semicontinuous at x, while $g(x) = h(x)$ if and only if f is continuous at x.

b. If f is bounded, the function g is lower semicontinuous, while h is upper semicontinuous.

c. If φ is any lower semicontinuous function such that $\varphi(x) \leq f(x)$ for all $x \in [a, b]$, then $\varphi(x) \leq g(x)$ for all $x \in [a, b]$.

7 BOREL SETS

Although the intersection of any collection of closed sets is closed and the union of any *finite* collection of closed sets is closed, the union of a *countable* collection of closed sets need not be closed. For example, the set of rational numbers is the union of a countable collection of closed sets each of which contains exactly one number. Thus if we are interested in σ-algebras of sets which contain all of the closed sets we must consider more general types of sets than the open and closed sets. This leads us to the following definition:

Definition: *The collection $\mathcal{B}$ of Borel sets is the smallest σ-algebra which contains all of the open sets.*

Such a smallest σ-algebra exists by Proposition 1.3. It is also the smallest σ-algebra which contains all closed sets and the smallest σ-algebra which contains the open intervals.

A set which is a countable union of closed sets is called an $\mathcal{F}_\sigma$ ($\mathcal{F}$ for closed, σ for sum). Thus every countable set is an $\mathcal{F}_\sigma$, as is of course every closed set. A countable union of sets in $\mathcal{F}_\sigma$ is again in $\mathcal{F}_\sigma$. Since $(a, b) = \bigcup_{n=1}^{\infty}\left[a + \frac{1}{n}, b - \frac{1}{n}\right]$, each open interval is an $\mathcal{F}_\sigma$, and hence each open set is an $\mathcal{F}_\sigma$.

We say that a set is a $\mathcal{G}_\delta$ if it is the intersection of a countable collection of open sets ($\mathcal{G}$ for open, δ for *durchschnitt*). Thus the complement of an $\mathcal{F}_\sigma$ is a $\mathcal{G}_\delta$, and conversely.

The $\mathcal{F}_\sigma$ and $\mathcal{G}_\delta$ are relatively simple types of Borel sets. We could also consider sets of type $\mathcal{F}_{\sigma\delta}$ which are the intersections of countable collections of sets each of which is an $\mathcal{F}_\sigma$. Similarly, we can construct the classes $\mathcal{G}_{\delta\sigma}$, $\mathcal{F}_{\sigma\delta\sigma}$, etc. Thus the classes in the two sequences

$$\mathcal{F}_\sigma, \mathcal{F}_{\sigma\delta}, \mathcal{F}_{\sigma\delta\sigma}, \ldots, \mathcal{G}_\delta, \mathcal{G}_{\delta\sigma}, \mathcal{G}_{\delta\sigma\delta}, \ldots$$

are all classes of Borel sets. However, not every Borel set belongs to one of these classes. Further theory of Borel sets can be found in Kuratowski [12], but we shall need only the facts that follow easily from their definition as forming the smallest σ-algebra containing the open and closed sets.

Problems

46. Let f be a lower semicontinuous function defined for all real numbers. What can you say about the sets $\{x: f(x) > \alpha\}$, $\{x: f(x) \geq \alpha\}$, $\{x: f(x) < \alpha\}$, $\{x: f(x) \leq \alpha\}$, and $\{x: f(x) = \alpha\}$?

47. Let f be a real-valued function defined for all real numbers. Prove that the set of points at which f is continuous is a $\mathcal{G}_\delta$.

3 Lebesgue Measure

1 INTRODUCTION

The length $l(I)$ of an interval I is defined, as usual, to be the difference of the endpoints of the interval. Length is an example of a *set function;* that is, a function which associates an extended real number to each set in some collection of sets. In the case of length the domain is the collection of all intervals. We should like to extend the notion of length to more complicated sets than intervals. For instance, we could define the "length" of an open set to be the sum of the lengths of the open intervals of which it is composed. Since the class of open sets is still too restricted for our purposes, we would like to construct a set function m which assigns to each set E in some collection $\mathcal{M}$ of sets of real numbers a nonnegative extended real number mE called the measure of E. Ideally, we should like m to have the following properties:

1. mE is defined for each set E of real numbers; that is, $\mathcal{M} = \mathcal{P}(R)$.
2. for an interval I, $mI = l(I)$.
3. if $\langle E_n \rangle$ is a sequence of disjoint sets (for which m is defined), $m(\bigcup E_n) = \Sigma mE_n$.
4. m is translation invariant; that is, if E is a set for which m is defined and if $E + y$ is the set $\{x + y : x \in E\}$, obtained by replacing each point x in E by the point $x + y$, then $m(E + y) = mE$.

Unfortunately, as we shall see in Section 4, it is impossible to construct a set function having all four of these properties, and it is not known whether there is a set function satisfying the first three properties.[1] Consequently, one of these properties must be weakened, and it is most useful to retain the last three properties and to weaken the first condition so that mE need not be defined for all sets E of real numbers.[2] We shall want mE to be defined for as many sets as possible, and will find it convenient to require the family $\mathcal{M}$ of sets for which m is defined to be a σ-algebra. Thus, we shall say that m is a **countably additive** measure if it is a nonnegative extended real valued function whose domain of definition is a σ-algebra $\mathcal{M}$ of sets (of real numbers) and we have $m(\bigcup E_n) = \Sigma mE_n$ for each sequence $\langle E_n \rangle$ of disjoint sets in $\mathcal{M}$. Thus our goal in the next two sections will be the construction of a countably additive measure which is translation invariant and has the property that $mI = l(I)$ for each interval I.

Problems

Let m be a countably additive measure defined for all sets in a σ-algebra $\mathcal{M}$.

1. If A and B are two sets in $\mathcal{M}$ with $A \subset B$, then $mA \leq mB$. This property is called monotonicity.

2. Let $\langle E_n \rangle$ be any sequence of sets in $\mathcal{M}$. Then $m(\bigcup E_n) \leq \Sigma mE_n$. (Hint: use Proposition 1.2.) This property of a measure is called countable subadditivity.

3. If there is a set A in $\mathcal{M}$ such that $mA < \infty$, then $m\varnothing = 0$.

4. Let nE be ∞ for an infinite set E and be equal to the number of elements in E for a finite set. Show that n is a countably additive set function which is translation invariant and defined for all sets of real numbers.

2 OUTER MEASURE

For each set A of real numbers consider the countable collections $\{I_n\}$ of open intervals which cover A, that is, collections for which $A \subset \bigcup I_n$, and for each such collection consider the sum of the

[1] If we assume the continuum hypothesis (that every noncountable set of real numbers can be put in one-to-one correspondence with the set of all real numbers) then such a measure is impossible.

[2] Weakening property (1) is not the only approach; it is also possible to replace property (3) of countable additivity by the weaker property of finite additivity: for each finite sequence $\langle E_n \rangle$ of disjoint sets we have $m(\bigcup E_n) = \Sigma mE_n$. (See Problem 10.21). Another possible alternative to property (3) is countable subadditivity which is satisfied by the outer measure we construct in the next section. (See Problem 2 below.)

lengths of the intervals in the collection. Since the lengths are positive numbers, this sum is uniquely defined independently of the order of the terms. We define the **outer measure**[3] m^*A of A to be the infimum of all such sums. In an abbreviated notation

$$m^*A = \inf_{A \subset \bigcup I_n} \sum l(I_n).$$

It follows immediately from the definition of m^* that $m^*\varnothing = 0$ and that if $A \subset B$, then $m^*A \leq m^*B$. Also each set consisting of a single point has outer measure zero. We establish two propositions concerning outer measure:

1. Proposition: *The outer measure of an interval is its length.*

Proof: We begin with the case in which we have a closed finite interval, say $[a, b]$. Since the open interval $(a - \epsilon, b + \epsilon)$ contains $[a, b]$ for each positive ϵ, we have $m^*[a, b] \leq l(a - \epsilon, b + \epsilon) = b - a + 2\epsilon$. Since $m^*[a, b] \leq b - a + 2\epsilon$ for each positive ϵ, we must have $m^*[a, b] \leq b - a$. Thus we have only to show that $m^*[a, b] \geq b - a$. But this is equivalent to showing that if $\{I_n\}$ is any countable collection of open intervals covering $[a, b]$, then

$$(1) \qquad \sum l(I_n) \geq b - a.$$

By the Heine-Borel theorem, any collection of open intervals covering $[a, b]$ contains a finite subcollection which also covers $[a, b]$, and since the sum of the lengths of the finite subcollection is no greater than the sum of the lengths of the original collection, it suffices to prove the inequality (1) for finite collections $\{I_n\}$ which cover $[a, b]$. Since a is contained in $\bigcup I_n$, there must be one of the I_n's which contains a. Let this be the interval (a_1, b_1). We have $a_1 < a < b_1$. If, $b_1 \leq b$, then $b_1 \in [a, b]$, and since $b_1 \notin (a_1, b_1)$, there must be an interval (a_2, b_2) in the collection $\{I_n\}$ such that $b_1 \in (a_2, b_2)$; that is, $a_2 < b_1 < b_2$. Continuing in this fashion we obtain a sequence $(a_1, b_1), \ldots, (a_k, b_k)$ from the collection $\{I_n\}$ such that $a_i < b_{i-1} < b_i$.

[3] In order to distinguish this outer measure from the more general outer measures to be considered in Chapter 12, we call this outer measure *Lebesgue* outer measure after Henri Lebesgue. Since we consider no other outer measure in this chapter, we refer to m^* simply as outer measure.

Since $\{I_n\}$ is a finite collection, our process must terminate with some interval (a_k, b_k). But it terminates only if $b \varepsilon (a_k, b_k)$; that is, if $a_k < b < b_k$. Thus

$$\begin{aligned}\sum l(I_n) \geq \sum l(a_i, b_i) &= (b_k - a_k) + (b_{k-1} - a_{k-1}) + \cdots (b_1 - a_1)\\ &= b_k - (a_k - b_{k-1}) - (a_{k-1} - b_{k-2})\\ &\quad - \cdots - (a_2 - b_1) - a_1 > b_k - a_1,\end{aligned}$$

since $a_i < b_{i-1}$. But $b_k > b$ and $a_1 < a$, and so we have $b_k - a_1 > b - a$, whence $\Sigma l(I_n) > (b - a)$. This shows that $m^*[a, b] = b - a$.

If I is any finite interval, then given $\epsilon > 0$, there is a closed interval $J \subset I$, such that $l(J) > l(I) - \epsilon$. Hence

$$l(I) - \epsilon < l(J) = m^*J \leq m^*I \leq m^*\bar{I} = l(\bar{I}) = l(I).$$

Thus for each $\epsilon > 0$,

$$l(I) - \epsilon < m^*I \leq l(I),$$

and so $m^*I = l(I)$.

If I is an infinite interval, then given any real number Δ, there is a closed interval $J \subset I$ with $l(J) = \Delta$. Hence $m^*I \geq m^*J = l(J) = \Delta$. Since $m^*I \geq \Delta$ for each Δ, $m^*I = \infty = l(I)$. ∎

2. Proposition: *Let $\{A_n\}$ be a countable collection of sets of real numbers. Then*

$$m^*(\bigcup A_n) \leq \sum m^*A_n.$$

Proof: If one of the sets A_n has infinite outer measure, the inequality holds trivially. If m^*A_n is finite, then given $\epsilon > 0$, there is a countable collection $\{I_{n,i}\}_i$ of open intervals such that $A_n \subset \bigcup_i I_{n,i}$ and $\sum_i l(I_{n,i}) < m^*A_n + 2^{-n}\epsilon$. Now the collection $\{I_{n,i}\}_{n,i} = \bigcup_n \{I_{n,i}\}_i$ is countable, being the union of a countable number of countable collections, and covers $\bigcup A_n$. Thus

$$\begin{aligned}m^*(\bigcup A_n) \leq \sum_{n,i} l(I_{n,i}) = \sum_n \sum_i l(I_{n,i}) &< \sum_n (m^*A_n + \epsilon 2^{-n})\\ &= \sum m^*A_n + \epsilon.\end{aligned}$$

Since ϵ was an arbitrary positive number,

$$m^*(\bigcup A_n) \leq \sum m^*A_n\,. \ ∎$$

3. Corollary: *If A is countable, $m^*A = 0$.*

4. Corollary: *The set* $[0, 1]$ *is not countable.*

5. Proposition: *Given any set A and any $\epsilon > 0$, there is an open set O such that $A \subset O$ and $m^*O \leq m^*A + \epsilon$. There is a $G \in \mathcal{G}_\delta$ such that $A \subset G$ and $m^*A = m^*G$.*

Problems

5. Let A be the set of rational numbers between 0 and 1, and let $\{I_n\}$ be a *finite* collection of open intervals covering A. Then $\Sigma l(I_n) \geq 1$.

6. Prove Proposition 5.

7. Prove that m^* is translation invariant.

8. Prove that if $m^*A = 0$, then $m^*(A \cup B) = m^*B$.

3 MEASURABLE SETS AND LEBESGUE MEASURE

While outer measure has the advantage that it is defined for all sets, it is not countably additive. It becomes countably additive, however, if we suitably reduce the family of sets on which it is defined. Perhaps the best way of doing this is to use the following definition due to Carathéodory:

Definition: *A set E is said to be measurable*[4] *if for each set A we have $m^*A = m^*(A \cap E) + m^*(A \cap \tilde{E})$.*

Since we always have $m^*A \leq m^*(A \cap E) + m^*(A \cap \tilde{E})$, we see that E is measurable if (and only if) for each A we have $m^*A \geq m^*(A \cap E) + m^*(A \cap \tilde{E})$. Since the definition of measurability is symmetric in E and $\tilde{E}$, we have $\tilde{E}$ measurable whenever E is. Clearly $\emptyset$ and the set R of all real numbers are measurable.

6. Lemma: *If $m^*E = 0$, then E is measurable.*

Proof: Let A be any set. Then $A \cap E \subset E$, and so $m^*(A \cap E) \leq m^*E = 0$. Also $A \supset A \cap \tilde{E}$, and so

$$m^*A \geq m^*(A \cap \tilde{E}) = m^*(A \cap \tilde{E}) + m^*(A \cap E),$$

and therefore E is measurable. ❙

7. Lemma: *If E_1 and E_2 are measurable, so is $E_1 \cup E_2$.*

Proof: Let A be any set. Since E_2 is measurable, we have

$$m^*(A \cap \tilde{E}_1) = m^*(A \cap \tilde{E}_1 \cap E_2) + m^*(A \cap \tilde{E}_1 \cap \tilde{E}_2),$$

[4] In the present case m^* is Lebesgue outer measure, and we say E is *Lebesgue* measurable. More general notions of measurable set are considered in Chapters 11 and 12.

and since $A \cap (E_1 \cup E_2) = [A \cap E_1] \cup [A \cap E_2 \cap \tilde{E}_1]$, we have

$$m^*(A \cap [E_1 \cup E_2]) \le m^*(A \cap E_1) + m^*(A \cap E_2 \cap \tilde{E}_1).$$

Thus

$$\begin{aligned} m^*(A \cap [E_1 \cup E_2]) + m^*(A \cap \tilde{E}_1 \cap \tilde{E}_2) &\le m^*(A \cap E_1) \\ &\quad + m^*(A \cap E_2 \cap \tilde{E}_1) + m^*(A \cap \tilde{E}_1 \cap \tilde{E}_2) \\ &= m^*(A \cap E_1) + m^*(A \cap \tilde{E}_1) = m^*A, \end{aligned}$$

by the measurability of E_1. Since $\sim(E_1 \cup E_2) = \tilde{E}_1 \cap \tilde{E}_2$, this shows that $E_1 \cup E_2$ is measurable. ▎

8. Corollary: *The family $\mathcal{M}$ of measurable sets is an algebra of sets.*

9. Lemma: *Let A be any set, and $E_1, \ldots, E_n$ a finite sequence of disjoint measurable sets. Then*

$$m^*\left(A \cap \left[\bigcup_{i=1}^{n} E_i\right]\right) = \sum_{i=1}^{n} m^*(A \cap E_i).$$

Proof: We prove the lemma by induction on n. It is clearly true for $n = 1$, and we assume it is true if we have $n - 1$ sets E_i. Since the E_i are disjoint sets, we have

$$A \cap \left[\bigcup_{i=1}^{n} E_i\right] \cap E_n = A \cap E_n$$

and

$$A \cap \left[\bigcup_{i=1}^{n} E_i\right] \cap \tilde{E}_n = A \cap \left[\bigcup_{i=1}^{n-1} E_i\right].$$

Hence the measurability of E_n implies

$$\begin{aligned} m^*\left(A \cap \left[\bigcup_{i=1}^{n} E_i\right]\right) &= m^*(A \cap E_n) + m^*\left(A \cap \left[\bigcup_{i=1}^{n-1} E_i\right]\right) \\ &= m^*(A \cap E_n) + \sum_{i=1}^{n-1} m^*(A \cap E_i) \end{aligned}$$

by our assumption of the lemma for $n - 1$ sets. ▎

10. Theorem: *The collection $\mathcal{M}$ of measurable sets is a σ-algebra; that is, the complement of a measurable set is measurable and the union (and intersection) of a countable collection of measurable sets is measurable. Moreover, every set with outer measure zero is measurable.*

Proof: We have already observed that $\mathcal{M}$ is an algebra of sets, and so we have only to prove that if a set E is the union of a countable collection of measurable sets it is measurable. By Proposition 1.2 such an E must be the union of a sequence $\langle E_n \rangle$ of pairwise disjoint measurable sets. Let A be any set, and let $F_n = \bigcup_{i=1}^{n} E_i$. Then F_n is measurable, and $\tilde{F}_n \supset \tilde{E}$. Hence

$$m^*A = m^*(A \cap F_n) + m^*(A \cap \tilde{F}_n) \geq m^*(A \cap F_n) + m^*(A \cap \tilde{E}).$$

By Lemma 9

$$m^*(A \cap F_n) = \sum_{i=1}^{n} m^*(A \cap E_i).$$

Thus

$$m^*A \geq \sum_{i=1}^{n} m^*(A \cap E_i) + m^*(A \cap \tilde{E}).$$

Since the lefthand side of this inequality is independent of n, we have

$$\begin{aligned} m^*A &\geq \sum_{i=1}^{\infty} m^*(A \cap E_i) + m^*(A \cap \tilde{E}) \\ &\geq m^*(A \cap E) + m^*(A \cap \tilde{E}) \end{aligned}$$

by the countable subadditivity of m^*. ∎

11. Lemma: *The interval* (a, ∞) *is measurable.*

Proof: Let A be any set, $A_1 = A \cap (a, \infty)$, and $A_2 = A \cap (-\infty, a]$. Then we must show $m^*A_1 + m^*A_2 \leq m^*A$. If $m^*A = \infty$, then there is nothing to prove. If $m^*A < \infty$, then given $\epsilon > 0$ there is a countable collection $\{I_n\}$ of open intervals which cover A and for which

$$\sum l(I_n) \leq m^*A + \epsilon.$$

Let $I_n' = I_n \cap (a, \infty)$ and $I_n'' = I_n \cap (-\infty, a]$. Then I_n' and I_n'' are intervals (or empty) and

$$l(I_n) = l(I_n') + l(I_n'') = m^*I_n' + m^*I_n''.$$

Since $A_1 \subset \bigcup I_n'$, we have

$$m^*A_1 \leq m^*(\bigcup I_n') \leq \sum m^*I_n',$$

and since $A_2 \subset \bigcup I_n''$, we have

$$m^*A_2 \leq m^*(\bigcup I_n'') \leq \sum m^*I_n''.$$

Thus

$$m^*A_1 + m^*A_2 \leq \sum(m^*I'_n + m^*I''_n)$$
$$\leq \sum l(I_n) \leq m^*A + \epsilon.$$

But ϵ was an arbitrary positive number, and so we must have $m^*A_1 + m^*A_2 \leq m^*A$. ❙

12. Theorem: *Every Borel set is measurable. In particular each open set and each closed set is measurable.*

Proof: Since the collection $\mathcal{M}$ of measurable sets is a σ-algebra, we have $(-\infty, a]$ measurable for each a since $(-\infty, a] = \sim(a, \infty)$. Since $(-\infty, b) = \bigcup_{n=1}^{\infty} (-\infty, b - 1/n]$, we have $(-\infty, b)$ measurable. Hence each open interval $(a, b) = (-\infty, b) \cap (a, \infty)$ is measurable. But each open set is the union of a countable number of open intervals and so must be measurable. Thus $\mathcal{M}$ is a σ-algebra containing the open sets and must therefore contain the family $\mathcal{B}$ of Borel sets, since $\mathcal{B}$ is the smallest σ-algebra containing the open sets. *Note:* The theorem also follows immediately from the fact that $\mathcal{M}$ is a σ-algebra containing each interval of the form (a, ∞) and the fact that $\mathcal{B}$ is the smallest σ-algebra containing all such intervals. ❙

If E is a measurable set, we define the Lebesgue measure mE to be the outer measure of E. Thus m is the set function obtained by restricting the set function m^* to the family $\mathcal{M}$ of measurable sets. Two important properties of Lebesgue measure are summarized by the following propositions:

13. Proposition: *Let $\langle E_i \rangle$ be a sequence of measurable sets. Then*

$$m(\bigcup E_i) \leq \sum mE_i.$$

If the sets E_n are pairwise disjoint, then

$$m(\bigcup E_i) = \sum mE_i.$$

Proof: The inequality is simply a restatement of the subadditivity of m^* given by Proposition 2. If $\langle E_i \rangle$ is a finite sequence of disjoint measurable sets, then Lemma 9 with $A = \mathbf{R}$ implies that

$$m(\bigcup E_i) = \sum mE_i,$$

and so m is finitely additive. Let $\langle E_i \rangle$ be an infinite sequence of pairwise disjoint measurable sets. Then

$$\bigcup_{i=1}^{\infty} E_i \supset \bigcup_{i=1}^{n} E_i$$

and so

$$m\left(\bigcup_{i=1}^{\infty} E_i\right) \geq m\left(\bigcup_{i=1}^{n} E_i\right) = \sum_{i=1}^{n} mE_i.$$

Since the lefthand side of this inequality is independent of n, we have

$$m\left(\bigcup_{i=1}^{\infty} E_i\right) \geq \sum_{i=1}^{\infty} mE_i.$$

The reverse inequality follows from countable subadditivity, and we have

$$m\left(\bigcup_{i=1}^{\infty} E_i\right) = \sum_{i=1}^{\infty} mE_i. \quad \blacksquare$$

14. Proposition: *Let $\langle E_n \rangle$ be an infinite decreasing sequence of measurable sets, that is, a sequence with $E_{n+1} \subset E_n$ for each n. Let mE_1 be finite. Then*

$$m\left(\bigcap_{i=1}^{\infty} E_i\right) = \lim_{n\to\infty} mE_n.$$

Proof: Let $E = \bigcap_{i=1}^{\infty} E_i$, and let $F_i = E_i \sim E_{i+1}$. Then

$$E_1 \sim E = \bigcup_{i=1}^{\infty} F_i,$$

and the sets F_i are pairwise disjoint. Hence

$$m(E_1 \sim E) = \sum_{i=1}^{\infty} mF_i = \sum_{i=1}^{\infty} m(E_i \sim E_{i+1}).$$

But $mE_1 = mE + m(E_1 \sim E)$, and $mE_i = mE_{i+1} + m(E_i \sim E_{i+1})$, since $E \subset E_1$ and $E_{i+1} \subset E_i$. Since $mE_i \leq mE_1 < \infty$, we have $m(E_1 \sim E) = mE_1 - mE$ and $m(E_i \sim E_{i+1}) = mE_i - mE_{i+1}$. Thus

$$\begin{aligned} mE_1 - mE &= \sum_{i=1}^{\infty} (mE_i - mE_{i+1}) \\ &= \lim_{n\to\infty} \sum_{i=1}^{n} (mE_i - mE_{i+1}) \\ &= \lim_{n\to\infty} (mE_1 - mE_n) \\ &= mE_1 - \lim_{n\to\infty} mE_n \end{aligned}$$

Since $mE_1 < \infty$, we have

$$mE = \lim_{n \to \infty} mE_n . \ \blacksquare$$

The following proposition expresses a number of ways in which a measurable set is very nearly a nice set. The proof is left to the reader (Problem 11).

15. Proposition: *Let E be a given set. Then the following five statements are equivalent:*

i. E is measurable;
ii. given $\epsilon > 0$, *there is an open set* $O \supset E$ *with* $m^*(O \sim E) < \epsilon$;
iii. given $\epsilon > 0$, *there is a closed set* $F \subset E$ *with* $m^*(E \sim F) < \epsilon$;
iv. there is a G in $\mathcal{G}_\delta$ *with* $E \subset G$, $m^*(G \sim E) = 0$.
v. there is an F in $\mathcal{F}_\sigma$ *with* $F \subset E$, $m^*(E \sim F) = 0$.

If m^*E *is finite, the above statements are equivalent to*

vi. given $\epsilon > 0$, *there is a finite union U of open intervals such that* $m^*(U \,\Delta\, E) < \epsilon$.

The notation $U \,\Delta\, E$ is used to denote the symmetric difference of U and E defined by $U \,\Delta\, E = (U \sim E) \cup (E \sim U)$.

Problems

9. Show that if E is a measurable set, then each translate $E + y$ of E is also measurable.

10. Show that if E_1 and E_2 are measurable, then $m(E_1 \cup E_2) + m(E_1 \cap E_2) = mE_1 + mE_2$.

11. Prove Proposition 15. Hint:

a. showing that for $m^*E < \infty$, (i) $\Rightarrow$ (ii) $\Leftrightarrow$ (vi) (cf. Proposition 5);
b. use (a) to show that for arbitrary sets E (i) $\Rightarrow$ (ii) $\Rightarrow$ (iv) $\Rightarrow$ (i);
c. use (b) to show (i) $\Rightarrow$ (iii) $\Rightarrow$ (v) $\Rightarrow$ (i).

4 A NONMEASURABLE SET

We are going to show the existence of a nonmeasurable set. If x and y are real numbers in $[0, 1)$, we define the *sum modulo one* of x and y to be $x + y$, if $x + y < 1$, and to be $x + y - 1$ if $x + y \geqslant 1$. Let us denote the sum modulo one of x and y by $x \stackrel{\circ}{+} y$. Then $\stackrel{\circ}{+}$ is a commutative and associative operation taking pairs of numbers in $[0, 1)$ into numbers in $[0, 1)$. If we assign to each $x \in [0, 1)$ the angle $2\pi x$, then addition modulo one corresponds to the addition of angles. If E is a subset of $[0, 1)$, we define the translate modulo one of E to be the set $E \overset{\circ}{+} y = \{z: z = x \overset{\circ}{+} y \text{ for some } x \in E\}$. Considering addition modulo one as addition of angles, translation modulo one by y corresponds to rotation through an angle of $2\pi y$. The following lemma shows that Lebesgue measure is invariant under translation modulo 1.

16. Lemma: *Let $E \subset [0, 1)$ be a measurable set. Then for each $y \in [0, 1)$ the set $E \overset{\circ}{+} y$ is measurable and $m(E \overset{\circ}{+} y) = mE$.*

Proof: Let $E_1 = E \cap [0, 1 - y)$ and $E_2 = E \cap [1 - y, 1)$. Then E_1 and E_2 are disjoint measurable sets whose union is E, and so

$$mE = mE_1 + mE_2.$$

Now $E_1 \overset{\circ}{+} y = E_1 + y$, and so $E_1 \overset{\circ}{+} y$ is measurable and we have $m(E_1 \overset{\circ}{+} y) = mE_1$, since m is translation invariant. Also $E_2 \overset{\circ}{+} y = E_2 + (y - 1)$, and so $E_2 \overset{\circ}{+} y$ is measurable and $m(E_2 \overset{\circ}{+} y) = mE_2$. But $E \overset{\circ}{+} y = (E_1 \overset{\circ}{+} y) \cup (E_2 \overset{\circ}{+} y)$ and the sets $(E_1 \overset{\circ}{+} y)$ and $(E_2 \overset{\circ}{+} y)$ are disjoint measurable sets. Hence $E \overset{\circ}{+} y$ is measurable and

$$\begin{aligned} m(E \overset{\circ}{+} y) &= m(E_1 \overset{\circ}{+} y) + m(E_2 \overset{\circ}{+} y) \\ &= mE_1 + mE_2 \\ &= mE. \quad \blacksquare \end{aligned}$$

We are now in a position to define a nonmeasurable set. If $x - y$ is a rational number, we say that x and y are equivalent and write $x \sim y$. This is an equivalence relation and hence partitions $[0, 1)$ into equivalence classes, that is, classes such that any two elements of one class differ by a rational number, while any two elements of different classes differ by an irrational number. By the axiom of choice there is a set P which contains exactly one element from each equivalence class. Let $\langle r_i \rangle_{i=0}^{\infty}$ be an enumeration of the rational numbers in $[0, 1)$ with $r_o = 0$, and define $P_i = P \overset{\circ}{+} r_i$. Then $P_o = P$. Let $x \in P_i \cap P_j$. Then $x = p_i + r_i = p_j + r_j$ with p_i and p_j belonging to P. But $p_i - p_j = r_j - r_i$, is a rational number, whence $p_i \sim p_j$. Since P has only one element from each equivalence class, we must have $i = j$.

This implies that if $i \neq j$, $P_i \cap P_j = \varnothing$, that is, that $\langle P_i \rangle$ is a pairwise disjoint sequence of sets. On the other hand each real number x in $[0, 1)$ is in some equivalence class and so is equivalent to an element in P. But if x differs from an element in P by the rational number r_i, then $x \in P_i$. Thus $\bigcup P_i = [0, 1)$. Since each P_i is a translation modulo one of P, each P_i will be measurable if P is and will have the same measure. But if this were the case

$$m[0, 1) = \sum_{i=1}^{\infty} mP_i = \sum_{i=1}^{\infty} mP,$$

and the right hand side is either zero or infinite depending on whether mP is zero or positive. But this is impossible since $m[0, 1) = 1$, and consequently P can not be measurable.

While the above proof that P is not measurable is a proof by contradiction, it should be noted that (until the last sentence) we have made no use of properties of Lebesgue measure other than translation invariance and countable additivity. Hence the foregoing argument gives a direct proof of the following theorem:

17. Theorem: *If m is a countably additive, translation invariant measure defined on a σ-algebra containing the set P, then $m[0, 1)$ is either zero or infinite.*

The nonmeasurability of P with respect to any translation invariant countably additive measure m for which $m[0, 1)$ is one follows by contraposition.

5 MEASURABLE FUNCTIONS

Since not all sets are measurable, it is of great importance to know that sets which arise naturally in certain constructions are measurable. If we start with a function f the most important sets which arise from it are those listed in the following proposition:

18. Proposition: *Let f be an extended real-valued function whose domain is measurable. Then the following statements are equivalent:*

i. For each real number α the set $\{x: f(x) > \alpha\}$ is measurable.
ii. For each real number α the set $\{x: f(x) \geq \alpha\}$ is measurable.
iii. For each real number α the set $\{x: f(x) < \alpha\}$ is measurable.
iv. For each real number α the set $\{x: f(x) \leq \alpha\}$ is measurable.

These statements imply

v. For each extended real number α *the set* $\{x: f(x) = \alpha\}$ *is measurable.*

Proof: (i)$\Leftrightarrow$(iv), since $\{x: f(x) > \alpha\} = \sim\{x: f(x) \leq \alpha\}$, and a set is measurable if and only if its complement is. Similarly (ii)$\Leftrightarrow$(iii), since $\{x: f(x) \geq \alpha\} = \sim\{x: f(x) < \alpha\}$. Now (i)$\Rightarrow$(ii), since $\{x: f(x) \geq \alpha\} = \bigcap_{n=1}^{\infty} \left\{x: f(x) > \alpha - \frac{1}{n}\right\}$, and the intersection of a sequence of measurable sets is measurable. Similarly, (ii)$\Rightarrow$(i), since $\{x: f(x) > \alpha\} = \bigcup_{n=1}^{\infty} \left\{x: f(x) \geq \alpha + \frac{1}{n}\right\}$, and the union of a sequence of measurable sets is measurable. This shows that the first four statements are equivalent. If α is a real number, $\{x: f(x) = \alpha\} = \{x: f(x) \geq \alpha\} \cap \{x: f(x) \leq \alpha\}$, and so (ii) and (iv)$\Rightarrow$(v) for α real. Since $\{x: f(x) = \infty\} = \bigcap_{n=1}^{\infty} \{x: f(x) \geq n\}$, (ii)$\Rightarrow$(v), for $\alpha = \infty$. Similarly, (iv)$\Rightarrow$(v) for $\alpha = -\infty$, and we have (ii) & (iv)$\Rightarrow$(v). ∎

Definition: *An extended real-valued function f is called (Lebesgue) measurable if its domain is measurable and if it satisfies one of the first four statements of Proposition* 18.

Thus if we restrict ourselves to measurable functions, the most important sets connected with them are measurable. It should be noted that a continuous function (with a measurable domain) is measurable, and of course each step function is measurable. If f is a measurable function and E is a measurable subset of the domain of f, then the function obtained by restricting f to E is also measurable. The following theorem tells us that certain operations performed on measurable functions lead again to measurable functions:

19. Theorem: *If* c *is a constant and the functions* f *and* g *are measurable, then so are the functions* $f + c$, cf, $f + g$, $f - g$, *and* fg.

Proof: We shall use condition (iii) of Proposition 18. Then

$$\{x: f(x) + c < \alpha\} = \{x: f(x) < \alpha - c\}$$

and so $f + c$ measurable when f is. A similar argument shows cf to be measurable.

If $f(x) + g(x) < \alpha$, then $f(x) < \alpha - g(x)$ and by the corollary to the axiom of Archimedes there is a rational number r such that

$$f(x) < r < \alpha - g(x).$$

Hence

$$\{x: f(x) + g(x) < \alpha\} = \bigcup_r (\{x: f(x) < r\} \cap \{x: g(x) < \alpha - r\}).$$

Since the rationals are countable, this set is measurable and so $f + g$ is measurable. Since $-g = (-1)g$ is measurable when g is, we have $f - g$ measurable.

The function f^2 is measurable, since

$$\{x: f^2(x) > \alpha\} = \{x: f(x) > \sqrt{\alpha}\} \cup \{x: f(x) < -\sqrt{\alpha}\}$$

for $\alpha \geq 0$ and

$$\{x: f^2(x) > \alpha\} = D$$

if $\alpha < 0$, where D is the domain of f. Thus

$$fg = \tfrac{1}{2}[(f + g)^2 - f^2 - g^2]$$

is measurable. ∎

20. Theorem: *Let $\langle f_n \rangle$ be a sequence of measurable functions (with the same domain of definition). Then the functions* $\sup \{f_1, \ldots, f_n\}$, $\inf \{f_1, \ldots, f_n\}$, $\sup_n f_n$, $\inf_n f_n$, $\overline{\lim} f_n$, *and* $\underline{\lim} f_n$ *are all measurable.*

Proof: If h is defined by $h(x) = \sup \{f_1(x), \ldots, f_n(x)\}$, then $\{x: h(x) > \alpha\} = \bigcup_{i=1}^{n} \{x: f_i(x) > \alpha\}$. Hence the measurability of the f_i implies that of h. Similarly, if g is defined by $g(x) = \sup f_n(x)$, then $\{x: g(x) > \alpha\} = \bigcup_{n=1}^{\infty} \{x: f_n(x) > \alpha\}$, and so g is measurable. A similar argument establishes the corresponding statements for inf. Since $\overline{\lim} f_n = \inf_n \sup_{k \geq n} f_k$, we have $\overline{\lim} f_n$ measurable, and similarly for $\underline{\lim} f_n$. ∎

A property is said to hold **almost everywhere**[5] (abbreviated a.e.) if the set of points where it fails to hold is a set of measure zero. Thus in particular we say that $f = g$ a.e. if f and g have the same domain

[5] French: *presque partout* (p.p.).

and $m\{x: f(x) \neq g(x)\} = 0$. Similarly, we say that f_n converges to g almost everywhere if there is a set E of measure zero such that $f_n(x)$ converges to $g(x)$ for each x not in E. One consequence of equality a.e. is the following:

21. Proposition: *If f is a measurable function and $f = g$ a.e., then g is measurable.*

Proof: Let E be the set $\{x: f(x) \neq g(x)\}$. By hypothesis $mE = 0$. Now

$$\{x: g(x) > \alpha\} = \{x: f(x) > \alpha\} \cup \{x \in E: g(x) > \alpha\} \sim \{x \in E: g(x) \leq \alpha\}.$$

The first set on the right is measurable, since f is a measurable function. The last two sets on the right are measurable since they are subsets of E and $mE = 0$. Thus $\{x: g(x) > \alpha\}$ is measurable for each α, and so g is measurable. ▌

The following proposition tells us that a measurable function is "almost" a continuous function. The proof is left to the reader (cf Problem 16).

22. Proposition: *Let f be a measurable function defined on an interval $[a, b]$, and assume that f takes the values $\pm\infty$ only on a set of measure zero. Then given $\epsilon > 0$, we can find a step function g and a continuous function h such that*

$$|f - g| < \epsilon \quad \textit{and} \quad |f - h| < \epsilon$$

except on a set of measure less than ϵ, i.e. $m\{x: |f(x) - g(x)| \geq \epsilon\} < \epsilon$ and $m\{x: |f(x) - h(x)| \geq \epsilon\} < \epsilon$. If in addition $m \leq f \leq M$, then we may choose the functions g and h so that $m \leq g \leq M$ and $m \leq h \leq M$.

If A is any set, we define the **characteristic function** χ_A of the set A to be the function given by

$$\chi_A(x) = \begin{cases} 1 & \text{if } x \in A \\ 0 & \text{if } x \notin A. \end{cases}$$

The function χ_A is measurable if and only if A is measurable. Thus the existence of a nonmeasurable set implies the existence of a nonmeasurable function.

A real-valued function φ is called **simple** if it is measurable and assumes only a finite number of values. If φ is simple and has the values $\alpha_1, \ldots, \alpha_n$ then $\varphi = \sum_{i=1}^{n} \alpha_i \chi_{A_i}$, where $A_i = \{x: \varphi(x) = \alpha_i\}$. The sum, product and difference of two simple functions are simple.

Problems

12. Show that (v) does not imply (iv) in Proposition 18 by constructing a function f such that $\{x: f(x) > 0\} = E$, a given nonmeasurable set, and such that f assumes each value at most once.

13. Show that if f is a measurable real-valued function and g a continuous function defined on $(-\infty, \infty)$, then $g \circ f$ is measurable.

14. Show that the sum and product of two simple functions are simple. Show that

$$\chi_{A \cap B} = \chi_A \cdot \chi_B$$
$$\chi_{A \cup B} = \chi_A + \chi_B - \chi_A \cdot \chi_B$$
$$\chi_{\tilde{A}} = 1 - \chi_A.$$

15. Let f be measurable and B a Borel set. Then $f^{-1}[B]$ is a measurable set.

16. Prove Proposition 22 by establishing the following lemmas:

a. Given a measurable function f on $[a, b]$ which takes the values $\pm\infty$ only on a set of measure zero, and given $\epsilon > 0$ there is an M such that $|f| \leq M$ except on a set of measure less than $\epsilon/3$.

b. Let f be a measurable function on $[a, b]$. Given $\epsilon > 0$ and M there is a simple function φ such that $|f(x) - \varphi(x)| < \epsilon$ except where $|f(x)| \geq M$. If $m \leq f \leq M$, then we may take φ so that $m \leq \varphi \leq M$.

c. Given a simple function φ on $[a, b]$ show that there is a step function g on $[a, b]$ such that $g(x) = \varphi(x)$ except on a set of measure less than $\epsilon/3$. (Hint use Proposition 15.) If $m \leq \varphi \leq M$, then we can take g so that $m \leq g \leq M$.

d. Given a step function g on $[a, b]$, there is a continuous function h such that $g(x) = h(x)$ except on a set of measure less than $\epsilon/3$. If $m \leq g \leq M$, then we may take h so that $m \leq h \leq M$.

17. ***Borel measurability;*** A function f is said to be **Borel measurable** if for each α the set $\{x: f(x) > \alpha\}$ is a Borel set. Verify that Proposition 18 and Theorems 19 and 20 remain valid if we replace "measurable set" by

"Borel set" and "(Lebesgue) measurable" by "Borel measurable." Every Borel measurable function is Lebesgue measurable. If f is Borel measurable, and B is a Borel set then $f^{-1}[B]$ is a Borel set. If f and g are Borel measurable, so is $f \circ g$. If f is Borel measurable and g is Lebesgue measurable then $f \circ g$ is Lebesgue measurable.

18. How much of the preceding problem can be carried out if we replace the class B of Borel sets by an arbitrary σ-algebra $\mathcal{A}$ of sets?

6 LITTLEWOOD'S THREE PRINCIPLES

Speaking of the theory of functions of a real variable, J. E. Littlewood says,[6] "The extent of knowledge required is nothing like so great as is sometimes supposed. There are three principles, roughly expressible in the following terms: Every (measurable) set is nearly a finite union of intervals; every [measurable] function is nearly continuous; every convergent sequence of [measurable] functions is nearly uniformly convergent. Most of the results of [the theory] are fairly intuitive applications of these ideas, and the student armed with them should be equal to most occasions when real variable theory is called for. If one of the principles would be the obvious means to settle the problem if it were 'quite' true, it is natural to ask if the 'nearly' is near enough, and for a problem that is actually solvable it generally is."

We have already met two of Littlewood's principles: Various forms of the first principle are given by Proposition 15. One version of the second principle is given by Proposition 22, another version by Problem 21, and a third is given by Problems 4.10 and 6.14. The following proposition gives one version of the third principle. A slightly stronger form is given by Egoroff's theorem (Problem 20), but you will generally find the weak form adequate.

23. Proposition: *Let E be a measurable set of finite measure, and $\langle f_n \rangle$ a sequence of measurable functions defined on E. Let f be a measurable real-valued function such that for each x in E we have $f_n(x) \to f(x)$. Then given $\epsilon > 0$ and $\delta > 0$, there is a measurable set $A \subset E$ with $mA < \delta$ and an integer N such that for all $x \notin A$ and all $n \geq N$*

$$|f_n(x) - f(x)| < \epsilon.$$

[6] Lectures on the Theory of Functions, Oxford, 1944, p. 26.

Proof: Let

$$G_n = \{x \in E \colon |f_n(x) - f(x)| \geq \epsilon\},$$

and set

$$E_N = \bigcup_{n=N}^{\infty} G_n = \{x \in E \colon |f_n(x) - f(x)| \geq \epsilon \text{ for some } n \geq N\}.$$

We have $E_{N+1} \subset E_N$, and for each $x \in E$ there must be some E_N to which x does not belong, since $f_n(x) \to f(x)$. Thus $\bigcap E_N = \varnothing$, and so by Proposition 14, $\lim mE_N = 0$. Hence given $\delta > 0$, $\exists N$ so that $mE_N < \delta$; that is,

$$m\{x \in E \colon |f_n(x) - f(x)| \geq \epsilon \text{ for some } n \geq N\} < \delta .$$

If we write A for this E_N, then $mA < \delta$ and

$$\tilde{A} = \{x \in E \colon |f_n(x) - f(x)| < \epsilon \text{ for all } n \geq N\}. \ \blacksquare$$

If, as in the hypothesis of the proposition we have $f_n(x) \to f(x)$ for each x, we say that the sequence $\langle f_n \rangle$ converges **pointwise** to f on E. If there is a subset B of E with $mB = 0$ such that $f_n \to f$ pointwise on $E \sim B$, we say that $f_n \to f$ a.e. on E. We have the following trivial modification of the last proposition:

24. Proposition: *Let E be a measurable set of finite measure, and* $\langle f_n \rangle$ *a sequence of measurable functions which converge to* f a.e. *on E. Then given* $\epsilon > 0$, *and* $\delta > 0$, *there is a set* $A \subset E$ *with* $mA < \delta$, *and an N such that for all* $x \notin A$ *and all* $n \geq N$.

$$|f_n(x) - f(x)| < \epsilon.$$

Problems

19. Give an example to show that we must require $mE < \infty$ in Proposition 23.

20. Prove Egoroff's theorem: If $\langle f_n \rangle$ is a sequence of measurable functions such that $f_n \to f$ a.e. on a measurable set E of finite measure, then given $\eta > 0$, there is a subset $A \subset E$ with $mA < \eta$ such that f_n converges to f *uniformly* on $E \sim A$. (Hint: apply Proposition 24 repeatedly with $\epsilon_n = 1/n$ and $\delta_n = 2^{-n}\eta$.)

21. Let f be a measurable function on an interval $[a, b]$. Then given $\delta > 0$, there is a continuous function φ on $[a, b]$ such that $m\{x \colon f(x) \neq \varphi(x)\} < \delta$. Can you do the same on the interval $(-\infty, \infty)$? (Hint: Use Egoroff's theorem, Propositions 15 and 22 and Problem 2.37.)

4 The Lebesgue Integral

1 THE RIEMANN INTEGRAL

We recall a few definitions pertaining to the Riemann integral. Let f be a bounded real-valued function defined on the interval $[a, b]$ and let

$$a = \xi_0 < \xi_1 < \cdots < \xi_n = b$$

be a subdivision of $[a, b]$. Then for each subdivision we can define the sums

$$S = \sum_{i=1}^{n} (\xi_i - \xi_{i-1})M_i$$

and

$$s = \sum_{i=1}^{n} (\xi_i - \xi_{i-1})m_i$$

where

$$M_i = \sup_{\xi_{i-1} < x \leq \xi_i} f(x); \qquad m_i = \inf_{\xi_{i-1} < x \leq \xi_i} f(x).$$

We then define the upper Riemann integral of f by

$$R\overline{\int_a^b} f(x)\,dx = \inf S.$$

with the infimum taken over all possible subdivisions of $[a, b]$. Similarly we define the lower integral

$$R\underline{\int_a^b} f(x)\,dx = \sup s.$$

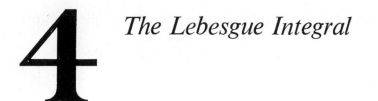

The upper integral is always at least as large as the lower integral, and if the two are equal we say that f is Riemann integrable and call this common value the Riemann integral of f. We shall denote it by

$$R\int_a^b f(x)\,dx$$

to distinguish it from the Lebesgue integral which we shall consider later.

By a step function we mean a function ψ which has the form

$$\psi(x) = c_i, \qquad \xi_{i-1} < x < \xi_i$$

for some subdivision of $[a, b]$ and some set of constants c_i. Under practically anybody's definition of an integral we have

$$\int_a^b \psi(x)\,dx = \sum_{i=1}^{n} c_i(\xi_i - \xi_{i-1}).$$

With this in mind we see that

$$\overline{\int_a^b} f(x)\,dx = \inf \int_a^b \psi(x)\,dx$$

for all step functions $\psi(x) \geq f(x)$. Similarly

$$\underline{\int_a^b} f(x)\,dx = \sup \int_a^b \varphi(x)\,dx$$

for all step functions $\varphi(x) \leq f(x)$.

Problem

1. a. Show that if

$$f(x) = \begin{cases} 0 & x \text{ irrational} \\ 1 & x \text{ rational} \end{cases}$$

then $R\,\overline{\int_a^b} f(x)\,dx = b - a$ and $R\,\underline{\int_a^b} f(x)\,dx = 0$.

b. Construct a sequence $\{f_n\}$ of nonnegative, Riemann integrable functions such that f_n increases monotonically to f. What does this imply about changing the order of integration and the limiting process?

2 THE LEBESGUE INTEGRAL OF A BOUNDED FUNCTION OVER A SET OF FINITE MEASURE

The problems of the preceding section show some of the shortcomings of the Riemann integral. In particular, we would like a function which is one on a measurable set and zero elsewhere to be integrable and have as its integral the measure of the set.

The function χ_E defined by

$$\chi_E(x) = \begin{cases} 1 & x \in E \\ 0 & x \notin E \end{cases}$$

is called the characteristic function of E. A linear combination

$$\varphi(x) = \sum_{i=1}^{n} a_i \chi_{E_i}(x)$$

is called a **simple** function if the sets E_i are measurable. This representation for φ is not unique. However, we note that a function φ is simple if and only if it is measurable and assumes only a finite number of values. If φ is a simple function and $\{a_1, \ldots, a_n\}$ the set of nonzero values of φ, then

$$\varphi = \sum a_i \chi_{A_i}$$

where $A_i = \{x: \varphi(x) = a_i\}$. This representation for φ is called the canonical representation and it is characterized by the fact that the A_i are disjoint and the a_i distinct and nonzero.

If φ vanishes outside a set of finite measure we define the integral of φ by

$$\int \varphi(x)\, dx = \sum_{i=1}^{n} a_i m A_i$$

when φ has the canonical representation $\varphi = \sum_{i=1}^{n} a_i \chi_{A_i}$. We sometimes abbreviate the expression for this integral to $\int \varphi$. If E is any measurable set, we define

$$\int_E \varphi = \int \varphi \cdot \chi_E \,.$$

It is often convenient to use representations which are not canonical, and the following lemma is useful:

1. Lemma: *Let* $\varphi = \sum_{i=1}^{n} a_i \chi_{E_i}$, *with* $E_i \cap E_j = \varnothing$ *for* $i \neq j$. *Suppose each set* E_i *is a measurable set of finite measure. Then*

$$\int \varphi = \sum_{i=1}^{n} a_i m E_i .$$

Proof: The set $A_a = \{x: \varphi(x) = a\} = \bigcup_{a_i = a} E_i$. Hence $a\, m A_a = \sum_{a_i = a} a_i m E_i$, by the additivity of m and so

$$\begin{aligned} \int \varphi(x)\, dx &= \sum a\, m A_a \\ &= \sum a_i m E_i . \end{aligned}$$ ❙

2. Proposition: *Let* φ *and* ψ *be simple functions which vanish outside a set of finite measure. Then*

$$\int (a\varphi + b\psi) = a \int \varphi + b \int \psi$$

and if $\varphi \geq \psi$ a.e., *then*

$$\int \varphi \geq \int \psi .$$

Proof: Let $\{A_i\}$ and $\{B_i\}$ be the sets which occur in the canonical representations of φ and ψ. Then the sets E_k obtained by taking all the intersections $A_i \cap B_j$ form a finite disjoint collection of measurable sets, and we may write

$$\varphi = \sum_{k=1}^{N} a_k \chi_{E_k} ,$$

$$\psi = \sum_{k=1}^{N} b_k \chi_{E_k} ,$$

and so

$$a\varphi + b\psi = \sum (a a_k + b b_k) \chi_{E_k} ,$$

whence $\int (a\varphi + b\psi) = a \int \varphi + b \int \psi$ follows from Lemma 1. To prove the second statement, we note that

$$\int \varphi - \int \psi = \int (\varphi - \psi) \geq 0 ,$$

since the integral of a simple function which is greater than or equal to zero a.e. is nonnegative by the definition of the integral. ❙

It follows from this proposition that if $\varphi = \sum_{i=1}^{n} a_i\chi_{E_i}$, then $\int \varphi = \Sigma a_i mE_i$, and so the restriction of Lemma 1 that the sets E_i be disjoint is unnecessary.

Let f be a bounded real-valued function and E a measurable set of finite measure. By analogy with the Riemann integral we consider for simple functions φ and ψ the numbers

$$\inf_{\psi \geq f} \int_E \psi$$

and

$$\sup_{\varphi \leq f} \int_E \varphi ,$$

and ask when these two numbers are equal. The answer is given by the following proposition:

3. Proposition: *Let f be defined and bounded on a measurable set E with mE finite. In order that*

$$\inf_{f \leq \psi} \int_E \psi(x)\,dx = \sup_{f \geq \varphi} \int_E \varphi(x)\,dx$$

for all simple functions φ and ψ it is necessary and sufficient that f be measurable.

Proof: Let f be bounded by M and suppose that f is measurable. Then the sets

$$E_k = \left\{x: \frac{kM}{n} \geq f(x) > \frac{(k-1)M}{n}\right\}, \qquad -n \leq k \leq n$$

are measurable, disjoint and have union E. Thus

$$\sum_{k=-n}^{n} mE_k = mE.$$

The simple functions defined by

$$\psi_n(x) = \frac{M}{n} \sum_{k=-n}^{n} k\chi_{E_k}(x)$$

and

$$\varphi_n(x) = \frac{M}{n} \sum_{k=-n}^{n} (k-1)\chi_{E_k}(x)$$

satisfy

$$\varphi_n(x) \leq f(x) \leq \psi_n(x).$$

Thus

$$\inf \int_E \psi(x)\,dx \le \int_E \psi_n(x)\,dx = \frac{M}{n} \sum_{k=-n}^{n} k\,mE_k$$

and

$$\sup \int_E \varphi(x)\,dx \ge \int_E \varphi_n(x)\,dx = \frac{M}{n} \sum_{k=-n}^{n} (k-1)\,mE_k$$

whence

$$0 \le \inf \int_E \psi(x)\,dx - \sup \int_E \varphi(x)\,dx \le \int_E \psi_n(x)\,dx - \int_E \varphi_n(x)\,dx$$

$$\le \frac{M}{n} \sum_{k=-n}^{n} mE_k = \frac{M}{n}\,mE.$$

Since n is arbitrary we have

$$\inf \int_E \psi(x)\,dx - \sup \int_E \varphi(x)\,dx = 0$$

and the condition is sufficient.

Suppose now that

$$\inf_{\psi \ge f} \int_E \psi(x)\,dx = \sup_{\varphi \le f} \int_E \varphi(x)\,dx.$$

Then given n there are simple functions φ_n and ψ_n such that

$$\varphi_n(x) \le f(x) \le \psi_n(x)$$

and

$$\int \psi_n(x)\,dx - \int \varphi_n(x)\,dx < \frac{1}{n}.$$

Then the functions

$$\psi^* = \inf \psi_n(x)$$

and

$$\varphi^* = \sup \varphi_n(x)$$

are measurable by Theorem 3.20 and

$$\varphi^*(x) \le f(x) \le \psi^*(x).$$

Now the set

$$\Delta = \{x\colon \varphi^*(x) < \psi^*(x)\}$$

is the union of the sets

$$\Delta_\nu = \left\{x\colon \varphi^*(x) < \psi^*(x) - \frac{1}{\nu}\right\}.$$

But each Δ_ν is contained in the set $\left\{x\colon \varphi_n(x) < \psi_n(x) - \frac{1}{\nu}\right\}$ and this latter set has measure less than ν/n. Since n is arbitrary, $m\Delta_\nu = 0$

and hence also $m\Delta = 0$. Thus $\varphi^* = \psi^*$ except on a set of measure zero and so $\varphi^* = f$ except on a set of measure zero whence f is measurable by Proposition 3.21. Thus the condition is also necessary. ▌

Definition: *If f is a bounded measurable function defined on a measurable set E with mE finite, we define the (Lebesgue) integral of f over E by*

$$\int_E f(x)\,dx = \inf \int_E \psi(x)\,dx$$

for all simple functions $\psi \geq f$.

We sometimes write the integral as $\int_E f$. If $E = [a, b]$, we write $\int_a^b f$ instead of $\int_{[a,b]} f$. If f is a bounded measurable function which vanishes outside a set E of finite measure, we write $\int f$ for $\int_E f$. Note that $\int_E f = \int f \cdot \chi_E$. The following corollary to Proposition 3 shows that the Lebesgue integral is in fact a generalization of the Riemann integral.

4. Proposition: *Let f be a bounded function defined on $[a, b]$. If f is Riemann integrable on $[a, b]$, then it is measurable and*

$$R\int_a^b f(x)\,dx = \int_a^b f(x)\,dx.$$

Proof: Since every step function is also a simple function we have

$$\underline{\int_a^b} f(x)\,dx \leq \sup_{\varphi \leq f} \int_a^b \varphi(x)\,dx \leq \inf_{\psi \geq f} \int_a^b \psi(x)\,dx \leq \overline{\int_a^b} f(x)\,dx.$$

Since f is Riemann integrable the inequalities are all equalities and f is measurable by Proposition 3. ▌

5. Proposition: *If f and g are bounded measurable functions defined on a set E of finite measure then*

a.
$$\int_E (af + bg) = a\int_E f + b\int_E g;$$

b. *If $f = g$ a.e., then*

$$\int_E f = \int_E g;$$

c. *If* $f \leq g$ a.e., *then*

$$\int_E f \leq \int_E g;$$

Hence $|\int f| \leq \int |f|$.

d. *If* $A \leq f(x) \leq B$, *then*

$$AmE \leq \int_E f \leq BmE;$$

e. *If A and B are disjoint measurable sets of finite measure, then*

$$\int_{A \cup B} f = \int_A f + \int_B f.$$

Proof: If ψ is a simple function so is $a\psi$ and conversely (if $a \neq 0$). Hence for $a > 0$

$$\int_E af = \inf_{\psi \geq f} \int_E a\psi = a \inf_{\psi \geq f} \int_E \psi = a \int_E f.$$

If $a < 0$,

$$\int_E af = \inf_{\varphi \leq f} \int_E a\varphi = a \sup_{\varphi \leq f} \int_E \varphi = a \inf_{\psi \geq f} \int_E \psi = a \int_E f$$

using Proposition 3.

If ψ_1 is a simple function not less than f and ψ_2 a simple function not less than g, then $\psi_1 + \psi_2$ is a simple function not less than $f + g$. Hence

$$\int_E f + g \leq \int_E (\psi_1 + \psi_2) = \int_E \psi_1 + \int_E \psi_2.$$

Since the infimum of the right hand side is $\int f + \int g$, we have

$$\int_E f + g \leq \int f + \int g.$$

On the other hand $\varphi_1 \leq f$ and $\varphi_2 \leq g$ imply $\varphi_1 + \varphi_2$ is a simple function not greater than $f + g$. Hence

$$\int_E f + g \geq \int_E (\varphi_1 + \varphi_2) = \int_E \varphi_1 + \int_E \varphi_2.$$

Since now the supremum of the right hand side is $\int f + \int g$, we have

$$\int_E f + g \geq \int_E f + \int_E g,$$

and statement (a) of the theorem follows.

To prove (b) it now suffices to show that

$$\int_E f - g = 0.$$

Since $f - g = 0$ a.e., it follows that if $\psi \geq f - g$, $\psi \geq 0$ a.e. From this it follows that

$$\int_E \psi \geq 0$$

whence

$$\int_E f - g \geq 0.$$

Similarly

$$\int_E f - g \leq 0$$

whence (b). This proof also serves to establish (c). Statement (d) follows from (c) and the fact that

$$\int_E 1 = mE.$$

Statement (e) follows from (a) and the fact that $\chi_{A \cup B} = \chi_A + \chi_B$. ∎

We next prove a proposition which will be used to prove Theorem 15. The proposition is a special case of Theorem 15.

6. Proposition (The Bounded Convergence Theorem): *Let $\langle f_n \rangle$ be a sequence of measurable functions defined on a set E of finite measure, and suppose that there is a real number M such that $|f_n(x)| \leq M$ for all n and all x. If $f(x) = \lim f_n(x)$ for each x in E, then*

$$\int_E f = \lim \int_E f_n.$$

Proof: The proof of this proposition furnishes a nice illustration of the use of Littlewood's "three principles." The conclusion of the proposition would be trivial if $\langle f_n \rangle$ converged to f uniformly. Littlewood's third principle states that, if $\langle f_n \rangle$ converges to f pointwise, then $\langle f_n \rangle$ is "nearly" uniformly convergent to f. A precise version of this principle is given by Proposition 3.23 which states that for a given $\epsilon > 0$ there is an N and a measurable set $A \subset E$ with $mA < \frac{\epsilon}{4M}$ such that for $n \geq N$ and $x \in E \sim A$ we have $|f_n(x) - f(x)| < \epsilon/2mE$. Thus

$$\left|\int_E f_n - \int_E f\right| = \left|\int_E f_n - f\right|$$
$$\leq \int_E |f_n - f|$$
$$= \int_{E \sim A} |f_n - f| + \int_A |f_n - f|$$
$$< \epsilon/2 + \epsilon/2 = \epsilon.$$

Hence

$$\int_E f_n \to \int_E f. \ \blacksquare$$

Problem

2. a. Let f be a bounded function on $[a, b]$, and let h be the upper envelope of f (cf. Problem 2.45). Then $R \overline{\int_a^b} f = \int_a^b h$. (If $\varphi \geq f$ is a step function, then $\varphi \geq h$ except at a finite number of points and so $\int_a^b h \leq R \overline{\int_a^b} f$. But there is a sequence $\langle \varphi_n \rangle$ of step functions such that $\varphi_n \downarrow h$. By Proposition 6 we have $\int_a^b h = \lim \int_a^b \varphi_n \geq R \overline{\int_a^b} f$.)

b. Use part (a) to prove the following theorem:

Theorem (Lebesgue): *A bounded function on* $[a, b]$ *is Riemann integrable if and only if the set of points at which* f *is discontinuous has measure zero.*

3 THE INTEGRAL OF A NONNEGATIVE FUNCTION

If f is a nonnegative measurable function defined on a measurable set E we define

$$\int_E f = \sup_{h \leq f} \int_E h$$

where h is a bounded measurable function such that $m\{x: h(x) \neq 0\} < \infty$.

7. Proposition: *If f and g are nonnegative measurable functions then*

a.
$$\int_E cf = c\int_E f, \qquad c > 0.$$

b.
$$\int_E f + g = \int_E f + \int_E g.$$

c. *If $f \leq g$ a.e., then*

$$\int_E f \leq \int_E g.$$

Proof: This proposition follows from Proposition 5 and we shall prove only (b) in detail. If $h(x) \leq f(x)$ and $k(x) \leq g(x)$, we have $h(x) + k(x) \leq f(x) + g(x)$ and so

$$\int_E h + \int_E k \leq \int_E f + g.$$

Taking suprema, we have

$$\int_E f + \int_E g \leq \int_E f + g.$$

On the other hand let l be a bounded measurable function which vanishes outside a set of finite measure and which is not greater than $f + g$. Then we define the functions h and k by setting

$$h(x) = \min(f(x), l(x)),$$

and

$$k(x) = l(x) - h(x).$$

We have

$$h(x) \leq f(x),$$

and

$$k(x) \leq g(x),$$

while h and k are bounded by the bound for l and vanish where l vanishes. Hence $\int_E l = \int_E h + \int_E k \leq \int_E f + \int_E g$, and so

$$\int_E f + \int_E g \geq \int_E f + g. \blacksquare$$

8. Theorem (Fatou's Lemma): *If $\langle f_n \rangle$ is a sequence of nonnegative measurable functions and $f_n(x) \to f(x)$ almost everywhere on a set E then*

$$\int_E f \leq \underline{\lim} \int_E f_n.$$

Proof: Without loss of generality we may assume that the convergence is everywhere, since integrals over sets of measure zero are zero. Let h be a bounded measurable function which is not greater than f and which vanishes outside a set E' of finite measure. Define a function h_n by setting

$$h_n(x) = \min \{h(x), f_n(x)\}.$$

Then h_n is bounded by the bound for h and vanishes outside E'. Now $h_n(x) \to h(x)$ for each x in E'. Thus by Proposition 6 we have

$$\int_E h = \int_{E'} h = \lim \int_{E'} h_n \leq \underline{\lim} \int_E f_n.$$

Taking the supremum over h, we get

$$\int_E f \leq \underline{\lim} \int_E f_n. \quad \blacksquare$$

9. Theorem: (Monotone Convergence Theorem): *Let $\langle f_n \rangle$ be an increasing sequence of nonnegative measurable functions, and let $f =$ $\lim f_n$. Then*

$$\int f = \lim \int f_n.$$

Proof: By Theorem 8 we have

$$\int f \leq \underline{\lim} \int f_n.$$

But for each n we have $f_n \leq f$ and so $\int f_n \leq \int f$. But this implies

$$\overline{\lim} \int f_n \leq \int f.$$

Hence

$$\int f = \lim \int f_n. \quad \blacksquare$$

10. Corollary: *Let u_n be a sequence of nonnegative measurable functions, and let $f = \sum_{n=1}^{\infty} u_n$. Then*

$$\int f = \sum_{n=1}^{\infty} \int u_n.$$

11. Proposition: *Let f be a nonnegative function and $\langle E_i \rangle$ a disjoint sequence of measurable sets. Let $E = \bigcup E_i$. Then*

$$\int_E f = \sum \int_{E_i} f.$$

Proof: Let $u_i = f \cdot \chi_{E_i}$. Then $f \cdot \chi_E = \Sigma u_i$, and so the proposition follows from the preceding corollary. ∎

Definition: *A nonnegative measurable function f is called integrable over the measurable set E if*

$$\int_E f < \infty.$$

12. Proposition: *Let f and g be two nonnegative measurable functions. If f is integrable over E and $g(x) < f(x)$ on E then g is also integrable on E and*

$$\int_E f - g = \int_E f - \int_E g.$$

Proof: By Proposition 7

$$\int_E f = \int_E (f - g) + \int_E g.$$

Since the lefthand side is finite, the terms on the right must also be finite, and so g is integrable. ∎

13. Proposition: *Let f be a nonnegative function which is integrable over a set E. Then given $\epsilon > 0$ there is a $\delta > 0$ such that for every set $A \subset E$ with $mA < \delta$ we have*

$$\int_A f < \epsilon.$$

Proof: Suppose not. Then for some $\epsilon > 0$ we can find sets A of arbitrarily small measure such that $\int_A f \geq \epsilon$, and in particular there must be a measurable set A_n for each n such that

$$\int_{A_n} f \geq \epsilon$$

and $mA_n < 2^{-n}$. Let $g_n = f \cdot \chi_{A_n}$. Then $g_n \to 0$ except on the set $\bigcap_{n=1}^{\infty} \bigcup_{i=n}^{\infty} A_i$. Since $m\left[\bigcup_{i=n}^{\infty} A_i\right] < 2^{-n+1}$, we have $g_n \to 0$ a.e. Let $f_n = f - g_n$. Then $\langle f_n \rangle$ is a sequence of nonnegative functions and $f_n \to f$ a.e. Hence by Fatou's lemma we have

$$\begin{aligned}\int f &\leq \underline{\lim} \int f_n \\ &\leq \int f - \overline{\lim} \int g_n \\ &\leq \int f - \epsilon.\end{aligned}$$

But this inequality can only hold if $\int f = \infty$, and so f is not integrable. The proposition follows by contraposition. ▌

Problems

3. Let f be a nonnegative measurable function. Show that $\int f = 0$ implies $f = 0$ a.e.

4. Let f be a nonnegative measurable function.

a. Show that there is an increasing sequence $\langle \varphi_n \rangle$ of nonnegative simple functions each of which vanishes outside a set of finite measure such that $f = \lim \varphi_n$.

b. Show that $\int f = \sup \int \varphi$ over all simple functions $\varphi \leq f$.

5. Let f be a nonnegative measurable function and E a measurable set of finite measure.

a. Show that $\int_E f = \lim_{N \to \infty} \int_E f_N$ where $f_N(x) = \min\{f(x), N\}$.

b. Show that $\int f = \lim_{N \to \infty} \int_{-N}^{N} f$.

6. Let f be a nonnegative integrable function. Show that the function F defined by

$$F(x) = \int_{-\infty}^{x} f$$

is continuous by using Theorem 9.

7. Let $\langle f_n \rangle$ be a sequence of nonnegative functions on $(-\infty, \infty)$ such that $f_n \to f$ a.e., and suppose that $\int f_n \to \int f < \infty$. Then for each measurable set E we have $\int_E f_n \to \int_E f$.

4 THE GENERAL LEBESGUE INTEGRAL

By the positive part f^+ of a function f we mean the function $f^+ = f \vee 0$; that is,

$$f^+(x) = \max \{f(x), 0\}.$$

Similarly we define the negative part f^- by $f^- = (-f) \vee 0$. If f is measurable so are f^+ and f^-. We have

$$f = f^+ - f^-$$

and

$$|f| = f^+ + f^-.$$

With these notions in mind we make the following definition:

Definition: *A measurable function f is said to be integrable over E if f^+ and f^- are both integrable over E. In this case we define*

$$\int_E f = \int_E f^+ - \int_E f^-.$$

As a consequence of Propositions 7 and 12 we have the following proposition:

14. Proposition: *Let f and g be integrable over E.*

a. *The function $(af + bg)$ is integrable over E and* $\int_E (af + bg) = a\int_E f + b\int_E g$.

b. *If $f \leq g$ a.e. then* $\int_E f \leq \int_E g$.

c. *If A and B are disjoint measurable sets contained in E, then*

$$\int_{A \cup B} f = \int_A f + \int_B f.$$

It should be noted that $af + bg$ is not defined at points where $af = \infty$ and $bg = -\infty$ and where $af = -\infty$ and $bg = \infty$. However, the set of such points must have measure zero since f and g are integrable. Hence the integrability and the value of $\int (af + bg)$ is independent of the choice of values in these ambiguous cases.

15. Theorem (Lebesgue Convergence Theorem): *Let g be integrable over E and let $\langle f_n \rangle$ be a sequence of measurable functions such that $|f_n| \leq g$ on E and for almost all x in E we have $f(x) = \lim f_n(x)$. Then*

$$\int_E f = \lim \int_E f_n.$$

Proof: The function $g - f_n$ is nonnegative, and so by Theorem 8

$$\int_E (g - f) \leq \underline{\lim} \int_E g - f_n.$$

Since $|f| \leq g$, f is integrable and we have

$$\int_E g - \int_E f \leq \int_E g - \overline{\lim} \int_E f_n$$

whence

$$\int_E f \geq \overline{\lim} \int_E f_n.$$

Similarly, considering $g + f_n$ we get

$$\int_E f \leq \underline{\lim} \int_E f_n,$$

and the theorem follows. ▌

Problems

8. a. Show that if f is integrable over E then so is $|f|$ and

$$\left| \int_E f \right| \leq \int_E |f|.$$

Does the integrability of $|f|$ imply that of f?

b. The improper Riemann integral of a function may exist without the function being integrable (in the sense of Lebesgue), e.g., if $f(x) = (\sin x)/x$ on $[0, \infty)$. If f is integrable, show that the improper Riemann integral is equal to the Lebesgue integral whenever the former exists.

9. Let g be an integrable function on a set E and suppose $\langle f_n \rangle$ is a sequence of measurable functions such that $|f_n(x)| \le g(x)$ a.e. on E. Then

$$\int_E \varliminf f_n \le \varliminf \int_E f_n \le \varlimsup \int_E f_n \le \int_E \varlimsup f_n.$$

10. a. Let f be integrable over E. Then given $\epsilon > 0$, there is a simple function φ such that

$$\int_E |f - \varphi| < \epsilon.$$

(Apply Problem 4 to the positive and negative parts of f).

b. Under the same hypothesis there is a step function ψ such that

$$\int_E |f - \psi| < \epsilon.$$

(Combine part (a) with Proposition 3.22).

c. Under the same hypothesis there is a continuous function g such that

$$\int_E |f - g| < \epsilon.$$

11. Let $\langle f_n \rangle$ be a sequence of integrable functions such that $f_n \to f$ a.e. Then $\int |f - f_n| \to 0$ if and only if $\int |f_n| \to \int |f|$. (Problem 7 is useful here.)

12. Let f be a function of two variables $\langle x, t \rangle$, which is defined in the square $Q = \{\langle x, t \rangle : 0 \le x \le 1, 0 \le t \le 1\}$, and which is a measurable function of x for each fixed value of t. Suppose that $\lim_{t \to 0} f(x, t) = f(x)$ and that for all t we have $|f(x, t)| \le g(x)$ where g is an integrable function on $[0, 1]$. Then

$$\lim_{t \to 0} \int f(x, t)\, dx = \int f(x)\, dx.$$

(Problem 2.43(f) is useful here.) Show also that, if the function $f(x, t)$ is continuous in t for each x, then

$$h(t) = \int f(x, t)\, dx$$

is a continuous function of t.

13. Let f be a function defined and bounded in the square $Q = \{\langle x, t \rangle : 0 \le x \le 1, 0 \le t \le 1\}$, and suppose that for each fixed t the function f is a measurable function of x. For each $\langle x, t\rangle \in Q$ let the partial derivative $\dfrac{\partial f}{\partial t}$ exist. Suppose that $\dfrac{\partial f}{\partial t}$ is bounded in Q. Then

$$\frac{d}{dt}\int_0^1 f(x, t)\,dx = \int_0^1 \frac{\partial f}{\partial t}\,dx.$$

*5 CONVERGENCE IN MEASURE

Suppose that $\langle f_n\rangle$ is a sequence of measurable functions such that $\int |f_n| \to 0$. What can we say about the sequence $\langle f_n\rangle$? Perhaps the most important property of such a sequence is that for each positive η the measure of the sets $\{x : |f_n(x)| > \eta\}$ must tend to zero. This leads us to the following definition:

Definition: *A sequence $\langle f_n\rangle$ of measurable functions is said to converge to f in measure if given $\epsilon > 0$ there is an N such that for all $n \geq N$ we have*

$$m\{x : |f(x) - f_n(x)| \geq \epsilon\} < \epsilon.$$

An example of a sequence $\langle f_n\rangle$ which converges to zero in measure on $[0, 1]$ but such that $\langle f_n(x)\rangle$ does not converge for any x in $[0, 1]$ can be constructed as follows: Let $n = k + 2^\nu$, $0 \leq k < 2^\nu$, and set $f_n(x) = 1$ if $x \in [k2^{-\nu}, (k + 1)2^{-\nu}]$ and $f_n(x) = 0$ otherwise. Then

$$m\{x : |f_n(x)| > \epsilon\} \leq \frac{2}{n},$$

and so $f_n \to 0$ in measure, although for any $x \in [0, 1]$, the sequence $\langle f_n(x)\rangle$ has the value 1 for arbitrarily large values of n and so does not converge. We do, however, have the following proposition.

16. Proposition: *Let $\langle f_n\rangle$ be a sequence of measurable functions which converges in measure to f. Then there is a subsequence $\langle f_{n_k}\rangle$ which converges to f almost everywhere.*

Proof: Given ν, there is an integer n_ν such that for all $n \geq n_\nu$ we have

$$m\{x : |f_n(x) - f(x)| \geq 2^{-\nu}\} < 2^{-\nu}.$$

Let $E_\nu = \{x : |f_{n_\nu}(x) - f(x)| \geq 2^{-\nu}\}$. Then if $x \notin \bigcup_{\nu=k}^{\infty} E_\nu$, we have $|f_{n_\nu}(x) - f(x)| < 2^{-\nu}$ for $\nu \geq k$, and so $f_{n_\nu}(x) \to f(x)$. Hence

$f_{n_\nu}(x) \to f(x)$ for any $x \notin A = \bigcap_{k=1}^{\infty} \bigcup_{\nu=k}^{\infty} E_\nu$. But $mA \le m\left[\bigcup_{\nu=k}^{\infty} E_\nu\right] \le \sum_{\nu=k}^{\infty} mE_\nu = 2^{-k+1}$. Hence $mA = 0$. ∎

17. Proposition: *Fatou's lemma and the monotone and Lebesgue convergence theorems remain valid if 'convergence a.e.' is replaced by 'convergence in measure'.*

Problems

14. Show that if $\langle f_n \rangle$ is a sequence which converges to f in measure, then each subsequence $\langle f_{n_k} \rangle$ converges to f in measure.

15. Deduce Proposition 17 from Proposition 16 using Problems 14 and 2.10.

16. Prove that a sequence $\langle f_n \rangle$ of measurable functions converges to f in measure if and only if every subsequence of $\langle f_n \rangle$ has in turn a subsequence which converges in measure to f.

17. Prove that a sequence $\langle f_n \rangle$ of measurable functions on a set E of finite measure converges to f in measure if and only if every subsequence of $\langle f_n \rangle$ has in turn a subsequence which converges to f a.e. on E.

18. Use Proposition 13 to prove directly that, if $f_n \to f$ in measure and if there is an integrable function g such that for all n we have $|f_n| \le g$, then $\int |f_n - f| \to 0$.

19. A sequence $\langle f_n \rangle$ of measurable functions is said to be a Cauchy sequence in measure if given $\epsilon > 0$ there is an N such that for all $m, n \ge N$ we have

$$m\{x : |f_n(x) - f_m(x)| \ge \epsilon\} < \epsilon.$$

Show that if $\langle f_n \rangle$ is a Cauchy sequence in measure then there is a function f to which the sequence $\langle f_n \rangle$ converges in measure. (Choose $n_{\nu+1} > n_\nu$ so that $m\{x : |f_{n_\nu} - f_{n_{\nu+1}}| > 2^{-\nu}\} < 2^{-\nu}$. Then the series $\Sigma(f_{n_{\nu+1}} - f_{n_\nu})$ converges almost everywhere to a function g. Let $f = g + f_{n_1}$. Then $f_{n_\nu} \to f$ in measure, and one can show that consequently $f_n \to f$ in measure.)

5 *Differentiation and Integration*

In this chapter we shall consider the sense in which differentiation is the inverse of integration. In particular we shall be concerned with the following questions:
When does

$$\int_a^b f'(x)\,dx = f(b) - f(a)?$$

When does

$$\frac{d}{dx}\int_a^x f(y)\,dy = f(x)?$$

From the theory of Riemann integration it is known that the second relation is true if x is a point of continuity of f. We shall show that more generally this relation holds almost everywhere. Thus differentiation is the inverse of Lebesgue integration. The first question, however, is more difficult and even using the Lebesgue integral it is true only for a certain class of functions which we shall characterize.

1 DIFFERENTIATION OF MONOTONE FUNCTIONS

Let $\mathscr{I}$ be a collection of intervals. Then we say that $\mathscr{I}$ covers a set E *in the sense of Vitali*, if for each $\epsilon > 0$ and any x in E there is an interval $I \in \mathscr{I}$ such that $x \in I$ and $l(I) < \epsilon$.

1. Lemma (Vitali): *Let E be a set of finite outer measure and $\mathscr{I}$ a collection of closed intervals which cover E in the sense of Vitali. Then* *given $\epsilon > 0$ there is a finite disjoint collection $\{I_1, \ldots, I_N\}$ of intervals in $\mathscr{I}$ such that*

$$m^*\left[E \sim \bigcup_{n=1}^{N} I_n\right] < \epsilon.$$

Proof: Let O be an open set of finite measure containing E. Since $\mathscr{I}$ is a Vitali covering of E, we may assume without loss of generality that each I of $\mathscr{I}$ is contained in O. We choose a sequence $\langle I_n \rangle$ of disjoint intervals of $\mathscr{I}$ by induction as follows: Let I_1 be any interval in $\mathscr{I}$, and suppose $I_1, \ldots, I_n$ have already been chosen. Let k_n be the supremum of the lengths of the intervals of $\mathscr{I}$ which do not meet any of the intervals $I_1, \ldots, I_n$. Since each I is contained in O, we have $k_n \leq mO < \infty$. Unless $E \subset \bigcup_{i=1}^{n} I_n$, we can find I_{n+1} in $\mathscr{I}$ so that $l(I_{n+1}) > \frac{1}{2}k_n$.

Thus we have a sequence $\langle I_n \rangle$ of disjoint intervals of $\mathscr{I}$, and since $\bigcup I_n \subset O$, we have $\Sigma l(I_n) \leq mO < \infty$. Hence we can find an integer N such that

$$\sum_{N+1}^{\infty} l(I_n) < \epsilon/5.$$

Let

$$R = E \sim \bigcup_{n=1}^{N} I_n.$$

The lemma will be established if we can show that $m^*R < \epsilon$. Let x be an arbitrary point of R. Since $\bigcup_{n=1}^{N} I_n$ is a closed set not containing x, we can find an interval I in $\mathscr{I}$ which contains x and whose length is so small that I does not meet any of the intervals $I_1, \ldots, I_N$. If now $I \cap I_i = \varnothing$ for $i \leq n$, we must have $l(I) \leq k_n < 2l(I_{n+1})$. Since $\lim l(I_n) = 0$, the interval I must meet at least one of the intervals I_n. Let n be the smallest integer such that I meets I_n. We have $n > N$, and $l(I) \leq k_{n-1} \leq 2l(I_n)$. Since x is in I and I has a point in common with I_n, it follows that the distance from x to the midpoint of I_n is at most $l(I) + \frac{1}{2}l(I_n) \leq \frac{5}{2}l(I_n)$. Thus x belongs to the interval J_n having the same midpoint as I_n and five times the length. Thus we have shown that

$$R \subset \bigcup_{N+1}^{\infty} J_n.$$

Hence

$$m^*R \leq \sum_{N+1}^{\infty} lJ_n = 5 \sum_{N+1}^{\infty} l(I_n)$$
$$< \epsilon. \;\blacksquare$$

In order to talk about the derivatives of a function f, we first define a set of four quantities called the **derivates** of f at x as follows:

$$D^+f(x) = \overline{\lim_{h\to 0+}} \frac{f(x+h)-f(x)}{h} \qquad D^-f(x) = \overline{\lim_{h\to 0+}} \frac{f(x)-f(x-h)}{h}$$

$$D_+f(x) = \underline{\lim_{h\to 0+}} \frac{f(x+h)-f(x)}{h} \qquad D_-f(x) = \underline{\lim_{h\to 0+}} \frac{f(x)-f(x-h)}{h}.$$

Clearly we have $D^+f(x) \geq D_+f(x)$ and $D^-f(x) \geq D_-f(x)$. If $D^+f(x) = D_+f(x) = D^-f(x) = D_-f(x) \neq \pm\infty$, we say that f is differentiable at x and define $f'(x)$ to be the common value of the derivates at x.

2. Theorem: *Let f be an increasing real-valued function on the interval $[a, b]$. Then f is differentiable almost everywhere. The derivative f' is measurable, and*

$$\int_a^b f'(x)\,dx \leq f(b) - f(a).$$

Proof: Let us show that the sets where any two derivates are unequal is of measure zero. We consider only the set E where $D^+f(x) > D_-f(x)$, the sets arising from other combinations of derivates being similarly handled. Now the set E is the union of the sets

$$E_{u,v} = \{x : D^+f(x) > u > v > D_-f(x)\}$$

for all rational u and v. Hence it suffices to prove that $m^*E_{u,v} = 0$. Let $s = m^*E_{u,v}$ and, choosing $\epsilon > 0$, enclose $E_{u,v}$ in an open set O with $mO < s + \epsilon$. For each point x in $E_{u,v}$, there is an arbitrarily small interval $[x - h, x]$ contained in O such that

$$f(x) - f(x-h) < vh.$$

By Lemma 1 we can choose a finite collection $\{I_1, \ldots, I_N\}$ of them whose interiors cover a subset A of $E_{u,v}$ of outer measure greater than $s - \epsilon$. Then summing over these intervals we have

$$\begin{aligned}\sum_{n=1}^{N} f(x_n) - f(x_n - h_n) &< v \sum_{n=1}^{N} h_n \\ &< v\, mO \\ &< v(s + \epsilon).\end{aligned}$$

Now each point $y \varepsilon A$ is the left endpoint of an arbitrarily small interval $(y, y + k)$ which is contained in some I_n and such that $f(y + k) - f(y) > uk$. Using Lemma 1 again, we can pick out a finite collection $\{J_1, \ldots, J_M\}$ of such intervals such that their union contains a subset of A of outer measure greater than $s - 2\epsilon$. Then summing over these intervals

$$\begin{aligned}\sum_{i=1}^{M} f(y_i + k_i) - f(y_i) &> u \sum k_i \\ &> u(s - 2\epsilon).\end{aligned}$$

Each interval J_i is contained in some interval I_n, and if we sum over those i for which $J_i \subset I_n$, we have

$$\sum f(y_i + k_i) - f(y_i) \le f(x_n) - f(x_n - h_n),$$

since f is increasing. Thus

$$\sum_{n=1}^{N} f(x_n) - f(x_n - h_n) \ge \sum_{i=1}^{M} f(y_i + k_i) - f(y_i),$$

and so

$$v(s + \epsilon) > u(s - 2\epsilon).$$

Since this is true for each positive ϵ, we have $vs \ge us$. But $u > v$, and so s must be zero.

This shows that

$$g(x) = \lim_{h \to 0} \frac{f(x + h) - f(x)}{h}$$

is defined almost everywhere, and that f is differentiable wherever g is finite. Let

$$g_n(x) = n[f(x + 1/n) - f(x)]$$

where we set $f(x) = f(b)$ for $x \ge b$. Then $g_n(x) \to g(x)$ for almost all

x, and so g is measurable. Since f is increasing, we have $g_n \geq 0$. Hence by Fatou's lemma

$$\int_a^b g \leq \underline{\lim} \int_a^b g_n = \underline{\lim}\, n \int_a^b [f(x + 1/n) - f(x)]\, dx$$

$$= \underline{\lim}\, n \int_b^{b+1/n} f - n \int_a^{a+1/n} f$$

$$= \underline{\lim}\, f(b) - n \int_a^{a+1/n} f$$

$$\leq f(b) - f(a).$$

This shows that g is integrable and hence finite almost everywhere. Thus f is differentiable a.e. and $g = f'$ a.e. ▌

Problems

1. Let f be the function defined by $f(0) = 0$ and $f(x) = x \sin (1/x)$ for $x \neq 0$. Find $D^+f(0)$, $D_+f(0)$, $D^-f(0)$, $D_-f(0)$.

2. If the function f assumes its maximum at c, then $D^+f(c) \leq 0$ and $D_-f(c) \geq 0$.

3. If f is continuous on $[a, b]$ and one of its derivates (say D^+) is everywhere nonnegative on $[a, b]$, then $f(b) \geq f(a)$. (Hint: Show that if $c = \sup \{x : f(x) \geq f(a)\}$ then $f(c) \geq f(a)$, and then show $c = b$.)

2 FUNCTIONS OF BOUNDED VARIATION

Let f be a real-valued function defined on the interval $[a, b]$ and let $a = x_0 < x_1 < \cdots < x_k = b$ be any subdivision of $[a, b]$. Define

$$p = \sum_{i=1}^{k} [f(x_i) - f(x_{i-1})]^+$$

$$n = \sum_{i=1}^{k} [f(x_i) - f(x_{i-1})]^-$$

$$t = n + p = \sum_{i=1}^{k} |f(x_i) - f(x_{i-1})|,$$

where we use r^+ to denote r, if $r \geq 0$ and 0, if $r \leq 0$, and set $r^- = |r| - r^+$. We have $f(b) - f(a) = p - n$. Set

$$P = \sup p$$
$$N = \sup n$$
$$T = \sup t,$$

where we take the suprema over all possible subdivisions of $[a, b]$. We clearly have $P \leq T \leq P + N$. We call P, N, T the positive, negative, and total variations of f over $[a, b]$. We sometimes write T_a^b, $T_a^b[f]$, etc., to denote the dependence on the interval $[a, b]$ or on the function f. If $T < \infty$, we say that f is of **bounded variation** over $[a, b]$. This notion is sometimes abbreviated by writing $f \in BV$.

3. Lemma: *If f is of bounded variation on $[a, b]$ then*

$$T_a^b = P_a^b + N_a^b$$

and

$$f(b) - f(a) = P_a^b - N_a^b.$$

Proof: For any subdivision of $[a, b]$,

$$\begin{aligned} p &= n + f(b) - f(a) \\ &\leq N + f(b) - f(a), \end{aligned}$$

and taking suprema over all possible subdivisions

$$P \leq N + f(b) - f(a).$$

Since $N \leq T < \infty$,

$$P - N \leq f(b) - f(a).$$

Similarly

$$N - P \leq f(a) - f(b),$$

and so

$$P - N = f(b) - f(a).$$

Thus

$$T \geq p + n = p + p - \{f(b) - f(a)\} = 2p + N - P,$$

and

$$T \geq 2P + N - P = P + N.$$

Since $T \leq P + N$, we have $T = P + N$. ∎

4. Theorem: *A function f is of bounded variation on $[a, b]$ if and only if f is the difference of two monotone real-valued functions on $[a, b]$.*

Proof: Let f be of bounded variation, and set $g(x) = P_a^x$ and $h(x) = N_a^x$. Then g and h are monotone increasing functions which are real-valued since $0 \le P_a^x \le T_a^x \le T_a^b < \infty$ and $0 \le N_a^x \le T_a^x \le T_a^b < \infty$. But $f(x) = g(x) - h(x) + f(a)$ by Lemma 3. Since $h - f(a)$ is a monotone function, we have f expressed as the difference of two monotone functions.

On the other hand, if $f = g - h$ on $[a, b]$ with g and h increasing, then for any subdivision we have

$$\sum |f(x_i) - f(x_{i-1})| \le \sum [g(x_i) - g(x_{i-1})] + \sum [h(x_i) - h(x_{i-1})]$$
$$= g(b) - g(a) + h(b) - h(a).$$

Hence

$$T_a^b(f) \le g(b) + h(b) - g(a) - h(a). \quad \blacksquare$$

5. Corollary: *If f is of bounded variation on $[a, b]$ then $f'(x)$ exists for almost all x in $[a, b]$.*

Problems

4. Let f be of bounded variation on $[a, b]$. Show that for each $c \in (a, b)$ the limit of $f(x)$ exists as $x \to c^-$ and also as $x \to c^+$. Prove that a monotone function (and hence a function of bounded variation) can have only a countable number of discontinuities.

5. Show that if $a \le c \le b$, then $T_a^b = T_a^c + T_c^b$ and that hence $T_a^c \le T_a^b$.

6. Show that $T_a^b(f + g) \le T_a^b(f) + T_a^b(g)$, and $T_a^b(cf) = |c|\, T_a^b(f)$.

7. a. Let f be defined by $f(0) = 0$ and $f(x) = x^2 \sin(1/x^2)$ for $x \ne 0$. Is f of bounded variation on $[-1, 1]$?

b. Let g be defined by $g(0) = 0$ and $g(x) = x^2 \sin(1/x)$ for $x \ne 0$. Is g of bounded variation on $[-1, 1]$?

3 DIFFERENTIATION OF AN INTEGRAL

In this section we shall show that the derivative of the indefinite integral of an integrable function is (a.e.) the integrand. We begin by establishing some lemmas.

6. Lemma: *If f is integrable on $[a, b]$ then the function F defined by*

$$F(x) = \int_a^x f(t)\, dt$$

is a continuous function of bounded variation on $[a, b]$.

Proof: The continuity follows from Proposition 4.13. To show that F is of bounded variation, let $a = x_0 < x_1 < \cdots < x_k = b$ be any subdivision of $[a, b]$. Then

$$\sum_{i=1}^{k} \left| F(x_i) - F(x_{i-1}) \right| = \sum_{i=1}^{k} \left| \int_{x_{i-1}}^{x_i} f(t)\, dt \right| \le \sum_{i=1}^{k} \int_{x_{i-1}}^{x_i} |f(t)|\, dt$$
$$= \int_a^b |f(t)|\, dt.$$

Thus

$$T_a^b(F) \le \int_a^b |f(t)|\, dt < \infty. \ \blacksquare$$

7. Lemma: *If f is integrable on $[a, b]$ and*

$$\int_a^x f(t)\, dt = 0$$

for all $x \in [a, b]$, then $f(t) = 0$ a.e., *in $[a, b]$.*

Proof: Suppose $f(x) > 0$ on a set E of positive measure. Then by Proposition 3.15 there is a closed set $F \subset E$ with $mF > 0$. Let $O = (a, b) \sim F$. Then either $\int_a^b f \neq 0$, or else

$$0 = \int_a^b f = \int_F f + \int_O f,$$

and

$$\int_O f = - \int_F f \neq 0.$$

But O is the disjoint union of a countable collection $\{(a_n, b_n)\}$ of open intervals, and so by Proposition 4.11

$$\int_O f = \sum \int_{a_n}^{b_n} f.$$

Thus for some n we have

$$\int_{a_n}^{b_n} f \neq 0,$$

and so either

$$\int_a^{a_n} f \neq 0.$$

or

$$\int_a^{b_n} f \neq 0.$$

In any case we see that if f is positive on a set of positive measure then for some $x \in [a, b]$ we have

$$\int_a^{x} f \neq 0.$$

Similarly, for f negative on a set of positive measure, and the lemma follows by contraposition. ∎

8. Lemma: *If f is bounded and measurable on* $[a, b]$ *and*

$$F(x) = \int_a^x f(t)\,dt + F(a),$$

then $F'(x) = f(x)$ for almost all x in $[a, b]$.

Proof: Since F is of bounded variation over $[a, b]$ by Lemma 6, $F'(x)$ exists for almost all x in $[a, b]$. Let $|f| \leq K$. Then setting

$$f_n(x) = \frac{F(x+h) - F(x)}{h},$$

with $h = 1/n$, we have

$$f_n(x) = \frac{1}{h}\int_x^{x+h} f(t)\,dt,$$

and so

$$|f_n| \leq K.$$

Since

$$f_n(x) \to F'(x) \qquad \text{a.e.},$$

the bounded convergence theorem implies that

$$\int_a^c F'(x)\,dx = \lim \int_a^c f_n(x)\,dx = \lim_{h\to 0} \frac{1}{h}\int_a^c (F(x+h) - F(x))\,dx$$

$$= \lim \frac{1}{h}\int_c^{c+h} F(x)dx - \frac{1}{h}\int_a^{a+h} F(x)dx$$

$$= F(c) - F(a) = \int_a^c f(x)\,dx,$$

since F is continuous. Hence

$$\int_a^c \{F'(x) - f(x)\}\,dx = 0$$

for all $c \in [a, b]$, and so

$$F'(x) = f(x) \quad \text{a.e.}$$

by Lemma 7. ▌

9. Theorem: *Let f be an integrable function on $[a, b]$, and suppose*

$$F(x) = F(a) + \int_a^x f(t)\,dt.$$

Then $F'(x) = f(x)$ for almost all x in $[a, b]$.

Proof: Without loss of generality we may assume $f \geq 0$. Let f_n be defined by $f_n(x) = f(x)$, if $f(x) \leq n$, and $f_n(x) = n$ if $f(x) > n$. Then $f - f_n \geq 0$, and so

$$G_n(x) = \int_a^x f - f_n$$

is an increasing function of x which must have a derivative almost everywhere, and this derivative will be nonnegative. Now by Lemma 8

$$\frac{d}{dx}\int_a^x f_n = f_n(x) \quad \text{a.e.,}$$

and so

$$F'(x) = \frac{d}{dx} G_n + \frac{d}{dx}\int_a^x f_n$$

$$\geq f_n(x) \quad \text{a.e.}$$

Since n is arbitrary,

$$F'(x) \geq f(x) \quad \text{a.e.}$$

Consequently

$$\int_a^b F'(x)\,dx \geq \int_a^b f(x)\,dx = F(b) - F(a)\,.$$

Thus by Theorem 2 we have

$$\int_a^b F'(x)\,dx = F(b) - F(a) = \int_a^b f(x)\,dx\,,$$

and

$$\int_a^b (F'(x) - f(x))\,dx = 0\,.$$

Since $F'(x) - f(x) \geq 0$, this implies that $F'(x) - f(x) = 0$ a.e., and so $F'(x) = f(x)$ a.e. ▌

4 ABSOLUTE CONTINUITY

A real-valued function f defined on $[a, b]$ is said to be **absolutely continuous** on $[a, b]$ if, given $\epsilon > 0$, there is a $\delta > 0$ such that

$$\sum_{i=1}^{n} |f(x_i') - f(x_i)| < \epsilon$$

for every finite collection $\{(x_i, x_i')\}$ of nonoverlapping intervals with

$$\sum_{i=1}^{n} |x_i' - x_i| < \delta\,.$$

An absolutely continuous function is continuous, and it follows from Proposition 4.13 that every indefinite integral is absolutely continuous.

10. Lemma: *If f is absolutely continuous on $[a, b]$ then it is of bounded variation on $[a, b]$.*

Proof: Let δ be the δ in the definition of absolute continuity which corresponds to $\epsilon = 1$. Then any subdivision of $[a, b]$ can be split (by inserting fresh division points, if necessary) into K sets of intervals, each of total length less than δ, where K is the largest integer less than $1 + (b - a)/\delta$. Thus for any subdivision we have $t \leq K$ and so $T \leq K$. ▌

11. Corollary: *If f is absolutely continuous, then f has a derivative almost everywhere.*

12. Lemma: *If f is absolutely continuous on $[a, b]$ and $f'(x) = 0$* a.e., *then f is constant.*

Proof: We wish to show that $f(a) = f(c)$ for any $c \in [a, b]$. Let E be the set of measure $c - a$ in which $f'(x) = 0$, and let ϵ and η be arbitrary positive numbers. To each x in E there is an arbitrarily small interval $[x, x + h]$ contained in $[a, c]$ such that $|f(x + h) - f(x)| < \eta h$. By Lemma 1 we can find a finite collection $\{[x_k, y_k]\}$ of nonoverlapping intervals of this sort which cover all of E except for a set of measure less than δ, where δ is the positive number corresponding to ϵ in the definition of the absolute continuity of f. If we label the x_k so that $x_k \le x_{k+1}$, we have

$$y_0 = a \le x_1 < y_1 \le x_2 < \cdots \le y_n \le c = x_{n+1}$$

and

$$\sum_{k=0}^{n} |x_{k+1} - y_k| < \delta .$$

Now

$$\begin{aligned}\sum_{k=1}^{n} |f(y_k) - f(x_k)| &\le \eta \sum (y_k - x_k) \\ &< \eta(b - a)\end{aligned}$$

by the way the intervals $\{[x_k, y_k]\}$ were constructed, and

$$\sum_{k=0}^{n} |f(x_{k+1}) - f(y_k)| < \epsilon$$

by the absolute continuity of f. Thus

$$\begin{aligned}|f(c) - f(a)| &= \left|\sum_{k=0}^{n} [f(x_{k+1}) - f(y_k)] + \sum_{k=1}^{n} [f(y_k) - f(x_k)]\right| \\ &\le \epsilon + \eta(b - a) .\end{aligned}$$

Since ϵ and η are arbitrary positive numbers, we have $f(c) - f(a) = 0$. ∎

13. Theorem: *A function F is an indefinite integral if and only if it is absolutely continuous.*

Proof: If F is an indefinite integral, then F is absolutely continuous by Proposition 4.13. Suppose on the other hand that F is absolutely continuous on $[a, b]$. Then F is of bounded variation, and we may write see lemma 6

$$F(x) = F_1(x) - F_2(x) ,$$

where the functions F_i are monotone increasing. Hence $F'(x)$ exists almost everywhere and

$$|F'(x)| \le F_1'(x) + F_2'(x) .$$

Thus

$$\int |F'(x)|\, dx \le F_1(b) + F_2(b) - F_1(a) - F_2(a)$$

by Theorem 2, and $F'(x)$ is integrable. Let

$$G(x) = \int_a^x F'(t)\, dt .$$

Then G is absolutely continuous and so is the function $f = F - G$. It follows from Theorem 9 that $f'(x) = F'(x) - G'(x) = 0$ a.e., and so f is constant by Lemma 12. Thus

$$F(x) = \int_a^x F'(t)\, dt + F(a) . \blacksquare$$

14. Corollary: *Every absolutely continuous function is the indefinite integral of its derivative.*

Problems

8. Let f be absolutely continuous in the interval $[\epsilon, 1]$ for each $\epsilon > 0$. Does the continuity of f at 0 imply that f is absolutely continuous on $[0, 1]$? What if f is also of bounded variation on $[0, 1]$?

9. The Cantor ternary function (Problem 2.42) is continuous and monotone but not absolutely continuous.

$f(x) = x^2 \sin \frac{1}{x^2}$ is a.c. on $[\epsilon, 1]$

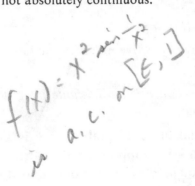

6 The Classical Banach Spaces

1 THE L^p SPACES

In this chapter we will study some spaces of functions of a real variable. Let p be a real number which is greater than or equal to 1. Then a measurable function defined on [0, 1] is said to belong to the space $L^p = L^p[0, 1]$ if $\int_0^1 |f|^p < \infty$. Thus L^1 consists precisely of the Lebesgue integrable functions on [0, 1]. For a function $f \in L^p$, we define

$$\|f\| = \|f\|_p = \left\{\int_0^1 |f|^p\right\}^{1/p}.$$

We see that $\|f\| = 0$ if and only if $f = 0$ a.e. If α is a constant, then $\|\alpha f\| = |\alpha|\,\|f\|$. In the next section we shall derive two inequalities, the second of which states that $\|f + g\| \leq \|f\| + \|g\|$.

It follows from this inequality that if f and g are in L^p, then so is $f + g$. A space X of functions is called a **linear space** (or vector space) if it has the property that $\alpha f + \beta g$ belongs to X for each pair f and g belonging to X and for each pair of constants α and β. Thus the L^p spaces are linear spaces. A linear space is said to be a normed linear space if we have assigned a nonnegative real number $\|f\|$ to each f such that $\|\alpha f\| = |\alpha|\,\|f\|$, $\|f + g\| \leq \|f\| + \|g\|$, and $\|f\| = 0 \Leftrightarrow f \equiv 0$. Unfortunately, the norm for the L^p spaces does not satisfy the last requirement, for from $\|f\| = 0$ we can only conclude that $f = 0$ a.e. We shall, however, consider two measurable functions to be equivalent if they are equal almost everywhere, and if we do not distinguish between equivalent functions, then the L^p spaces are normed linear spaces.[1]

[1] To be pedantic we should say the elements of L^p are not functions but rather equivalence classes of functions. Cf. Problem 10.10.

It is convenient to denote by L^∞ the space of all bounded measurable functions on [0, 1] (or rather all measurable functions which are bounded except possibly on a subset of measure zero). Again we identify functions which are equivalent. Then L^∞ is a linear space, and it becomes a normed linear space if we define

$$\|f\| = \|f\|_\infty = \text{ess sup } |f(t)|,$$

where ess sup $f(t)$ is the infimum of sup $g(t)$ as g ranges over all functions which are equal to f almost everywhere, thus

$$\text{ess sup} f(t) = \inf \{M: m\{t: f(t) > M\} = 0\}.$$

Problems

1. Show that $\|f + g\|_\infty \le \|f\|_\infty + \|g\|_\infty$.

2. Let f be a bounded measurable function on [0, 1]. Then $\lim_{p\to\infty} \|f\|_p = \|f\|_\infty$.

3. Prove that $\|f + g\|_1 \le \|f\|_1 + \|g\|_1$.

4. If $f \in L^1$ and $g \in L^\infty$, then

$$\int |fg| \le \|f\|_1 \cdot \|g\|_\infty$$

true on any set of finite measure

2 THE HÖLDER AND MINKOWSKI INEQUALITIES

Before proving inequalities about the L^p norm, we first establish the following lemma which is a generalization of the inequality between the arithmetic and geometric mean:

1. Lemma: *Let α and β be nonnegative real numbers, and suppose $0 < \lambda < 1$. Then $\alpha^\lambda \beta^{1-\lambda} \le \lambda\alpha + (1 - \lambda)\beta$ with equality only if $\alpha = \beta$.*

Proof: Consider the function φ defined for nonnegative real numbers t by

$$\varphi(t) = (1 - \lambda) + \lambda t - t^\lambda.$$

Then

$$\varphi'(t) = \lambda(1 - t^{\lambda-1}).$$

Since $\lambda - 1 < 0$, we have $\varphi'(t) < 0$ for $t < 1$ and $\varphi'(t) > 0$ for $t > 1$. Thus for $t \ne 1$, we have $\varphi(t) > \varphi(1) = 0$. Hence

$$(1 - \lambda) + \lambda t \ge t^\lambda,$$

with equality only for $t = 1$. If $\beta \neq 0$, the lemma follows by substituting α/β for t, while if $\beta = 0$, the lemma is trivial. ▌

2. Hölder Inequality: *If p and q are nonnegative extended real numbers such that* $\frac{1}{p} + \frac{1}{q} = 1$, *and if $f \in L^p$ and $g \in L^q$, then $f \cdot g \in L^1$ and*

$$\int |fg| \leq \|f\|_p \cdot \|g\|_q.$$

Equality holds if and only if, for some constant c, $|f|^p = |g|^q$ a.e.

Proof: The case $p = 1$, $q = \infty$ is straightforward and is left to the reader. Hence we assume $1 < p < \infty$ and consequently $1 < q < \infty$. Let us first suppose that $\|f\|_p = \|g\|_q = 1$, and apply our lemma with $\alpha = |f(t)|^p$, $\beta = |g(t)|^q$, $\lambda = \frac{1}{p}$, $1 - \lambda = \frac{1}{q}$. Then

$$\text{(1)} \qquad |f(t)g(t)| \leq \lambda |f(t)|^p + (1 - \lambda)\, |g(t)|^q,$$

and integrating both sides we have

$$\text{(2)} \qquad \int |fg| \leq \lambda \int |f|^p + (1 - \lambda) \int |g|^q = 1.$$

The inequality is trivial if $\|f\| = 0$ or $\|g\| = 0$. Let f and g be any elements of L^p and L^q with $\|f\| \neq 0$ and $\|g\| \neq 0$. Then $f/\|f\|_p$ and $g/\|g\|_q$ both have norm 1. Substituting them in (2) gives

$$\frac{1}{\|f\|_p \, \|g\|_q} \int |fg| = \int \frac{|f|}{\|f\|_p} \cdot \frac{|g|}{\|g\|_q} \leq 1.$$

Equality in (1) can occur only if $|f(t)|^p = |g(t)|^q$, and equality can hold in (2) only if it holds almost everywhere in (1). Hence equality holds only if $|f|^p = |g|^q$ a.e. ▌

3. Minkowski Inequality: *If f and g are in L^p, then so is $f + g$ and*

$$\|f + g\|_p \leq \|f\|_p + \|g\|_p.$$

Proof: The cases $p = 1$ and $p = \infty$ are straightforward and are left to the reader. Hence we assume $1 < p < \infty$.

Let us first suppose that f and g are bounded. Then $f + g$ is bounded, and

$$\int |f + g|^p \leq \int |f + g|^{p-1}\, |f| + \int |f + g|^{p-1}\, |g|.$$

By the Hölder inequality,

$$\int |f+g|^{p-1}\,|f| \le \|f\|_p\,\|(|f+g|^{p-1})\|_q$$

$$\int |f+g|^{p-1}\,|g| \le \|g\|_p\,\|(|f+g|^{p-1})\|_q$$

and

$$\|(|f+g|^{p-1})\|_q = \left\{\int |f+g|^{(p-1)q}\right\}^{1/q}$$

$$= \{\|f+g\|_p\}^{p/q}$$

since $p = q(p-1)$. Hence

$$\|f+g\|_p^p \le (\|f\|_p + \|g\|_p)(\|f+g\|_p)^{p/q},$$

or

$$\|f+g\|_p \le \|f\|_p + \|g\|_p.$$

The case of unbounded functions f and g now follows easily, for if h is any nonnegative bounded function less than $|f+g|$, then we set

$$k(t) = \min |f(t)|,\ |h(t)|$$

and

$$l(t) = h(t) - k(t).$$

Then

$$0 \le l(t) \le |g(t)|$$

and

$$0 \le k(t) \le |f(t)|.$$

Thus $\|k\| \le \|f\|$ and $\|l\| \le \|g\|$, and so by the inequality for bounded functions

$$\left\{\int h^p\right\}^{1/p} = \|h\| = \|k+l\| \le \|k\| + \|l\|$$
$$\le \|f\| + \|g\|.$$

Since

$$\int |f+g|^p = \sup \int h^p$$

over all bounded functions h which are less than $|f+g|$, we have

$$\left\{\int |f+g|^p\right\}^{1/p} \le \|f\| + \|g\|. \ \blacksquare$$

Problems

5. For $1 \leq p < \infty$, we denote by l^p the space of all sequences $\langle \xi_\nu \rangle_{\nu=1}^{\infty}$ such that $\sum_{\nu=1}^{\infty} |\xi_\nu|^p < \infty$. Show that if $\langle \xi_\nu \rangle \varepsilon\, l^p$, and $\langle \eta_\nu \rangle \varepsilon\, l^q$ with $\frac{1}{p} + \frac{1}{q} = 1$, then

$$\sum_{\nu=1}^{\infty} |\xi_\nu \eta_\nu| \leq \| \langle \xi_\nu \rangle \|_p \cdot \| \langle \eta_\nu \rangle \|_q$$

where

$$(\| \langle \xi_\nu \rangle \|_p)^p = \sum_{\nu=1}^{\infty} |\xi_\nu|^p.$$

This is the Hölder inequality for sequences.

6. Prove the Minkowski inequality for sequences:

$$\|\langle \xi_\nu + \eta_\nu \rangle\|_p \leq \|\langle \xi_\nu \rangle\|_p + \|\langle \eta_\nu \rangle\|_p$$

Here we have $1 \leq p < \infty$.

3 CONVERGENCE AND COMPLETENESS

The notion of convergence for a sequence of real numbers generalizes to give us a notion of convergence for sequences in a normed linear space.

Definition: *A sequence $\langle f_n \rangle$ in a normed linear space is said to converge to an element f in the space if, given $\epsilon > 0$, there is an N such that for all $n > N$ we have $\|f - f_n\| < \epsilon$. If f_n converges to f we write $f = \lim f_n$ or $f_n \to f$.*

Another way of formulating the convergence of f_n to f is by noting that $f_n \to f$ if $\|f_n - f\| \to 0$. Convergence in the space $L^p, 1 \leq p < \infty$, is often referred to as **convergence in the mean of order p.** Thus a sequence of functions $\langle f_n \rangle$ is said to converge to f in the mean of order p if each f_n belongs to L^p and $\|f - f_n\|_p \to 0$. Convergence in L^∞ is almost uniform convergence (Problem 8).

Since we are dealing with a linear space X of functions, we must be careful to distinguish the above notion of convergence in X from the notion of a sequence of functions which converges at each point. We shall call this latter type of convergence **pointwise convergence,** and say that $\langle f_n \rangle$ converges pointwise to f if for each x we have

$f(x) = \lim f_n(x)$. If there is a set E of measure zero such that for each x in $\tilde{E}$ we have $f(x) = \lim f_n(x)$, then we say that f_n converges to f almost everywhere.

Just as for the case of sequences of real numbers, we say that a sequence $\langle f_n \rangle$ in a normed linear space is a **Cauchy sequence** if, given $\epsilon > 0$, there is an N such that for all $n \geq N$ and all $m \geq N$ we have $\|f_n - f_m\| < \epsilon$. It is easily verified that each convergent sequence is a Cauchy sequence.

Definition: *A normed linear space is called* **complete** *if every Cauchy sequence in the space converges; that is, if for each Cauchy sequence $\langle f_n \rangle$ in the space there is an element f in the space such that $f_n \to f$. A complete normed linear space is called a Banach space.*

A series $\langle f_n \rangle$ in a normed linear space is said to be **summable** to a sum s if s is in the space and the sequence of partial sums of the series converges to s; that is

$$\left\| s - \sum_{i=1}^{n} f_i \right\| \to 0.$$

If this is the case, we write $s = \sum_{i=1}^{\infty} f_i$. The series $\langle f_n \rangle$ is said to be absolutely summable if $\sum_{n=1}^{\infty} \|f_n\| < \infty$.

For a series of real numbers we know that the absolute summability implies that the series is summable. While this is not true in general for series of elements in a normed linear space, the following proposition shows that this implication holds if the space is complete.

4. Proposition: *A normed linear space X is complete if and only if every absolutely summable series is summable.*

Proof: $\Rightarrow$: Let X be complete and $\langle f_n \rangle$ an absolutely summable series of elements of X. Since $\Sigma\|f_n\| = m < \infty$,, there is for each given $\epsilon > 0$ an N such that $\sum_{n=N}^{\infty} \|f_n\| < \epsilon$. Let $s_n = \sum_{i=1}^{n} f_i$ be the partial sum of the series $\langle f_n \rangle$. Then for $n \geq m \geq N$ we have

$$\|s_n - s_m\| = \left\| \sum_{i=m}^{n} f_i \right\| \leq \sum_{i=m}^{n} \|f_i\| \leq \sum_{i=N}^{\infty} \|f_i\| < \epsilon.$$

Hence the sequence $\langle s_n \rangle$ of partial sums is a Cauchy sequence and must converge to an element s in X since X is complete.

$\Leftarrow$: Let $\langle f_n \rangle$ be a Cauchy sequence in X. For each integer k there is an integer n_k such that $\|f_n - f_m\| < 2^{-k}$ for all n and m greater than n_k, and we may choose the n_k's so that $n_{k+1} > n_k$. Then $\langle f_{n_k} \rangle_{k=1}^{\infty}$ is a subsequence of $\langle f_n \rangle$, and if we set $g_1 = f_{n_1}$ and $g_k = f_{n_k} - f_{n_{k-1}}$ for $k > 1$ we obtain a series $\langle g_k \rangle$ whose k^{th} partial sum is f_{n_k}. But we have $\|g_k\| < 2^{-k}$, and thus $\Sigma \|g_k\| \le \Sigma 2^{-k} = 1$. Hence the series $\langle g_k \rangle$ is absolutely summable, and so by our hypothesis there is an element f in X to which the partial sums of the series converge. Thus the subsequence $\langle f_{n_k} \rangle$ converges to f.

We shall now show that $f = \lim f_n$. Since $\langle f_n \rangle$ is a Cauchy sequence, given $\epsilon > 0$, there is an N such that $\|f_n - f_m\| < \epsilon/2$ for all n and m larger than N. Since $f_{n_k} \to f$, there is a K such that for all $k \ge K$ we have $\|f_{n_k} - f\| < \epsilon/2$. Let us take k so large that $k > K$ and $n_k \ge N$. Then

$$\|f_n - f\| \le \|f_n - f_{n_k}\| + \|f_{n_k} - f\| \le \epsilon/2 + \epsilon/2 = \epsilon.$$

Thus for all $n > N$ we have $\|f_n - f\| < \epsilon$, and so $f_n \to f$. ∎

5. Theorem (Riesz-Fischer): *The L^p spaces are complete.*

Proof: Since the case $p = \infty$ is elementary, it is left to the reader, and we assume $1 \le p < \infty$. By virtue of the preceding proposition we need only show that each absolutely summable series in L^p is summable in L^p to some element of L^p.

Let $\langle f_n \rangle$ be a sequence in L^p with $\sum_{n=1}^{\infty} \|f_n\| = m < \infty$, and define functions g_n by setting $g_n(x) = \sum_{k=1}^{n} |f_k(x)|$. From the Minkowski inequality we have

$$\|g_n\| \le \sum_{k=1}^{n} \|f_k\| \le m.$$

Hence

$$\int (g_n)^p \le m^p.$$

For each x, $\langle g_n(x) \rangle$ is an increasing sequence of (extended) real numbers and so must converge to an extended real number $g(x)$. The function g so defined is measurable, and, since $g_n \ge 0$, we have

$$\int g^p \le m^p$$

by the Fatou Lemma. Hence g^p is integrable, and $g(x)$ is finite for almost all x.

For each x such that $g(x)$ is finite the series $\sum_{k=1}^{\infty} f_k(x)$ is an absolutely summable series of real numbers and so must be summable to a real number $s(x)$. If we set $s(x) = 0$ for those x where $g(x) = \infty$, we have defined a function s which is the limit almost everywhere of the partial sums $s_n = \sum_{k=1}^{n} f_k$. Hence s is measurable. Since $|s_n(x)| \leq g(x)$, we have $|s(x)| \leq g(x)$. Consequently, s is in L^p and we have

$$|s_n(x) - s(x)|^p \leq 2^p[g(x)]^p.$$

Since $2^p g^p$ is integrable and $|s_n(x) - s(x)|^p$ converges to 0 for almost all x, we have

$$\int |s_n - s|^p \to 0$$

by the Lebesgue Convergence Theorem. Thus $\|s_n - s\|^p \to 0$, whence $\|s_n - s\| \to 0$. Consequently the series $\langle f_n \rangle$ has in L^p the sum s. ▌

Problems

7. Prove that every convergent sequence is a Cauchy sequence.

8. Let $\langle f_n \rangle$ be a sequence of functions in L^∞. Prove that $\langle f_n \rangle$ converges to f in L^∞ if and only if there is a set E of measure zero such that f_n converges to f uniformly on $\tilde{E}$.

9. Prove that L^∞ is complete.

10. Prove that l^p is complete $(1 \leq p < \infty)$. (See Problem 5.)

11. Let $C = C[0,1]$ be the space of all continuous functions on $[0, 1]$ and define $\|f\| = \max |f(x)|$. Show that C is a Banach space.

12. We denote by l^∞ the space of all bounded sequences of real numbers, and define $\|\langle \xi_\nu \rangle\|_\infty = \sup |\xi_\nu|$. Show that l^∞ is a Banach space.

13. Show that the space c of all convergent sequences of real numbers and the space c_0 of all sequences which converge to zero are Banach spaces (with the l^∞ norm).

14. Let f be a function in L^p, $1 \leq p < \infty$. Show that given $\epsilon > 0$ there is a continuous function φ and a step function ψ such that $\|f - \varphi\| < \epsilon$ and $\|f - \psi\| < \epsilon$.

15. Let $\langle f_n \rangle$ be a sequence of functions in L^p, $1 \le p < \infty$, which converge almost everywhere to a function f in L^p. Show that $\langle f_n \rangle$ converges to f in L^p if and only if $\|f_n\| \to \|f\|$. (For $p = 1$ this is just Problem 4.11.)

16. Let $\langle f_n \rangle$ be a sequence of functions in L^p, $1 < p < \infty$, which converge almost everywhere to a function f in L^p, and suppose that there is a constant M such that $\|f_n\| \le M$ for all n. Then for each function g in L^q we have

$$\int fg = \lim \int f_n g.$$

Is the result true for $p = 1$?

4 BOUNDED LINEAR FUNCTIONALS ON THE L^p SPACES

We define a **linear functional** on a normed linear space X to be a mapping F of the space X into the set of real numbers such that $F(\alpha f + \beta g) = \alpha F(f) + \beta F(g)$. We say that the linear functional is **bounded** if there is a constant M such that $|F(f)| \le M \cdot \|f\|$ for all f in X. The smallest constant M for which this inequality is true is called the norm of F. Thus

$$\|F\| = \sup \frac{|F(f)|}{\|f\|},$$

as f ranges over all nonzero elements of X.

If g is a function in L^q, we can define a bounded linear functional F on L^p by setting

$$F(f) = \int fg.$$

The functional F is clearly linear, and the Hölder inequality states that $\|F\| \le \|g\|_q$. In fact we actually have $\|F\| = \|g\|_q$. To see this for the case $1 < p < \infty$, we set

$$f = |g|^{q/p} \operatorname{sgn} g.$$

Then $|f|^p = |g|^q = fg$. Hence f is in L^p and $\|f\|_p = (\|g\|_q)^{q/p}$. Now

$$\begin{aligned} F(f) &= \int fg = \int |g|^q \\ &= (\|g\|_q)^q = \|g\|_q \, \|f\|_p, \end{aligned}$$

and so $\|F\|$ must be at least as great as $\|g\|_q$. We state this result as a proposition, the cases $p = 1$ and $p = \infty$ being left to the reader. (See Problem 17).

6. Proposition: *Each function g in L^q defines a bounded linear functional F on L^p by*

$$F(f) = \int fg.$$

We have $\|F\| = \|g\|_q$.

The goal of the present section is to show that for $1 \leq p < \infty$ the converse of this proposition holds, that is that we obtain every bounded linear functional on L^p in this manner. We shall find it useful to first establish the following lemma.

7. Lemma: *Let g be an integrable function on* [0, 1], *and suppose that there is a constant M such that*

$$\left|\int fg\right| \leq M \|f\|_p$$

for all bounded measurable functions f. Then g is in L^q, and $\|g\|_q \leq M$.

Proof: We define a sequence of bounded measurable functions by setting

$$g_n(x) = \begin{cases} g(x) & \text{if } |g(x)| \leq n \\ 0 & \text{if } |g(x)| > n, \end{cases}$$

and letting

$$f_n = |g_n|^{q/p} \operatorname{sgn} g_n.$$

Now $\|f_n\|_p = (\|g_n\|_q)^{q/p}$, and $|g_n|^q = f_n \cdot g_n = f_n \cdot g$.

Hence

$$(\|g_n\|_q)^q = \int f_n g \leq M \|f_n\|_p = M(\|g_n\|_q)^{q/p}.$$

Since $q - q/p = 1$,

$$\|g_n\|_q \leq M,$$

and

$$\int |g_n|^q \leq M^q.$$

Since $|g_n|^q$ converges to $|g|^q$ almost everywhere, we have

$$\int |g|^q \leq \lim \int |g_n|^q \leq M^q$$

by the Fatou lemma. Thus $g \in L^q$, and $\|g\|_q \leq M$. ∎

We are now in a position to give the following characterization of the bounded linear functionals on L^p for $1 \leq p < \infty$:

8. Riesz Representation Theorem: *Let F be a bounded linear functional on L^p, $1 \leq p < \infty$. Then there is a function g in L^q such that*

$$F(f) = \int fg.$$

We have also $\|F\| = \|g\|_q$.

Proof: Let χ_s be the characteristic function of the interval $[0, s]$. We begin our investigation of F by observing what it does to χ_s. For each s the value of $F(\chi_s)$ is a real number $\Phi(s)$, and this defines a function Φ on $[0, 1]$. Now I maintain that Φ is absolutely continuous. For let $\{(s_i, s_i')\}$ be any finite collection of nonoverlapping subintervals of $[0, 1]$ of total length less than δ. Then

$$\sum_i |\Phi(s_i') - \Phi(s_i)| = F(f),$$

where

$$f = \sum_i (\chi_{s'_i} - \chi_{s_i}) \operatorname{sgn} (\Phi(s_i') - \Phi(s_i)).$$

Since $(\|f\|_p)^p < \delta$, we have

$$\begin{aligned}\sum_i |\Phi(s_i') - \Phi(s_i)| &= F(f)\\ &\leq \|F\| \, \|f\|_p\\ &\leq \|F\| \, \delta^{1/p}\end{aligned}$$

This shows that the total variation of Φ is less than ϵ over any finite collection of disjoint intervals of total length δ if we take $\delta = \epsilon^p/\|F\|^p$. Thus Φ is absolutely continuous.

By Theorem 5.13 there is an integrable function g on $[0, 1]$ such that

$$\Phi(s) = \int_0^s g.$$

Thus

$$F(\chi_s) = \int_0^1 g \cdot \chi_s.$$

Since every step function on $[0, 1]$ is (equal except at a finite number of points to) a suitable linear combination $\Sigma\, c_i \chi_{s_i}$, we must have

$$F(\psi) = \int_0^1 g\psi$$

for each step-function ψ by the linearity of F and of the integral.

Let f be any bounded measurable function on [0, 1]. Then it follows from Proposition 3.22 that there is a sequence $\langle\psi_n\rangle$ of step-functions which converge almost everywhere to f. Since the sequence $\langle|f - \psi_n|^p\rangle$ is uniformly bounded and tends to zero almost everywhere, the bounded convergence theorem implies that $\|f - \psi_n\|_p \to 0$. Since F is bounded, and

$$\begin{aligned} |F(f) - F(\psi_n)| &= |F(f - \psi_n)| \\ &\leq \|F\| \, \|f - \psi_n\|_p, \end{aligned}$$

we must have

$$F(f) = \lim F(\psi_n).$$

Since $g\psi_n$ is always less than $|g|$ times the uniform bound for the sequence $\langle\psi_n\rangle$, we have

$$\int fg = \lim \int g\psi_n$$

by the Lebesgue convergence theorem. Consequently we must have

$$\int fg = F(f)$$

for each bounded measurable function f. Since $|F(f)| \leq \|F\| \, \|f\|_p$, we have g in L^q and $\|g\|_q \leq \|F\|$ by Lemma 7.

Thus we have only to show that $F(f) = \int fg$ for each f in L^p. Let f be an arbitrary function in L^p. Then by Problem 14 there is for each $\epsilon > 0$ a step function ψ such that $\|f - \psi\|_p < \epsilon$. Since ψ is bounded we have

$$F(\psi) = \int \psi g.$$

Hence

$$\begin{aligned} \left|F(f) - \int fg\right| &= \left|F(f) - F(\psi) + \int \psi g - \int fg\right| \\ &\leq |F(f - \psi)| + \left|\int (\psi - f)g\right| \\ &\leq \|F\| \, \|f - \psi\|_p + \|g\|_q \, \|f - \psi\|_p \\ &< (\|F\| + \|g\|_q)\, \epsilon. \end{aligned}$$

Since ϵ is an arbitrary number, we must have

$$F(f) = \int fg.$$

The equality $\|F\| = \|g\|_q$ follows by Proposition 6. ▌

In the problems the reader is asked to carry out a similar representation for the bounded linear functionals on l^p, $1 \leq p < \infty$, c, and c_0. In Chapter 13, p. 256, we give a representation for the bounded linear functionals on C. Unfortunately, the bounded linear functionals on L^∞ (and on l^∞) do not admit of a similar representation.

Problems

17. a. Let g be an integrable function on [0, 1]. Show that there is a bounded measurable function f such that

$$\int fg = \|g\|_1 \cdot \|f\|_\infty.$$

b. Let g be a bounded measurable function. Show that for each $\epsilon > 0$ there is an integrable function f such that

$$\int fg \geq \|g\|_\infty \cdot \|f\|_1 - \epsilon.$$

(Hint: f may be taken to be a suitable characteristic function.)

18. Find a representation for the bounded linear functionals on l^p, $1 \leq p < \infty$.

19. Find a representation for the bounded linear functionals on c and on c_0. (*Caveat*: These representations are different.)

(ditto, which converge to 0

(set of all convergent sequences

Epilogue to Part I

In this part we have considered most of the central theory of functions of a real variable. This material falls roughly into three classes: sets of real numbers and their properties; measure and integration theory; properties of real-valued functions such as continuity, differentiability, etc. The books by Saks [15] and Hobson [8] give an excellent account of this classical theory and in particular of those results which depend strongly on special properties of the real numbers. A very elegant treatment of this classical theory is given in Part I of Riesz-Nagy [14].

In Chapters 11, 12, and 13 we shall generalize the concepts of measure and integration to an abstract setting. This will enable us (among other things) to discuss multiple integrals and the classical theorems on interchange of the order of integration.

In Chapters 7, 8, and 9 we shall consider in some detail generalization of the notions of convergence, continuity, open and closed sets, etc. In Chapter 10 we consider Banach and other linear spaces of which the L^p spaces are important examples.

Part Two

ABSTRACT SPACES

7 Metric Spaces

1 INTRODUCTION

The system of real numbers has two types of properties. The first type consists of the algebraic dealing with addition, multiplication, etc. The other type consists of properties having to do with the notion of distance between two numbers and with the concept of a limit. These latter properties are called topological or metric, and the object of the present chapter is to study these properties in a general space in which the notion of distance is defined. We make the following definition:

Definition: *A metric space $\langle X, \rho \rangle$ is a nonempty set X of elements (which we call points) together with a real-valued function ρ defined on $X \times X$ such that for all x, y, and z in X:*

i. $\rho(x, y) \geq 0$;

ii. $\rho(x, y) = 0$ *if and only if* $x = y$;

iii. $\rho(x, y) = \rho(y, x)$;

iv. $\rho(x, y) \leq \rho(x, z) + \rho(z, y)$.

The function ρ is called a metric.

An obvious example of a metric space is the set $\mathbf{R}^1$ of all numbers with $\rho(x, y) = |x - y|$. A second example is the n-dimensional Euclidean space $\mathbf{R}^n$ whose points are the n-tuples $x = \langle x_1, \ldots, x_n \rangle$ of real numbers and

$$\rho(x, y) = [(x_1 - y_1)^2 + \cdots + (x_n - y_n)^2]^{1/2}.$$

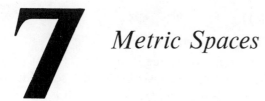

For $\mathbf{R}^n$ property (iv) of the metric is merely the statement that the length of a side of a triangle is less than the sum of the lengths of the other two sides. Consequently, (iv) is usually called the triangle inequality.

Other examples of metric spaces are the normed linear spaces of the last chapter if we set

$$\rho(x, y) = \|x - y\|,$$

the triangle inequality being equivalent to $\|x + y\| \le \|x\| + \|y\|$.

It should be emphasized that a metric space is not the set X of its points, since it is in fact the pair $\langle X, \rho \rangle$ consisting of the set of its points together with the metric ρ. For example the set of all n-tuples of real numbers can also be made into a metric space by use of the metric ρ^* given by

$$\rho^*(x, y) = |x_1 - y_1| + \cdots + |x_n - y_n|,$$

and this is not the metric space $\mathbf{R}^n$ (if $n > 1$). Often we are interested in only one metric for a given set of points, and in such cases we sometimes use the symbol X to denote both the set of points and the metric space $\langle X, \rho \rangle$.

If we have two metric spaces $\langle X, \rho \rangle$ and $\langle Y, \sigma \rangle$, we can form a new metric space called the **Cartesian product** $X \times Y$ whose set of points is the set $X \times Y = \{\langle x, y \rangle : x \in X, y \in Y\}$ and whose metric τ is given by

$$\tau(\langle x_1, y_1 \rangle, \langle x_2, y_2 \rangle) = [\rho(x_1, x_2)^2 + \sigma(y_1, y_2)^2]^{1/2}.$$

It is readily verified that τ has all of the properties required of a metric and that $\mathbf{R}^m \times \mathbf{R}^n = \mathbf{R}^{m+n}$.

Any nonempty subset of a metric space is itself a metric space if we restrict the metric to it. For example, the space C of the last chapter is a subspace of L^∞.

Problems

1. a. Show the set of all n-tuples of real numbers becomes a metric space under each of the following metrics:

$$\rho^*(x, y) = |x_1 - y_1| + \cdots + |x_n - y_n|,$$

$$\rho^+(x, y) = \max \{|x_1 - y_1|, \cdots, |x_n - y_n|\}.$$

b. For $n = 2$, and $n = 3$ describe the sets $\{x : \rho(x, y) < 1\}$, $\{x : \rho^*(x, y) < 1\}$, and $\{x : \rho^+(x, y) < 1\}$.

2. By the **spheroid** (or sphere) centered at x and having radius δ we mean the set

$$S_{x,\delta} = \{y : \rho(x, y) < \delta\}.$$

Prove that if $0 < \epsilon < \delta - \rho(x, z)$, then $S_{z,\epsilon} \subset S_{x,\delta}$.

3. *Pseudometrics.* A pair $\langle X, \rho \rangle$ is called a pseudometric space if ρ satisfies all the conditions of a metric except that $\rho(x, y) = 0$ need not imply $x = y$. Show that $\rho(x, y) = 0$ is an equivalence relation and that if X^* is the set of equivalence classes under this relation then $\rho(x, y)$ depends only on the equivalence classes of x and y and defines a metric on X^*.

2 OPEN AND CLOSED SETS

We shall find that a number of the properties of sets of real numbers apply immediately to sets in a metric space. Throughout the present section all sets mentioned are subsets of a given metric space $\langle X, \rho \rangle$. The following propositions and definitions correspond to those in Section 5 of Chapter 2, and the reader is asked to check that the proofs given there are valid for metric spaces.

Definition: *A set O is called **open** if for every $x \in O$, $\exists \delta > 0$ such that all y with $\rho(x, y) < \delta$ belong to O.*

1. Proposition: *The sets X and $\varnothing$ are open; the intersection of any two open sets is open; and the union of any collection of open sets is open.*

Definition: *A point $x \in X$ is called a **point of closure** of the set E if for every $\delta > 0$, there is a point $y \in E$ such that $\rho(x, y) < \delta$. We use $\bar{E}$ to denote the set of points of closure of E. Clearly $E \subset \bar{E}$.*

2. Proposition: *If $A \subset B$ then $\bar{A} \subset \bar{B}$. Also $\overline{(A \cup B)} = \bar{A} \cup \bar{B}$, and $\overline{(A \cap B)} \subset \bar{A} \cap \bar{B}$.*

Definition: *A set F is called **closed** if $\bar{F} = F$.*

3. Proposition: *The closure $\bar{E}$ of any set E is closed; that is, $\bar{E} = \bar{\bar{E}}$.*

4. Proposition: *The sets $\varnothing$ and X are closed; the union of any two closed sets is closed; and the intersection of any collection of closed sets is closed.*

5. Proposition: *The complement of an open set is closed; the complement of a closed set is open.*

Definition: *A metric space X is called* **separable** *if it has a subset D which has a countable number of points and which is dense in X, that is, for which $\bar{D} = X$.*

Since the set of rational numbers is a countable dense subset of $\mathbf{R}^1$, we see that $\mathbf{R}^1$ is separable. The following proposition shows that the Lindelöf theorem holds for a metric space if and only if it is separable.

6. Proposition: *A metric space X is separable if and only if there is a countable family $\{O_i\}$ of open sets such that for any open set $O \subset X$,*

$$O = \bigcup_{O_i \subset O} O_i.$$

Proof: If X is separable, let D be a countable dense set. By the spheroid at x with radius δ we mean the set

$$S_{x,\delta} = \{y : \rho(x, y) < \delta\}.$$

Let $\{O_i\}$ consist of those spheroids $S_{x,\delta}$ for which x is in D and δ is rational. Then $\{O_i\}$ is a countable collection of open sets. If O is any open set and $y \in O$, then we want to show that for some O_i we have $y \in O_i \subset O$. Since O is open, there is a spheroid $S_{y,\delta}$ such that $S_{y,\delta} \subset O$. By taking δ even smaller we may assume δ is rational. Since y is a point of closure of D, there is a point $x \in D$ such that $\rho(x, y) < \delta/2$. Hence

$$S_{x,\delta/2} \subset S_{y,\delta} \subset O.$$

But $S_{x,\delta/2}$ is one of the $\{O_i\}$, and the "only if" part of the theorem is proved.

Suppose on the other hand we are given the countable collection $\{O_i\}$. Let x_i be a point of O_i, and let D be the set of all these points x_i. We shall now see that D is dense. Let x be any point of X and S any spheroid centered at x. Then we must show that S contains a point of D. But S is an open set (Problem 6), and so we must have some O_i such that $x \in O_i \subset S$. Hence $x_i \in S$, and we see that $x \in \bar{D}$. ∎

Problems

4. a. Show that C is a closed subset of L^∞ (See Chapter 6).
   b. Show that the set of all integrable functions which vanish for $0 \le t < \frac{1}{2}$ is a closed subset of L^1.

c. Show that the set of all measurable functions $x(t)$ with $\int x < 1$ is an open subset of L^1.

5. Show that $\bar{E} = \bigcap_{E \subset F} F$ for closed sets F. The interior E° of a set E is the set of those points $y \in E$ for which there is a $\delta > 0$ such that $\rho(y, z) < \delta \Rightarrow z \in E$.

a. Show that

$$E^\circ = \bigcup_{O \subset E} O.$$

b. Show that

$$\sim(\bar{E}) = (\sim E)^\circ.$$

6. a. Show that each spheroid is open.

b. Show that the sets $\{x : \rho(x, y) \leq \delta\}$ are closed.

7. Which of the following spaces $\mathbf{R}^n$, C, L^∞, L^1 are separable?

3 CONTINUOUS FUNCTIONS AND HOMEOMORPHISMS

By a function f on a metric space $\langle X, \rho\rangle$ into a metric space $\langle Y, \sigma\rangle$ we mean one which associates to each $x \in X$ a unique $y \in Y$. We also call f a mapping of X into Y and shall use the terms function and mapping interchangeably. By a mapping f of X **onto** Y we mean, as usual, that for any $y \in Y$ there is some $x \in X$ such that $f(x) = y$, that is to say that Y is the range of f. Then as in Section 6 of Chapter 2 we have the following definition and proposition:

Definition: *The function f is said to be continuous at x if for every $\epsilon > 0$, there is a $\delta > 0$ such that if $\rho(x, y) < \delta$ then $\sigma[f(x), f(y)] < \epsilon$. The function f is called* **continuous** *if it is continuous at each $x \in X$.*

7. Proposition: *A function f from a metric space X to a metric space Y is continuous if and only if for each open set O in Y the set $f^{-1}[O]$ is an open set in X.*

8. Proposition: *If f is a continuous mapping from X to Y and if g is a continuous mapping from Y to Z, then the mapping $g \circ f$ from X to Z is also continuous.*

A one-to-one mapping f of X ***onto*** Y is called a **homeomorphism** between X and Y if f is continuous and the mapping f^{-1} inverse to f

is also continuous. The spaces X and Y are said to be homeomorphic if there is a homeomorphism between them. The study of topology is essentially the study of those properties which are unaltered by homeomorphisms, and such properties are called topological. By virtue of Proposition 7 a one-to-one correspondence between X and Y is a homeomorphism if and only if it makes open sets in X correspond to open sets in Y and conversely. Thus the property of being an open subset of a space is a topological one. Since a closed set is the complement of an open set, it follows that being a closed subset of X is a topological property. In fact every property which can be defined by means of open sets is a topological one and hence so is the property of being a continuous function, that is, if f is a continuous function on X and $h: X \to Y$ is a homeomorphism between X and Y, then $f \circ h^{-1}$ is a continuous function on Y.

Not all properties in a metric space are preserved under a homeomorphism, however. For example the distance between two points is usually altered by a homeomorphism. A homeomorphism which leaves distance unchanged, that is, one for which

$$\sigma[h(x_1), h(x_2)] = \rho(x_1, x_2)$$

for all x_1 and x_2 in X, is called an **isometry** between X and Y. The spaces X and Y are called isometric if there is an isometry between them. From an abstract point of view two isometric metric spaces are exactly the same, an isometry amounting merely to a relabeling of the points. A notion which arises naturally in this connection is that of equivalent metrics: Two metrics ρ and σ on the same set X of points are called equivalent if the identity mapping of $\langle X, \rho \rangle$ onto $\langle X, \sigma \rangle$ is a homeomorphism. Thus two metrics are equivalent if and only if they define the same open sets, that is, if a set is open with respect to one whenever it is open with respect to the other.

Problems

8. Show that the function h on $[0, 1)$ given by $h(x) = x/(1 + x)$ is a homeomorphism between $[0, 1)$ and $[0, \infty)$.

9. Let E be a set and x a point in a metric space. Define

$$\rho(x, E) = \inf_{y \in E} \rho(x, y).$$

a. Show that for a fixed E the function f given by $f(x) = \rho(x, E)$ is continuous.

b. Show that $\{x : \rho(x, E) = 0\} = \bar{E}$.

10. a. Prove that two metrics on a set X are equivalent if and only if given $x \in X$ and $\epsilon > 0$ there is an $\delta > 0$ such that for all $y \in X$

$$\rho(x, y) < \delta \Rightarrow \sigma(x, y) < \epsilon$$

and

$$\sigma(x, y) < \delta \Rightarrow \rho(x, y) < \epsilon.$$

b. Show that the following set of metrics for the set of n-tuples of real numbers are equivalent:

$$\rho(x, y) = [(x_1 - y_1)^2 + \cdots + (x_n - y_n)^2]^{1/2}$$

$$\rho^*(x, y) = |x_1 - y_1| + \cdots + |x_n - y_n|$$

$$\rho^+(x, y) = \max \{|x_1 - y_1|, \cdots, |x_n - y_n|\}.$$

c. Find a metric for the set of n-tuples which is not equivalent to these.

11. Show that if ρ is any metric on a set X, then $\sigma = \rho/(1 + \rho)$ is an equivalent metric for X. Prove $\langle X, \sigma \rangle$ is a bounded metric space, that is, $\sigma(x, y) \leq 1$ for all x and y in X.

4 CONVERGENCE AND COMPLETENESS

Just as for the case of real numbers we say that a sequence $\langle x_n \rangle$ from a metric space X **converges** to the point x in X (or has x as a limit) if given $\epsilon > 0$ there is an N such that $\rho(x, x_n) < \epsilon$ for all $n \geq N$. This definition can be rephrased in geometric terms by saying that $\langle x_n \rangle$ converges to x if every spheroid about x contains all but a finite number of terms of the sequence.

We often write $x = \lim x_n$ or $x_n \to x$ to mean that x is the limit of the sequence $\langle x_n \rangle$. If we have merely the weaker condition that each spheroid about x contains infinitely many terms of the sequence, then we say that x is a cluster point of the sequence $\langle x_n \rangle$. Thus x is a cluster point of $\langle x_n \rangle$ if given $\epsilon > 0$ and given N there is an $n \geq N$ such that $\rho(x, x_n) < \epsilon$. Thus if x is the limit of $\langle x_n \rangle$ then x is a cluster point of $\langle x_n \rangle$ but the converse is not necessarily true. A number of properties concerning limits and cluster points are given in the problems.

$h' = \frac{(1-y)+y}{(1-y)^2} = \frac{1}{(1-y)^2} \to$ cont.

A sequence $\langle x_n \rangle$ from a metric space is called a **Cauchy sequence** if given $\epsilon > 0$ there is an N such that for all n and m larger than N we have $\rho(x_n, x_m) < \epsilon$. If $\langle x_n \rangle$ converges to some point x, then given $\epsilon > 0$ we may choose N so large that $\rho(x_n, x) < \epsilon/2$ for $n \geq N$. Hence for all $n, m \geq N$ we have

$$\rho(x_n, x_m) \leq \rho(x_n, x) + \rho(x_m, x) < \epsilon,$$

and $\langle x_n \rangle$ is a Cauchy sequence. The converse statement that every Cauchy sequence converges is not true in an arbitrary metric space (for example, in the space of rational numbers with the usual metric). If a metric space has the property that every Cauchy sequence converges (to some point of the space), we say that the space is **complete.** The Cauchy criterion for real numbers merely states that the space $\mathbf{R}^1$ of real numbers is complete. Other examples of complete spaces are given by the Banach spaces discussed in the last chapter.

If X is an incomplete metric space, it can always be enlarged to become complete. A precise statement of this fact is given by the following theorem. One proof of this theorem is outlined in Problem 17 and another in Problem 10.16.

9. Theorem: *If* $\langle X, \rho \rangle$ *is an incomplete metric space it is possible to find a complete metric space* X^* *in which* X *is isometrically imbedded as a dense subset. If* X *is contained in an arbitrary complete space* Y *then* X^* *is isometric with the closure of* X *in* Y.

Problems

12. Show that a sequence $\langle x_n \rangle$ in a metric space has x as a cluster point if and only if there is a subsequence $\langle x_{n_k} \rangle$ of $\langle x_n \rangle$ which converges to x.

13. Show that a sequence $\langle x_n \rangle$ in a metric space converges to x if and only if every subsequence of $\langle x_n \rangle$ has x as a cluster point. Hence $\langle x_n \rangle$ converges to x if every subsequence has in turn a subsequence which converges to x.

14. Let E be a set in a metric space X. If x is a cluster point of a sequence from E, then $x \in \bar{E}$, while if $x \in \bar{E}$, there is a sequence from $\bar{E}$ which converges to x.

15. If a Cauchy sequence $\langle x_n \rangle$ in a metric space has a cluster point x, then $\langle x_n \rangle$ converges to x.

16. If X and Y are metric spaces and f a mapping from X to Y, then f is continuous at x if and only if for each sequence $\langle x_n \rangle$ in X converging to x we have $\langle f(x_n) \rangle$ converging to $f(x)$ in Y.

17. a. If $\langle x_n \rangle$ and $\langle y_n \rangle$ are Cauchy sequences from a metric space X, then $\rho(x_n, y_n)$ converges.

b. The set of all Cauchy sequences from a metric space X becomes a pseudo-metric space (cf. Problem 3) if $\rho^*(\langle x_n \rangle, \langle y_n \rangle) = \lim \rho(x_n, y_n)$.

c. This pseudometric space becomes (as in Problem 3) a metric space X^* when we identify elements for which $\rho^* = 0$, and X is isometrically imbedded in X^*.

d. The metric space $\langle X^*, \rho^* \rangle$ is complete. (Hint: if $\langle x_n \rangle$ is a Cauchy sequence from X we may assume (by taking subsequences) that $\rho(x_n, x_{n+1}) < 2^{-n}$. If $\langle \langle x_{n,m} \rangle_{n=1}^{\infty} \rangle_{m=1}^{\infty}$ is a sequence of such Cauchy sequences which represents a Cauchy sequence in X^*, then the sequence $\langle x_{n,n} \rangle_{n=1}^{\infty}$ is a Cauchy sequence from X which represents the limit of the Cauchy sequences from X^*.)

e. Use Propositions 10, 11, and 12 of the next sections to complete the proof of Theorem 9.

18. Prove that the Cartesian product of two complete metric spaces is complete.

5 UNIFORM CONTINUITY AND UNIFORMITY

Let f be a mapping from the metric space $\langle X, \rho \rangle$ to the metric space $\langle Y, \sigma \rangle$. We say that f is **uniformly continuous** if given $\epsilon > 0$ there is a $\delta > 0$ such that for all x and x' in X with $\rho(x, x') < \delta$ we have $\sigma(f(x), f(x')) < \epsilon$. The function h defined on $[0, 1)$ by $h(x) = x/(1 - x)$ is continuous but not uniformly continuous. Moreover, this function h takes the Cauchy sequence given by $x_n = 1 - 1/n$ into the sequence $y_n = n - 1$ which is not a Cauchy sequence. Thus the image under a continuous function of a Cauchy sequence need not be a Cauchy sequence. However, we have the following proposition:

10. Proposition: *Let f be a uniformly continuous mapping of the metric space X into the metric space Y. If $\langle x_n \rangle$ is a Cauchy sequence in X, then $\langle f(x_n) \rangle$ is a Cauchy sequence in Y.*

A homeomorphism f between metric spaces X and Y is called a **uniform homeomorphism** if both f and f^{-1} are uniformly continuous.

It follows from Proposition 10 that the property of being a Cauchy sequence is preserved under uniform homeomorphisms as is the property of being complete. Properties which are preserved under uniform homeomorphisms are called uniform properties. In addition to the properties of being a Cauchy sequence and of completeness we have also uniform continuity as a uniform property. These three properties are not topological properties, since the function h defined by $h(x) = x/(1 - x)$ is a homeomorphism between the incomplete space $[0, 1)$ and the complete space $[0, \infty)$ which takes a Cauchy sequence into a sequence which is not a Cauchy sequence and its inverse carries the uniformly continuous function sin back into a function which is not uniformly continuous on $[0, 1)$.

Two metrics ρ and σ for a set X of points are said to be **uniformly equivalent** if the identity map from $\langle X, \rho\rangle$ to $\langle X, \sigma\rangle$ is a uniform homeomorphism. Thus σ and ρ are uniformly equivalent if given $\epsilon > 0$ there is a $\delta > 0$ so that for all x and y we have $\rho(x, y) < \delta \Rightarrow \sigma(x, y) < \epsilon$ and $\sigma(x, y) < \delta \Rightarrow \rho(x, y) < \epsilon$.

We conclude this section by stating the following useful extension theorem for uniformly continuous mappings. Its proof is outlined in Problem 20.

11. Proposition: *Let $\langle X, \rho\rangle$ and $\langle Y, \sigma\rangle$ be metric spaces with Y complete. Let f be a uniformly continuous mapping from a subset E of X into Y. Then there is a unique continuous extension g of f from E to $\bar{E}$; that is, there is a unique continuous mapping g from $\bar{E}$ into Y such that $g(x) = f(x)$ for $x \in E$. Moreover, g is uniformly continuous.*

Problems

19. Prove Proposition 10.

20. Prove Proposition 11 by the following steps:

a. If $\langle x_n\rangle$ is a sequence from E which converges to a point $x \in \bar{E}$ then $\langle f(x_n)\rangle$ converges to a point $y \in Y$ (cf. Proposition 10).

b. The point y in (a) depends only on x and not on the sequence $\langle x_n\rangle$. Thus if we define $y = g(x)$ we have defined a function g on $\bar{E}$ which is an extension of f.

c. The function g is uniformly continuous on $\bar{E}$.

d. If h is any continuous function from $\bar{E}$ to Y which agrees with f on E, then $h \equiv g$.

21. a. Show that the metrics in Problem 10(b) are uniformly equivalent.
b. Find a metric for the set of n-tuples of real numbers which is equivalent but not uniformly equivalent to the usual metric.
c. If $\langle X, \rho \rangle$ is any metric space, the metric $\sigma = \rho/(1 + \rho)$ is uniformly equivalent to ρ.

22. a. Boundedness is a metric but not a uniform property [cf. Problem 21(c)].
b. A metric space X is said to be totally bounded if given $\epsilon > 0$ there are a finite number of spheroids of radius ϵ which cover (that is, whose union is) X. Show that total boundedness is a uniform property.
c. Show that total boundedness is not a topological property. [consider $[0, 1)$ and $[0, \infty)$.]

6 SUBSPACES

If $\langle X, \rho \rangle$ is a metric space and S is a subset of X, then S becomes a metric space if we restrict ρ to S, that is to say if we take as the distance between two points of S their distance as points of X. When we consider S as a metric space with this metric we call S a subspace of X. For example the rationals are a subspace of $\mathbf{R}^1$, and the set $\{\langle x, 0 \rangle\}$ in $\mathbf{R}^2$ is a subspace isometric with $\mathbf{R}^1$. The space C is a subspace of L^∞.

If E is a subset of S then we may consider the closure of E in S or in X, that is we may wish to consider the set of all points of X which are points of closure of E or else the set of all points of S which are points of closure of E. These sets are in general different. For example let X be the space $\mathbf{R}^1$ and S the interval $(0, 1)$. Then if E is the interval $(0, \frac{1}{2}]$, the closure of E in $\mathbf{R}^1$ is the interval $[0, \frac{1}{2}]$ while its closure in S is just $(0, \frac{1}{2}]$; that is, E is closed relative to S. Thus we see that the closure of a set as well as the properties of a set being closed or open are all relative to the space containing the set. However, we do have the following relations between these notions.

12. Proposition: *Let X be a metric space and S a subspace of it. Then the closure of E relative to S is $\bar{E} \cap S$ where $\bar{E}$ denotes the closure of E in X. A set $A \subset S$ is closed relative to S if and only if $A = S \cap F$ with F closed in X. A set $A \subset S$ is open relative to S if and only if $A = S \cap O$ with O open in X.*

Proof: If x is a point of closure of E in X then it is a point of closure of E in S if it belongs to S. Hence the closure in S of E is $\bar{E} \cap S$. If A is closed in S we must have $A = S \cap \bar{A}$, while on the other hand if F is closed in X, then the closure in S of $S \cap F$ is

$$S \cap \overline{(S \cap F)} \subset S \cap (\bar{S} \cap \bar{F}) \subset S \cap F$$

whence $S \cap F$ is closed relative to S.

If A is open relative to S, then $S \sim A$ is closed relative to S and we have $S \sim A = S \cap F$, or $S \cap A = S \cap (\sim F)$ and $\sim F$ is open in X. Similarly if O is open then $S \cap O$ is the complement in S of $S \cap (\sim O)$ which is closed in S. ❙

13. Proposition: *Every subspace of a separable metric space is separable.*

Proof: Let X be a separable metric space and S a subspace. Then by Proposition 6 there is a countable collection $\{O_i\}$ of open sets in X such that each open set in X is a union of some subcollection of $\{O_i\}$. By Proposition 12 the collection $\{O_i \cap S\}$ is a countable collection of open subsets of S such that every open subset of S is a union of a subcollection of them. Hence S is separable by Proposition 6. ❙

In contrast to the relative properties discussed above, there are some properties which are intrinsic. For example the property of x being a point of closure of E holds in any subspace of X containing x and E as soon as it holds in one of them. Another such property is that of being complete, since the definition of completeness of a space is given in terms of points in the space. However, the following proposition gives some relations between complete sets and closed sets.

14. Proposition: *If a subset A of a metric space X is complete, then it is closed. On the other hand a closed subset of a complete metric space is itself complete.*

Problem

23. Prove Proposition 14 using Problem 14.

7 BAIRE CATEGORY

In this section we shall go more deeply into certain aspects of metric spaces. We begin by defining a set E to be **nowhere dense** if $\sim\bar{E}$ is dense. This is equivalent to stating that $\bar{E}$ contains no spheroid. For example, the integers are nowhere dense in $\mathbf{R}^1$ and the Cantor ternary set is nowhere dense in $[0, 1]$. A set E is said to be of **first category** if it is the union of a countable collection of nowhere dense sets, and a set which is not of first category is said to be of second category. We shall show that a complete metric space is of second category when considered as a subset of itself. We begin with the following theorem:

15. Theorem: *Let X be a complete metric space and $\{O_n\}$ a countable collection of dense open subsets of X. Then $\bigcap O_n$ is not empty.*

Proof: Let x_1 be a point of O_1 and S_1 a spheroid (of radius r_1) which is centered at x_1 and contained in O_1. Since O_2 is dense, there must be a point x_2 in $O_2 \cap S_1$. Since O_2 is open, there is a spheroid S_2 centered at x_2 and contained in O_2, and we may take the radius r_2 of S_2 to be smaller than $\frac{1}{2}r_1$ and smaller than $r_1 - \rho(x_1, x_2)$. Then $\bar{S}_2 \subset S_1$. Proceeding inductively, we obtain a sequence $\langle S_n \rangle$ of spheroids such that $\bar{S}_n \subset S_{n-1}$ and $S_n \subset O_n$ and whose radii $\langle r_n \rangle$ tend to zero. Let $\langle x_n \rangle$ be the sequence of centers of these spheres. Then for $n, m \geq N$ we have $x_n \in S_N$ and $x_m \in S_N$. Hence $\rho(x_n, x_m) \leq 2r_N$, and $\langle x_n \rangle$ is a Cauchy sequence since $r_n \to 0$. By the completeness of X there is a point x such that $x_n \to x$. Since $x_n \in S_{N+1}$ for $n > N$, we have $x \in \bar{S}_{N+1} \subset S_N \subset O_N$. Hence $x \in \bigcap O_n$. ∎

16. Corollary (Baire Category Theorem): *A complete metric space is not the union of a countable collection of nowhere dense sets.*

Proof: Let $\{E_n\}$ be a countable collection of nowhere dense sets. Then $O_n = \sim\bar{E}_n$ is a dense open set, and so there is a point $x \in \bigcap O_n$. But this means $x \notin \bigcup E_n$. ∎

As an application of the Baire category theorem we establish the following theorem which is known as the uniform boundedness principle:

17. Theorem: *Let $\mathfrak{F}$ be a family of real-valued continuous functions on a complete metric space X, and suppose that for each $x \in X$ there is a number M_x such that $|f(x)| \leq M_x$ for all $f \in \mathfrak{F}$. Then there is a nonempty open set $O \subset X$ and a constant M such that $|f(x)| \leq M$ for all $f \in \mathfrak{F}$ and all $x \in O$.*

Proof: For each integer m, let $E_{m,f} = \{x\colon |f(x)| \leq m\}$, and set $E_m = \bigcap_{\mathfrak{F}} E_{m,f}$. Since each f is continuous, $E_{m,f}$ is closed, and consequently E_m is closed. For each $x \in X$, there is an m such that $|f(x)| \leq m$ for all $f \in \mathfrak{F}$, that is, there is an m such that $x \in E_m$. Hence

$$X = \bigcup_{m=1}^{\infty} E_m.$$

Since X is a complete metric space, there is a set E_m which is not nowhere dense. Since this E_m is a closed set, it must contain some spheroid O. But for every $x \in O$ we have $|f(x)| \leq m$ for all $f \in \mathfrak{F}$. ▌

Problems

24. a. Prove that a closed set F is nowhere dense if and only if it contains no open set.

b. Prove that E is nowhere dense if and only if for any nonempty open set O there is a spheroid contained in $O \sim E$.

25. a. Prove that if E is of first category and $A \subset E$ then A is also of first category.

b. Prove that if $\langle E_n \rangle$ is a sequence of sets of first category then $\bigcup E_n$ is also of first category.

26. If X is a complete metric space and E is a set of first category in E, then $\sim E$ is dense in X.

27. a. Show that on [0, 1] there is a nowhere dense closed set having Lebesgue measure $1 - 1/n$. (Hint: Form a Cantor set by removing different sized intervals.).

b. Construct a set of first category on [0, 1] which has measure 1.

28. A point x in a metric space is called isolated if the set $\{x\}$ is open. Prove that a complete metric space without isolated points has an uncountable number of points.

29. Let $\langle f_n \rangle$ be a sequence of continuous functions from a metric space X to a metric space Y such that for each x in X the sequence $\langle f_n(x) \rangle$

converges to a point $f(x)$ in Y. Then f defines a mapping of X into Y. Show that there is a set E of first category in X such that f is continuous at each point $x \in X \sim E$. Hence if X is complete, f is continuous at a dense set of points in X. (Hint: Let $F_{n,m} = \{x\colon \sigma(f_n(x), f_k(x)) < 1/m \text{ for all } k \geq n\}$. Let $F^\circ_{n,m}$ be the interior of $F_{n,m}$. Set $E = \bigcup_{n,m} [F_{n,m} \sim F^\circ_{n,m}]$.)

8 Topological Spaces

1 FUNDAMENTAL NOTIONS

In Chapter 7 we discussed a number of properties of metric spaces and found that a number of theorems depended only on the properties of open and closed sets. This leads us to our present study which is the consideration of spaces in which we start with the notion of an open set. Before defining these spaces we might say a word about the necessity for considering them; why not stick to metric spaces? Unfortunately, there are many examples of spaces of functions in which certain topological notions have a very natural meaning, but this meaning is not consistent with the topological concepts derived from any metric that might be defined on the space. Examples will occur in both this and the following chapter. We now proceed with an abstraction from the notion of a metric space:

Definition: *A topological space* $\langle X, \mathscr{T} \rangle$ *is a nonempy set* X *of points together with a family* $\mathscr{T}$ *of subsets* (*which we shall call open*) *possessing the following properties:*

i. $X \in \mathscr{T}$, $\varnothing \in \mathscr{T}$;

ii. $O_1 \in \mathscr{T}$ and $O_2 \in \mathscr{T}$ imply $O_1 \cap O_2 \in \mathscr{T}$;

iii. $O_\alpha \in \mathscr{T}$ implies $\bigcup_\alpha O_\alpha \in \mathscr{T}$.

The family $\mathscr{T}$ is called a topology for the set X.

The properties in this definition are all satisfied by open sets in a metric space $\langle X, \rho \rangle$, and hence to each metric space $\langle X, \rho \rangle$ we can associate a topological space $\langle X, \mathscr{T} \rangle$, where $\mathscr{T}$ is the family of open sets in $\langle X, \rho \rangle$. A topological space which is associated in this manner to some metric space is called metrizable, and the metric ρ is said to be a metric for the topological space. From a logical standpoint the distinction between a metric space and its associated topological space is essential, since different metric spaces can give rise to the same topological space. Two such metric spaces are of course equivalent, and we shall often disregard the distinction between a metric space and its associated topological space in cases where no confusion is likely to arise. In many cases we shall not trouble even to distinguish between a topological space $\langle X, \mathscr{T} \rangle$ and the set X of its points, using X to denote both. It is to be remembered, however, that metric and topological spaces are couples and in many cases it is necessary to express this fact explicitly.

Given any set X of points there are always two topologies that can be defined on X. One is the trivial topology in which the only open sets are $\varnothing$ and X. A second possible topology is the discrete topology: every subset of X an open set.

In terms of the notion of open sets we may define other topological properties, for example:

A subset F of X is called **closed** if $\tilde{F}$ is open.

1. Proposition: *The sets $\varnothing$ and X are closed. The union of any two closed sets is closed. The intersection of any collection of closed sets is closed.*

If A is a subset of a topological space $\langle X, \mathscr{T} \rangle$ we can define a topology $\mathcal{S}$ for A by taking for $\mathcal{S}$ those subsets B of A for which there is a set $O \in \mathscr{T}$ such that $B = A \cap O$. We call $\mathcal{S}$ the topology inherited from $\mathscr{T}$ and call the topological space $\langle A, \mathcal{S} \rangle$ a subspace of $\langle X, \mathscr{T} \rangle$. This is consistent with our usage concerning metric spaces.

A sequence $\langle x_n \rangle$ in a topological space is said to converge to the point x, or to have the limit x, if given any open set O containing x there is an integer N such that $x_n \in O$ for all $n \geq N$. Similarly a sequence $\langle x_n \rangle$ is said to have x as a cluster point if given any open set O containing x and any integer N there is an integer $n \geq N$ such that $x_n \in O$. Thus if $\langle x_n \rangle$ has a subsequence which converges to x then x is a cluster point of $\langle x_n \rangle$. The converse of this statement is not always true in an arbitrary topological space.

In view of Proposition 7.7 we may give a definition of a continuous function on a topological space which agrees with the usual concept of continuity in the case in which the topological space is also a metric space.

Definition: *A mapping f of a topological space $\langle X, \mathcal{T} \rangle$ into a topological space $\langle Y, \mathcal{S} \rangle$ is said to be* **continuous** *if the inverse image of every open set is open, i.e. if $O \in \mathcal{S} \Rightarrow f^{-1}[O] \in \mathcal{T}$.*

It should be noted that if f is a continuous function on a space X, then the restriction f_1 of f to a subspace A of X is a continuous function on A, for $f_1^{-1}[O] = A \cap f^{-1}[O]$ and must be open for open O by the continuity of f and the definition of open sets in A.

Definition: *A homeomorphism between two topological spaces is a one-to-one continuous mapping of X* **onto** *Y for which f^{-1} is continuous. The spaces X and Y are said to be homeomorphic if there is a homeomorphism between them.*

From an abstract point of view two homeomorphic topological spaces are indistinguishable, the homeomorphism amounting to a mere relabeling of the points of one set by the points of a second set. Thus the concept of homeomorphism plays the same role for topological spaces that isometry plays for metric spaces and isomorphism plays for algebraical systems.

Suppose that $\mathcal{T}$ and $\mathcal{S}$ are two topologies for the same set X. Then $\mathcal{S}$ is said to be stronger than $\mathcal{T}$ if $\mathcal{S} \supset \mathcal{T}$. Thus $\mathcal{S}$ is stronger than $\mathcal{T}$ if and only if the identity mapping of $(X, \mathcal{S})$ into $(X, \mathcal{T})$ is continuous. The trivial topology for a set X is the weakest possible topology on X, while the discrete topology is the strongest possible topology.

If $\mathcal{S}$ and $\mathcal{T}$ are two topologies for a set X, then $\mathcal{S} \cap \mathcal{T}$ is also a topology. In fact if $\{\mathcal{T}_\alpha\}$ is any collection of topologies, then $\bigcap_\alpha \mathcal{T}_\alpha$ is a topology. Thus if $\mathcal{C}$ is any collection of subsets of X, then the intersection of all topologies containing $\mathcal{C}$ is a topology containing $\mathcal{C}$. This topology is the weakest topology such that all of the sets of $\mathcal{C}$ are open.

2. Proposition: *Let X be a nonempty set of points and $\mathcal{C}$ any collection of subsets of X. Then there is a weakest topology $\mathcal{T}$ which contains $\mathcal{C}$.*

Problems

1. **a.** Given a set X, can you define a metric on X so that the associated topological space is discrete? Trivial?

b. Let X be a space with a trivial topology. Find all continuous mappings of X into $\mathbf{R}^1$.

c. Let X be a space with a discrete topology. Find all continuous mappings of X into $\mathbf{R}^1$.

2. We say that x is a point of closure of a set E if for every $O \in \mathscr{T}$ with $x \in O$ we have $O \cap E \neq \varnothing$. Prove that the set $\bar{E}$ of points of closure of E is the intersection of all closed sets containing E.

3. Prove that a set $A \subset X$ is open if and only if given $x \in A$ there is an open set O such that $x \in O \subset A$.

4. Prove that a mapping of X into Y is continuous if and only if the inverse image of every closed set is closed.

5. Show that if f is a continuous mapping of X into Y and g a continuous mapping of Y into Z, then $g \circ f$ is a continuous mapping of X into Z.

6. Prove that the sum and product of two real-valued continuous functions are themselves continuous.

7. a. Let F be a closed subset of topological space and $\langle x_n \rangle$ a sequence of points from F. Show that if x is a cluster point of $\langle x_n \rangle$ then $x \in F$.

b. Show that if f is continuous and $x = \lim x_n$ then $\langle f(x_n) \rangle$ has the limit $f(x)$.

c. Show that if f is continuous and x is a cluster point of $\langle x_n \rangle$ then $f(x)$ is a cluster point of $\langle f(x_n) \rangle$.

2 BASES AND COUNTABILITY

A collection $\mathscr{B}$ of open subsets of a topological space X is called a **base** for the topology $\mathscr{T}$ of X if for each open set O in X and each $x \in O$ there is a set $B \in \mathscr{B}$ such that $x \in B \subset O$. A collection $\mathscr{B}_x$ of open sets containing a point x is called a base at x if for each open set O containing x there is a $B \in \mathscr{B}_x$ such that $x \in B \subset O$. Thus a collection $\mathscr{B}$ of open sets is a base if and only if it contains a base at each point $x \in X$. If X is a metric space, the spheroids form a base, and the spheroids centered at x form a base at x.

If $\mathscr{B}$ is a base for the topology $\mathscr{T}$, then $O \in \mathscr{T}$ if and only if for each $x \in O$ there is a $B \in \mathscr{B}$ with $x \in B \subset O$. The "only if" part of the statement follows from the definition of a base, while if for each x in O we have $x \in B \subset O$, then O must be the union of those B in $\mathscr{B}$ with $B \subset O$, and O is open since it is a union of open sets.

We often find it convenient to specify a topology for a set X by specifying a base $\mathcal{B}$ of open sets and using the preceding criterion to define the open sets. Conditions on a collection $\mathcal{B}$ in order that it be a base for some topology are given by the following proposition:

3. Proposition: *A collection $\mathcal{B}$ of subsets of a set X is a base for some topology on X if and only if each x in X is contained in some B, and if $x \in B_1 \cap B_2$ then there is a $B_3 \in \mathcal{B}$ such that $x \in B_3 \subset B_1 \cap B_2$.*

Proof: That these conditions are necessary follows from the definition of a base and the fact that X and $B_1 \cap B_2$ must be open. Suppose now that $\mathcal{B}$ satisfies these conditions. If we set $\mathcal{T} = \{O\colon (x \in O)(\exists B \in \mathcal{B})(x \in B \subset O)\}$, then $\varnothing \in \mathcal{T}$, and the union of sets in $\mathcal{T}$ will be in $\mathcal{T}$, and the first condition on $\mathcal{B}$ implies that $X \in \mathcal{T}$. To show that the intersection of two sets O_1 and O_2 in $\mathcal{T}$ is itself in $\mathcal{T}$, let $x \in O_1 \cap O_2$. Then there are sets B_1 and B_2 in $\mathcal{B}$ such that $x \in B_1 \subset O_1$ and $x \in B_2 \subset O_2$. Let B_3 be a set in $\mathcal{B}$ with $x \in B_3 \subset B_1 \cap B_2$. Then $x \in B_3 \subset O_1 \cap O_2$, and it follows that $O_1 \cap O_2$ is open. ∎

A topological space is said to satisfy the first axiom of countability if there is a countable base at each point. Every metric space satisfies the first axiom of countability, since the spheroids centered at x and having rational radii are countable in number and form a base at x. A space is said to satisfy the second axiom of countability if there is a countable base for the topology. Thus Proposition 7.6 states that a metric space satisfies the second axiom of countability if and only if it is separable.

If $\langle X, \mathcal{T}\rangle$ and $\langle Y, \mathcal{S}\rangle$ are two topological spaces, we define a topology on the product $X \times Y$ by taking as a base the collection of all sets of the form $O_1 \times O_2$ where $O_1 \in \mathcal{T}$ and $O_2 \in \mathcal{S}$. This is called the **product topology** for $X \times Y$. If $\langle X_\alpha, \mathcal{T}_\alpha\rangle$ is any indexed family of topological spaces we define the product topology on $\underset{\alpha}{\times} X_\alpha$ by taking as a base all sets of the form $\underset{\alpha}{\times} O_\alpha$ where $O_\alpha \in \mathcal{T}_\alpha$ and $O_\alpha = X_\alpha$ except for a finite number of α. If the X_α are all the same space X and indexed by an index set A, we write X^A for $\underset{\alpha}{\times} X_\alpha$.

Problems

8. a. Let $\mathcal{B}$ be a base for the topological space $\langle X, \mathcal{T}\rangle$. Then $x \in \bar{E}$ if and only if for every $B \in \mathcal{B}$ with $x \in B$, there is a $y \in B \cap E$.

b. Let X satisfy the first axiom of countability. Then $x \in \bar{E}$ if and only if there is a sequence from E which converges to x.

c. Let X satisfy the first axiom of countability. Then x is a cluster point of a sequence $\langle x_n \rangle$ from X if and only if $\langle x_n \rangle$ has a subsequence which converges to x.

9. Let f be a mapping of the topological space X into the topological space Y. Let $\mathcal{B}_x$ be a base at x and $\mathcal{C}_y$ be a base at $y = f(x)$. Then f is continuous at x if and only if for each $C \in \mathcal{C}_y$ there is a $B \in \mathcal{B}_x$ such that $B \subset f^{-1}[C]$.

10. Let $\mathcal{C}$ be any collection of subsets of X. Let $\mathcal{B}$ consist of X and all finite intersections of sets in $\mathcal{C}$. Show that $\mathcal{B}$ is a base for the weakest topology which contains $\mathcal{C}$.

11. Let X be an uncountable set of points, and let $\mathcal{T}$ consist of the empty set and all subsets of X whose complement is finite. Show that $\mathcal{T}$ is a topology for X and that the space $\langle X, \mathcal{T} \rangle$ does not satisfy the first axiom of countability.

12. Let X be the set of real numbers, and let $\mathcal{B}$ be the set of all intervals of the form $[a, b)$. Show that $\mathcal{B}$ is the base of a topology $\mathcal{T}$ for X. (This topology is called the half open interval topology.) Show that $\langle X, \mathcal{T} \rangle$ satisfies the first but not the second axiom of countability and that the rationals are dense in X. Is $\langle X, \mathcal{T} \rangle$ metrizable?

13. Prove that the collections taken for bases in defining product topologies satisfy the conditions of Proposition 3. Show that if $\langle X, \rho \rangle$ and $\langle Y, \sigma \rangle$ are two metric spaces then the product topology on $X \times Y$ is the same as the topology induced by the product metric.

14. Show that X^A is the set of all functions mapping A into X with a base for its topology given by open sets of the form $\{ f : f(\alpha_1) \in O_1, f(\alpha_2) \in O_2, \ldots, f(\alpha_n) \in O_n \}$ where $\{\alpha_1, \ldots, \alpha_n\}$ is some finite subset of A and $\{O_1, \ldots, O_n\}$ a finite collection of open subsets of X. Prove that a sequence $\langle f_n \rangle$ converges to f in X^A if and only if $f_n(\alpha)$ converges to $f(\alpha)$ for each α in A.

15. Show that, if X is metrizable and A is countable, then X^A is metrizable. (Hint: X can always be metrized by a bounded metric ρ. Define a metric σ on X^A by $\sigma(x, y) = \sum_{\alpha \in A} 2^{-n} \rho(x_\alpha, y_\alpha)$.)

16. Let $\langle X_\alpha, \mathcal{T}_\alpha \rangle$ be a collection of topological spaces and let Y be their direct product. For each α we define a mapping π_α (called a projection) of Y onto X_α by letting $\pi_\alpha(x)$ be the α-th coordinate of x. Show that each π_α is continuous, and that the product topology is the weakest topology such that each π_α is continuous.

3 THE SEPARATION AXIOMS AND CONTINUOUS REAL-VALUED FUNCTIONS

The properties of topological spaces are in general quite different from those of metric spaces, and it is often convenient to suppose that our topological space satisfies some additional conditions which are true in metric spaces. Consider the following set of conditions on a topological space:

T_1: Given two distinct points x and y, there is an open set which contains y but not x.

T_2: Given two distinct points x and y, there are disjoint open sets O_1 and O_2 such that $x \in O_1$ and $y \in O_2$.

T_3: In addition to T_1, given a closed set F and a point x not in F there are disjoint open sets O_1 and O_2 such that $x \in O_1$ and $F \subset O_2$.

T_4: In addition to T_1, given two disjoint closed sets F_1 and F_2, there are disjoint open sets O_1 and O_2 such that $F_1 \subset O_1$ and $F_2 \subset O_2$.

These are called separation axioms, and all are satisfied in a metric space. A topological space which satisfies T_2 is called a Hausdorff space, one which satisfies T_3 is called a regular space, and one which satisfies T_4 is called a normal space. The following proposition tells us that the condition T_1 is equivalent to the statement that each set consisting of a single point is closed. With this in mind we see that $T_4 \Rightarrow T_3 \Rightarrow T_2 \Rightarrow T_1$.

4. Proposition: *A topological space X satisfies* T_1 *if and only if every set consisting of a single point is closed.*

Proof: If each set $\{x\}$ is closed, given two distinct points x and y, we may take $O = \sim\{x\}$. Then O is an open set containing y but not x. Suppose that T_1 holds. Then for each $y \in \sim\{x\}$ there is an open set $O \subset \sim\{x\}$. Thus the set $\sim\{x\}$ is the union of the open sets contained in it and so must be open. Hence $\{x\}$ is closed. ❙

One important consequence of normality is the following proposition whose proof is left to the reader (Problem 21):

5. Proposition (Urysohn's Lemma): *Let A and B be disjoint closed subsets of a normal space X. Then there is a continuous real-valued* *function f defined on X such that $0 \leq f \leq 1$ on X while $f \equiv 0$ on A and $f \equiv 1$ on B.*

If X is any set of points and $\mathfrak{F}$ is any collection of real-valued functions on X there is always a weakest topology on X such that every function in $\mathfrak{F}$ is continuous, for let $C = \{E : E = f^{-1}[O], f \in \mathfrak{F}$ and O an open subset of $\mathbf{R}^1\}$ and apply Proposition 3. This topology is called the weak topology generated (or induced) by $\mathfrak{F}$. If the functions in $\mathfrak{F}$ are all continuous in some topology $\mathscr{T}$, then the weak topology generated by $\mathfrak{F}$ is in general weaker than $\mathscr{T}$. A condition under which it coincides with $\mathscr{T}$ is given in Problem 24.

We conclude this section by stating the following theorem whose proof (and generalizations) can be found in Kelley [11], p. 125 ff.

Urysohn Metrization Theorem: *Every normal topological space satisfying the second axiom of countability is metrizable.*

Problems

17. a. Show that every metric space is Hausdorff.

b. Show that every metric space is normal. (Hint: If F_1 and F_2 are disjoint closed sets, let $O_1 = \{x : \rho(x, F_1) < \rho(x, F_2)\}$ and $O_2 = \{x : \rho(x, F_2) < \rho(x, F_1)\}$.)

18. Let f be a real-valued function on a topological space X. Show that f is continuous iff for each real number a the sets $\{x: f(x) < a\}$ and $\{x: f(x) > a\}$ are open. Show that f is continuous iff for each real number a the set $\{x : f(x) > a\}$ is open and the set $\{x : f(x) \geq a\}$ is closed.

19. If f and g are continuous real-valued functions on a topological space X, then the functions $f + g$, fg, $f \vee g$ and $f \wedge g$ are continuous. (Here as usual $(f \vee g)(x) = \max f(x), g(x)$.)

20. Let $\langle f_n \rangle$ be a sequence of continuous functions from a topological space X to a metric space Y. If $\langle f_n \rangle$ converges uniformly to a function f, then f is continuous.

21. a. Show that a Hausdorff space is normal if and only if given a closed set F and an open set O containing F there is an open set U such that $F \subset U$ and $\bar{U} \subset O$.

b. Let F be a closed subset of a normal space contained in an open set O. By repeating the result in (a) indefinitely, show that it is possible to construct a family $\{U_r\}$ of open sets, one corresponding to each rational in (0, 1) of the form $r = p \cdot 2^{-n}$, such that $F \subset U_r \subset O$ and $\bar{U}_r \subset U_s$ for $r < s$.

c. Let $\{U_r\}$ be the family constructed in (b) with $U_1 = X$. Let f be the real-valued function on X defined by $f(x) = \inf\{r : x \in U_r\}$. Then f is a continuous function, $0 \leq f \leq 1$, with $f \equiv 0$ on F and $f \equiv 1$ on $\tilde{O}$.

d. Let X be a Hausdorff space. Prove that X is normal if and only if for every pair of disjoint closed sets A and B on X there is a continuous real-valued function f on X such that $0 \leq f \leq 1$, $f \equiv 0$ on A and $f \equiv 1$ on B.

22. ***Tietze's Extension Theorem:*** Let X be a normal topological space, A a closed subset and f a continuous real-valued function on A. Then there is a continuous real-valued function g on X such that $g(x) = f(x)$ for $x \in A$. Give a proof using the following steps:

a. It suffices to suppose that $|f(x)| < 1$ for all $x \in A$. (Replace f by $f/(1 + |f|)$.)

b. Let $B = \{x : f(x) \leq -\frac{1}{3}\}$, $C = \{x : f(x) \geq \frac{1}{3}\}$. Then by the Urysohn lemma there is a continuous real-valued function f_1 on X which is $-\frac{1}{3}$ on B and $\frac{1}{3}$ on C, while $|f_1(x)| \leq \frac{1}{3}$ for all $x \in X$. Clearly $|f(x) - f_1(x)| < \frac{2}{3}$ for all $x \in A$.

c. By induction there is a continuous function f_n on X such that $|f_n(x)| < \dfrac{2^{n-1}}{3^n}$ for all $x \in X$ and $|f(x) - \sum_{i=1}^{n} f_i(x)| < \dfrac{2^n}{3^n}$ for all $x \in A$.

d. The sequence $\langle f_n \rangle$ is uniformly summable to a continuous function g on X, and $g = f$ on A.

23. Let $\mathfrak{F}$ be a family of real-valued functions on a set X. Show that a base for the weak topology on X generated by $\mathfrak{F}$ is given by the sets of the form $\{x : |f_i(x) - f_i(y)| < \epsilon$, for some $\epsilon > 0$, $y \in X$, and some finite set $f_1, \ldots, f_n$ of functions in $\mathfrak{F}\}$. Show that this topology is Hausdorff if and only if given any pair $\{x, y\}$ of distinct points in X there is an $f \in \mathfrak{F}$ with $f(x) \neq f(y)$.

24. Let $\mathfrak{F}$ be a family of real-valued continuous functions on a topological space $\langle X, \mathscr{T} \rangle$. Show that the weak topology generated by $\mathfrak{F}$ is $\mathscr{T}$ if for each closed set F and each $x \notin F$ there is an $f \in \mathfrak{F}$ with $f(x) = 0$ and $f \equiv 1$ on F.

25. Prove that the direct product of Hausdorff spaces is a Hausdorff space.

26. Prove that every subset of a Hausdorff space is Hausdorff.

4 CONNECTEDNESS

A topological space X is said to be connected if there do not exist two nonempty disjoint open sets O_1 and O_2 such that $X = O_1 \cup O_2$. Such a pair of open sets is called a separation of X. Since each set is the complement of the other, they are closed sets as well as open sets. Any pair of disjoint nonempty closed sets whose union is X is a separation for X, since each of these sets must also be open. A space X is connected if and only if the only subsets of X which are both open and closed are the sets $\varnothing$ and X. A subset E of X is said to be connected when it is a connected space in the topology it inherits from X: thus E is connected if there do not exist open sets O_1 and O_2 in X with $E \subset O_1 \cup O_2$ and $E \cap O_1 \cap O_2 = \varnothing$.

6. Proposition: *Let f be a continuous mapping of a connected space X onto a topological space Y. Then Y is connected.*

Proof: Let O_1 and O_2 be a separation of Y. Then $f^{-1}[O_1]$ and $f^{-1}[O_2]$ are disjoint open sets in X whose union is X. Since f is onto, neither $f^{-1}[O_1]$ nor $f^{-1}[O_2]$ is empty, and so this pair is a separation of X. Thus if Y is not connected, X is not connected, and the proposition follows by contraposition. ▍

7. Proposition: *Let f be a real-valued continuous function on a connected space X. Let x and y be two points in X and c a real number such that $f(x) < c < f(y)$. Then there is a $z \in X$ such that $f(z) = c$.*

Proof: If f does not assume the value c then $f^{-1}[(-\infty, c)]$ and $f^{-1}[(c, \infty)]$ are disjoint open sets whose union is X. They are nonempty since x belongs to the first and y to the second. Thus X is not connected. ▍

8. Proposition: *A subset E of $\mathbf{R}^1$ is connected if and only if it is either an interval or a single point.*

Problems

27. Let A be a connected subset of a topological space, and suppose $A \subset B \subset \bar{A}$. Then B is connected.

28. a. Let E be a connected subset of $\mathbf{R}^1$ having more than one point. Prove that E is an interval. (If x and y are in E, $x < y$, then $[x, y] \subset E$. Let $a = \inf E$, $b = \sup E$. Then $(a, b) \subset E \subset [a, b]$.)

b. Prove that an interval in $\mathbf{R}^1$ is connected. (Let $I = (a, b)$ and let O be a subset of I which is both open and closed in I. Show that $\sup \{y : (x, y) \subset O\} = b$, and use Problem 27 to take care of nonopen intervals.)

29. A space X is said to be arcwise connected if given two points x and y in X there is a continuous map f of $[0, 1]$ into X such that $f(0) = x$ and $f(1) = y$.

a. Show that an arcwise connected space is connected.

b. In the plane $\mathbf{R}_2$ consider the subspace

$$X = \{\langle x, y\rangle : x = 0, -1 \leq y \leq 1\} \cup \{\langle x, y\rangle : y = \sin 1/x, 0 < x \leq 1\}.$$

Show that X is connected but not arcwise connected.

c. Show that each connected open set G in $\mathbf{R}^n$ is arcwise connected. (Let $x \in G$ and let H be the set of points in G which can be connected to x by a polygonal arc. Then H is open and closed in G.)

30. Let X be a topological space and $\{E_\alpha\}$ a collection of connected subsets of X each of which contains a fixed point x. Then $\bigcup E_\alpha$ is connected.

*5 NETS

By a directed system we mean a set A together with a relation $\prec$ satisfying the following conditions.

i. $\alpha \prec \beta$ and $\beta \prec \gamma \Rightarrow \alpha \prec \gamma$.
ii. If $\alpha, \beta \in A$, there is a $\gamma \in A$ with $\alpha \prec \gamma$ and $\beta \prec \gamma$.

One example of a directed system is the set N of positive integers with $\prec$ replaced by $\leq$. Another commonly used directed set is the set of all open sets containing a point x, with $O_1 \prec O_2$ defined to mean $O_1 \supset O_2$.

A net is a mapping of a directed system into a topological space X. If the directed system is the integers, we have a sequence, and nets may be thought of as generalizations of sequences. We usually write x_α for the value of the net at α and $\langle x_\alpha\rangle$ for the net itself. A point

$x \in X$ is said to be the limit of a net $\langle x_\alpha \rangle$ if for each open set O containing x there is an $\alpha_0 \in A$ such that $x_\alpha \in O$ for all $\alpha \succ \alpha_0$. A point x is called a cluster point of $\langle x_\alpha \rangle$ if given O containing x and given $\alpha \in A$ there is a $\beta \succ \alpha$ such that $x_\beta \in O$. For sequences these notions coincide with our earlier notions of limit and cluster point.

9. Proposition: *A point x is a point of closure of a set E if and only if it is the limit of a net $\langle x_\alpha \rangle$ from E.*

Proof: The "if" part follows directly from the definitions of limit and point of closure. Hence we assume x is a point of closure of E. We take as our directed system A the collection of open sets which contain x and set $O_1 \prec O_2$ if $O_1 \supset O_2$. Since x is a point of closure of E, for each $O \in A$ there is a point x_0 in $O \cap E$. Then $\langle x_O \rangle$ is a net from E, and it converges to x, since given O containing x, we have $x_{O'} \in O$ for all $O' \succ O$. ❙

Problems

31. Prove that X is Hausdorff if and only if every net in X has at most one limit. (To prove the "if" part, let x and y be two points which cannot be separated and let the directed system be the collection of all pairs $\langle A, B \rangle$ of open sets with $x \in A$, $y \in B$. Choose $x_{\langle A, B \rangle}$ to be in $A \cap B$ and show that both x and y are limits of this net.)

32. Prove that a function f from X to Y is continuous at x if and only if for each net $\langle x_\alpha \rangle$ which converges to x the net $\langle f(x_\alpha) \rangle$ converges to $f(x)$.

33. Let X be any set and f a real-valued function on X. Let A be the system consisting of all finite subsets of X, with $F \prec G$ meaning $F \subset G$. For each $F \in A$, let $y_F = \sum_{x \in F} f(x)$. Prove that the net $\langle y_F \rangle$ has a limit if and only if $f(x) = 0$ except for x in a countable subset $\{x_n\}$ and $\Sigma\, |f(x_n)| < \infty$. In this case $\lim y_F = \sum_{n=1}^{\infty} f(x_n)$.

34. Let $X = \times_\alpha X_\alpha$. Then a net $\langle x_\beta \rangle$ in X converges to x if and only if each coordinate of x_β converges to the corresponding coordinate of x.

9 Compact Spaces

1 BASIC PROPERTIES

Many of the important properties of the interval [0, 1] follow from the Heine-Borel theorem. We introduce a class of topological spaces in which the conclusion of the Heine-Borel theorem is valid and show that many properties of [0, 1] are also true for these spaces. These spaces are called compact spaces. To give an exact definition, we say that a collection $\mathcal{U}$ of open sets in a topological space is an open covering for a set K if K is contained in the union of the sets in $\mathcal{U}$. A topological space X is said to be **compact** if every open covering $\mathcal{U}$ of X has a finite subcovering, that is, if there is a finite collection $\{O_1, O_2, \ldots, O_N\} \subset \mathcal{U}$ such that $X = \bigcup_{i=1}^{N} O_i$. A subset K of a topological space is called compact if it is compact as a subspace of X. In view of the topology of a subspace this definition is equivalent to saying that a subset K of X is compact if every covering $\mathcal{U}$ of K by open sets of X has a finite subcovering. The Heine-Borel theorem states that every closed and bounded subset of real numbers is compact.

If $\mathcal{U}$ is an open covering of a space X, then the collection $\mathcal{F}$ of complements of sets in $\mathcal{U}$ is a collection of closed sets whose intersection is empty, and conversely. Thus a space X is compact if and only if every collection of closed sets with an empty intersection has a finite subcollection whose intersection is empty. A collection $\mathcal{F}$ of sets in X is said to have the finite intersection property if any finite subcollection of $\mathcal{F}$ has a nonempty intersection. Hence we have the following proposition:

1. Proposition: *A topological space X is compact if and only if every collection $\mathfrak{F}$ of closed sets with the finite intersection property has a nonempty intersection.*

The notion of compactness is intimately connected with that of being closed, as the following proposition shows. Thus compactness may be viewed as an absolute type of closedness.

2. Proposition: *A closed subset of a compact space is compact. A compact subset of a Hausdorff space is closed.*

Proof: Let X be compact, F a closed subset of X, and $\mathcal{U}$ an open covering for F. Then $\mathcal{U} \cup \{\tilde{F}\}$ is an open covering for X and so must have a finite subcovering $\{\tilde{F}, O_1, \ldots, O_N\}$. Then the sets $O_1, O_2, \ldots, O_N$ cover F, and so $\mathcal{U}$ has a finite subcovering.

Suppose now that X is a Hausdorff space and K a compact subset of X. We shall show that $\tilde{K}$ is open. Let $y \in \tilde{K}$. Since X is Hausdorff, for each $x \in K$ there are disjoint open sets O_x and N_x such that $x \in O_x$ and $y \in N_x$. The sets $\{O_x : x \in K\}$ form an open covering of K, and so there is a finite subcollection $\{O_{x_1}, O_{x_2}, \ldots, O_{x_n}\}$ which covers K. Let

$$N = \bigcap_{i=1}^{n} N_{x_i}.$$

Then N is an open set containing y and not meeting any of the sets O_{x_i}. Since $K \subset \bigcup O_{x_i}$, N does not meet K and so is contained in $\tilde{K}$. Thus $\tilde{K}$ is open and K closed. ∎

3. Corollary: *Every compact set of real numbers is closed and bounded.*

Proof: Since $\mathbf{R}^1$ is Hausdorff, a compact subset K of $\mathbf{R}^1$ must be closed. Moreover, the intervals $I_n = (-n, n)$ form an open covering of K and so a finite number of them must cover K. Hence K must be bounded. ∎

4. Proposition: *The continuous image of a compact set is compact.*

Proof: Let f be a continuous function which maps the compact set K *onto* a topological space Y. If $\mathcal{U}$ is an open covering for Y then the collection of sets $f^{-1}[O]$ for all $O \in \mathcal{U}$ is an open covering of K. By the compactness of K, there are a finite number $O_1, \ldots, O_n$ of sets of O such that the sets $f^{-1}[O_i]$ cover K. Since f is onto, the sets $O_1, \ldots, O_n$ cover Y. ▌

5. Proposition: *A one-to-one continuous mapping of a compact space onto a Hausdorff space is a homeomorphism.*

Proof: Let X be compact, Y Hausdorff, and f a one-to-one continuous mapping onto Y. In order to show that f is a homeomorphism it is only necessary to show that it carries open sets into open sets or equivalently closed sets into closed sets. But if F is a closed subset of X it is compact by Proposition 2 and so $f[F]$ is compact by Proposition 4 and so must be closed by Proposition 2. ▌

Problems

1. a. Prove that a compact Hausdorff space is regular.

b. Prove that a compact Hausdorff space is normal.

2. Let f be a continuous mapping of the compact space X onto the Hausdorff space Y. Then any mapping g of Y into Z for which $g \circ f$ is continuous must itself be continuous.

3. a. Prove that if $(X, \mathscr{T})$ is a compact space, then $(X, \mathscr{T}_1)$ is compact for all $\mathscr{T}_1$ weaker than $\mathscr{T}$.

b. Show that if $(X, \mathscr{T})$ is a Hausdorff space then $(X, \mathscr{T}_2)$ is a Hausdorff space for all $\mathscr{T}_2$ stronger than $\mathscr{T}$.

c. Show that if $(X, \mathscr{T})$ is a compact Hausdorff space, then any weaker topology is not Hausdorff and any stronger topology is not compact.

2 COUNTABLE COMPACTNESS AND THE BOLZANO-WEIERSTRASS PROPERTY

A somewhat weaker notion than compactness is countable compactness. A space X is said to be **countably compact** if every countable open covering has a finite subcovering. Since every space satisfying the second axiom of countability has the property that every open covering of it has a countable subcovering, it follows that countable compactness is equivalent to compactness in the presence of the second axiom of countability. The proof of Proposition 4 applies in the countably compact case to give the following proposition:

6. Proposition: *The continuous image of a countably compact space is countably compact.*

A topological space X is said to have the **Bolzano-Weierstrass property** if every sequence $\langle x_n \rangle$ in X has at least one cluster point, i.e. if there is an $x \in X$ such that for each open set O containing x and for each N there is an $n \geq N$ with $x_n \in O$.

7. Proposition: *A topological space has the Bolzano-Weierstrass property if and only if it is countably compact.*

Proof: We first observe that X is countably compact if and only if every countable family $\mathfrak{F}$ of closed sets with the finite intersection property has a nonempty intersection. Suppose now that X has the Bolzano-Weierstrass property and that $\mathfrak{F} = \{F_i\}$ is a countable family of closed sets with the finite intersection property. Since the intersection $H_n = \bigcap_{k=1}^{n} F_k$ is empty for no n, we may choose for each n an element $x_n \in H_n$. By the Bolzano-Weierstrass property the sequence $\langle x_n \rangle$ has a cluster point x. But $x_n \in F_i$ for all $n \geq i$, and so x must belong to F_i since F_i is closed. Thus x belongs to every F_i and so to their intersection.

Suppose on the other hand that X is countably compact and that $\langle x_i \rangle$ is a sequence from X. Let B_n be the set $\{x_n, x_{n+1}, \ldots, \}$. Then $\{\bar{B}_n\}$ is a countable collection of closed sets with the finite intersection property, and so there is a point x which belongs to $\bigcap \bar{B}_n$. The point x is a cluster point of the sequence, since given any open set O containing x and N we have $x \in \bar{B}_N$, and so there must be an $x_n \in O$ with $n \geq N$. ▌

A somewhat old-fashioned concept which resembles the Bolzano-Weierstrass property is that of sequential compactness. A space X is said to be **sequentially compact** if every infinite sequence from X has a convergent subsequence. The relationship of sequential compactness to countable compactness is the following:

8. Proposition: *A sequentially compact space is countably compact. A countably compact space satisfying the first countability axiom is sequentially compact.*

Proof: Sequential compactness implies the Bolzano-Weierstrass property which is equivalent to countable compactness. The second part is an immediate consequence of Problem 8.8(c). ▎

9. Proposition: *Let f be a continuous real-valued function on a countably compact space X. Then f is bounded and assumes its maximum and minimum.*

This proposition can be proved by using Proposition 8 and the fact that every countably compact subset of $\mathbf{R}^1$ is closed and bounded. However, we can give a direct proof which proves more. A real-valued function f on a topological space is called **upper semicontinuous** if for each real number α the set $\{x: f(x) < \alpha\}$ is open. If f is continuous both f and $-f$ are upper semicontinuous. This implies that Proposition 9 is a corollary of the following proposition:

10. Proposition: *Let f be an upper semicontinuous real-valued function on a countably compact space X. Then f is bounded (from above) and assumes its maximum.*

Proof: The sets $O_n = \{x: f(x) < n\}$ form a countable open covering for X and so there must be a finite subcovering $\{O_1, \ldots, O_N\}$. But this implies $X \subset O_N$. Hence $f(x) < N$ for all x, and f is bounded from above. Let $\beta = \sup\,\{f(x): x \in X\}$. Then the sets

$$F_n = \left\{x: f(x) \geq \beta - \frac{1}{n}\right\}$$

form a countable collection of closed sets with the finite intersection property. Hence there is a y belonging to every F_n. Then $f(y) = \beta$, and f assumes its maximum at y. ▎

11. Proposition (Dini): *Let $\langle f_n \rangle$ be a sequence of upper semicontinuous real-valued functions on a countably compact space X, and suppose that for each $x \in X$ the sequence $\langle f_n(x) \rangle$ decreases monotonically to zero. Then $\langle f_n \rangle$ converges to zero uniformly.*

Proof: Choose $\epsilon > 0$, and let $O_n = \{x: f_n(x) < \epsilon\}$. Since f_n is upper semicontinuous, O_n is open. Since $f_n(x) \to 0$ for each x, we have $X \subset \bigcup O_n$. By the countable compactness of X, there are a finite number of open sets $\{O_1, \ldots, O_N\}$ whose union contains X.

But this implies that $O_N = X$, and hence $f_N(x) < \epsilon$ for all x. If $n \geq N$, we have $0 \leq f_n(x) \leq f_N(x) < \epsilon$, and the sequence $\langle f_n \rangle$ converges to 0 uniformly. ▎

Problems

4. **a.** A real-valued function f is called lower semicontinuous if $-f$ is upper semicontinuous. Show that a real-valued function on a space X is continuous if and only if it is both upper and lower semicontinuous.
   b. Show that if f and g are upper semicontinuous so is $f + g$.
   c. Let $\langle f_n \rangle$ be a decreasing sequence of upper semicontinuous functions which converge pointwise to a real-valued function f. Then f is upper semicontinuous.
   d. Let $\langle f_n \rangle$ be a decreasing sequence of upper semicontinuous functions on a countably compact space, and suppose that $\lim f_n(x) = f(x)$ where f is a lower semicontinuous real-valued function. Then f is continuous and $\langle f_n \rangle$ converges to f uniformly.
   e. Show that if a sequence $\langle f_n \rangle$ of upper semicontinuous functions converges uniformly to a function f, then f is also upper-semicontinuous.

3 COMPACT METRIC SPACES

In this section we investigate special properties of compactness that are true in metric spaces. We shall show that in a metric space the notions of compactness, countable compactness and sequential compactness coincide.

12. Lemma: *Let X be a countably compact metric space. Then given $\epsilon > 0$ there are a finite number of points $x_1, \ldots, x_N$ of X such that for each $x \in X$ there is an x_k with $\rho(x, x_k) < \epsilon$.*

Proof: Suppose that no such finite collection of points exists. Then we can choose an infinite sequence $\langle x_n \rangle$ of points in X so that $\rho(x_n, x_m) \geq \epsilon$ for $m \neq n$. Since each spheroid of radius $\epsilon/3$ can contain at most one term of this sequence, the Bolzano-Weierstrass property does not hold, and X is not countably compact. ▎

13. Proposition: *A countably compact metric space is separable.*

Proof: For each positive integer n let F_n be a finite set of points such that for each $x \in X$ there is a $y \in F_n$ with $\rho(x, y) < 1/n$. Then $\bigcup_{n=1}^{\infty} F_n$ is a countable dense subset of X. ∎

14. Corollary: *For a metric space the notions of compactness, countable compactness, and sequential compactness are equivalent.*

Proof: Since a metric space satisfies the first axiom of countability, the notions of countable compactness and sequential compactness coincide by Proposition 8. Compactness trivially implies countable compactness. If X is countably compact, it must satisfy the second axiom of countability by Proposition 13, and so be compact. ∎

A metric space X is said to be **totally bounded** if for each $\epsilon > 0$ there is a finite collection of spheroids of radius ϵ which covers X. Every compact space is totally bounded, and every subset of a totally bounded space is totally bounded. The following proposition characterizes compactness in terms of completeness and total boundedness:

15. Proposition: *A metric space X is compact if and only if it is both complete and totally bounded.*

Proof: If X is compact it is trivially totally bounded. If $\langle x_n \rangle$ is a Cauchy sequence in X, then $\langle x_n \rangle$ must have a cluster point. But a Cauchy sequence which has a cluster point converges to the cluster point. Thus X is complete.

Suppose that X is complete and totally bounded. In order to show that X is compact, it suffices to show that each infinite sequence $\langle x_n \rangle$ has a convergent subsequence. Since X is totally bounded, we may cover X by a finite number of spheres of radius 1. Among these spheres there must be a sphere S_1 which contains infinitely many terms of the sequence $\langle x_n \rangle$. Covering X by a finite number of spheres of radius $\frac{1}{2}$, we can find among them a sphere S_2 such that $S_1 \cap S_2$ contains infinitely many terms of the sequence $\langle x_n \rangle$. Continuing, we obtain a sequence $\langle S_k \rangle$ of spheres, S_k having radius $1/k$, such that $S_1 \cap \cdots \cap S_k$ contains infinitely many terms of the sequence. Since there are infinitely many terms of the sequence in $S_1 \cap \cdots \cap S_k$, we may choose n_k so that $n_k > n_{k-1}$ and $x_{n_k} \in S_1 \cap \cdots \cap S_k$. Then

$\langle x_{n_k} \rangle$ is a subsequence of $\langle x_n \rangle$, and it must be a Cauchy sequence since $\rho(x_{n_k}, x_{n_l}) \leq 2/N$ for $k, l \geq N$. Since X is complete, this subsequence converges. ❙

16. Proposition: *Let f be a continuous mapping of a compact metric space X into a metric space Y. Then f is uniformly continuous.*

Proof: Given $\epsilon > 0$ and $x \in X$, there is a $\delta_x > 0$ such that $\rho(x, y) < \delta_x$ implies $\sigma(f(x), f(y)) < \epsilon/2$. Let O_x be the spheroid $\{y: \rho(x, y) < \frac{1}{2}\delta_x\}$. Then $\{O_x: x \in X\}$ is an open covering of X and so has a finite subcovering $\{O_{x_1}, \ldots, O_{x_n}\}$. Let $\delta = \frac{1}{2}\min\{\delta_{x_1}, \ldots, \delta_{x_n}\}$. Then $\delta > 0$. Given two points y and z in X such that $\rho(y, z) < \delta$, the point y must belong to some O_{x_i}, and hence $\rho(y, x_i) < \frac{1}{2}\delta_{x_i}$. Consequently, $\rho(z, x_i) \leq \rho(z, y) + \rho(y, x_i) < \frac{1}{2}\delta_{x_i} + \delta \leq \delta_{x_i}$. Thus we have $\sigma(f(y), f(x_i)) < \epsilon/2$ and $\sigma(f(z), f(x_i)) < \epsilon/2$. This implies that $\sigma(f(z), f(y)) < \epsilon$, showing that f is uniformly continuous on X. ❙

Problems

5. Let X be a metric space, K a compact subset and F a closed subset. Then $F \cap K = \varnothing$ if and only if $\rho(F, K) > 0$, i.e., iff there is a $\delta > 0$ such that $\rho(x, y) > \delta$ for all $x \in F$ and all $y \in K$. (Consider the function $\rho(x, F) = \inf_{y \in F} \rho(x, y)$.)

6. Let X be a compact metric space and $\mathcal{U}$ an open covering of X. Then there is a $\delta > 0$ such that every spheroid of radius δ is contained in some element of $\mathcal{U}$.

4 PRODUCTS OF COMPACT SPACES

In this section we prove the theorem of Tychonoff that a product of compact spaces is compact. It is probably the most important theorem in general topology. Most applications in analysis need only the special case of a product of (closed) intervals, but this special cases does not seem to be easier to prove than the general case. We begin with two lemmas concerning the finite intersection property.

17. Lemma: *Let $\mathcal{A}$ be a collection of subsets of a set X, and suppose that $\mathcal{A}$ has the finite intersection property. Then there is a* *collection* $\mathcal{B} \supset \mathcal{A}$ *such that* $\mathcal{B}$ *has the finite intersection property and is maximal with respect to this property; that is, no collection properly containing* $\mathcal{B}$ *has the finite intersection property.*

Proof: Consider the family of all collections containing $\mathcal{A}$ and having the finite intersection property. This family is partially ordered by inclusion. By the Hausdorff maximal principle there is a maximal linearly ordered subfamily $\mathcal{F}$. Let $\mathcal{B}$ be the union of the collections in $\mathcal{F}$. If $B_1, \ldots, B_n$ are in $\mathcal{B}$, then each B_i belongs to some $\mathcal{C}_i \in \mathcal{F}$. Since $\mathcal{F}$ is linearly ordered by inclusion, one of the collections $\mathcal{C}_k$ contains the others, and so all B_i belong to $\mathcal{C}_k$. Since $\mathcal{C}_k$ has the finite intersection property, $\bigcap B_i \neq \varnothing$. Thus $\mathcal{B}$ has the finite intersection property. If $\mathcal{B}' \supset \mathcal{B}$ and $\mathcal{B}'$ has the finite intersection property, then $\mathcal{B}'$ contains every $\mathcal{C}$ in $\mathcal{F}$ and so must belong to $\mathcal{F}$ by the maximality of $\mathcal{F}$. Thus $\mathcal{B}$ is a union of collections one of which is $\mathcal{B}'$, and so $\mathcal{B}' \subset \mathcal{B}$. This shows that $\mathcal{B}$ is maximal with respect to the finite intersection property. ▌

18. Lemma: *Let* $\mathcal{B}$ *be a collection of subsets of* X *which is maximal with respect to the finite intersection property. Then each intersection of a finite number of sets in* $\mathcal{B}$ *is again in* $\mathcal{B}$*, and each set which meets each set in* $\mathcal{B}$ *is itself in* $\mathcal{B}$.

Proof: Let $\mathcal{B}'$ be the collection of all sets which are finite intersections of sets in $\mathcal{B}$. Then $\mathcal{B}'$ is a collection having the finite intersection property and containing $\mathcal{B}$. Thus $\mathcal{B}' = \mathcal{B}$ by the maximality of $\mathcal{B}$.

Suppose that a set C meets each element of $\mathcal{B}$. Since $\mathcal{B}$ contains each finite intersection of sets in $\mathcal{B}$, it follows that $\mathcal{B} \cup \{C\}$ has the finite intersection property. By maximality $\mathcal{B} \cup \{C\} = \mathcal{B}$, and so $C \in \mathcal{B}$. ▌

19. Theorem (Tychonoff): *Let* $\langle X_\alpha \rangle$ *be an indexed family of compact topological spaces. Then the product space* $\underset{\alpha}{\times} X_\alpha$ *is compact in the product topology.*

Proof: Let π_α be the mapping of X to X_α which assigns to each $x \in X$ its αth coordinate. Then the sets obtained by taking finite intersections of sets of the form $\pi_\alpha^{-1}(O_\alpha)$ with O_α open in X_α form a base $\mathcal{N}$ for the topology of X.

Let $\mathcal{A}$ be any collection of closed subsets of X with the finite intersection property, and let $\mathcal{B}$ be a collection (of not necessarily closed) sets which contains $\mathcal{A}$ and is maximal with respect to the finite intersection property. Let $\mathcal{B}_\alpha$ be the collection of subsets of X_α of the form $\pi_\alpha(B)$ with $B \in \mathcal{B}$. Then $\mathcal{B}_\alpha$ has the finite intersection property, and by the compactness of X_α it is possible to choose a point x_α belonging to $\bigcap_{\mathcal{B}} [\overline{\pi_\alpha(B)}]$, that is, a point x_α which is a point of closure of each set $\pi_\alpha(B)$. Let x be that point in X whose αth coordinate is x_α.

Consider a set S which is of the form $\pi_\alpha^{-1}(O_\alpha)$ for some α and some open set O_α in X_α with $x_\alpha \in O_\alpha$. Since x_α is a point of closure of $\pi_\alpha(B)$ for each B in $\mathcal{B}$, the set S must intersect each B in $\mathcal{B}$. By Lemma 18 we must have $S \in \mathcal{B}$. Each set containing x in the base $\mathcal{N}$ for the topology of X is a finite intersection of sets of this form and so must be in $\mathcal{B}$ by Lemma 18. Let F be a closed set in $\mathcal{B}$. Then F meets each $N \in \mathcal{N}$ with $x \in N$. Consequently, x is a point of closure of F and so in F. Hence x belongs to each set in $\mathcal{A}$, and $\mathcal{A}$ has nonempty intersection. ❙

Problems

7. Each closed and bounded set in $\mathbf{R}^n$ is compact.

8. Prove without using the axiom of choice that if X is compact and I is a closed interval then $X \times I$ is compact. (Hint: Let $\mathcal{U}$ be an open covering of $X \times I$, and consider the smallest value of $t \in I$ such that for each $t' < t$ the set $X \times [0, t']$ can be covered by a finite number of sets in $\mathcal{U}$. Use the compactness of X to show that $X \times [0, t]$ can also be covered by a finite number of sets in $\mathcal{U}$ and that if $t < 1$, then for some $t'' > t$, $X \times [0, t'']$ can be covered by a finite number of sets in $\mathcal{U}$.)

9. Prove that the product of a countable number of sequentially compact spaces is sequentially compact. (If $\langle x_n \rangle$ is a sequence in the product, choose a subsequence $\langle x_n^1 \rangle$ whose first coordinate converges, choose a subsequence $\langle x_n^2 \rangle$ of this whose second coordinate converges, etc. Then the "diagonal" sequence $\langle x_n^n \rangle$ converges in the product space.)

10. A product I^A of unit intervals is called a (generalized) cube. Prove that every compact Hausdorff space X is homeomorphic to a closed subset of some cube. (Let $\mathcal{F}$ be the family of continuous real-valued functions on

X with values in [0, 1]. Let $Q = \mathop{\times}_{f \varepsilon \mathfrak{F}} I_f$. Then the mapping g of X into Q which takes x into the point whose fth coordinate is $f(x)$ is one-to-one into Q and continuous.)

11. Let $Q = I^A$ be a cube, and let f be a continuous real-valued function on Q. Then given $\epsilon > 0$, there is a continuous real-valued function g on Q such that $|f - g| < \epsilon$ and g is a function of only a finite number of coordinates. (Hint: Cover the range of f by a finite number of intervals of length ϵ and look at the inverse images of these intervals.)

5 LOCALLY COMPACT SPACES

A topological space X is called locally compact if for each $x \varepsilon X$ there is an open set O containing x such that $\bar{O}$ is compact. Thus X is locally compact iff the collection of open sets with compact closures form a base for the topology of X. Every compact space is locally compact, while the Euclidean spaces $\mathbf{R}^n$ are examples of a locally compact but not compact space.

If X is a locally compact Hausdorff space, we can form a new space X^* by adding to X a single point ω not in X and taking a set in X^* to be open if it is either an open subset of X or the complement of a compact subset in X. Then X^* is a compact Hausdorff space, and the identity mapping of X into X^* is a homeomorphism of X and $X^* \sim \{\omega\}$. The space X^* is called the **Alexandroff one point compactification** of X, and ω is often referred to as the point at infinity in X^*.

Problems

12. a. Prove that the subsets of X^* which are either open subsets of X or the complement of a compact subset of X form a topology for X^*, that is, that the intersection of two such sets is such a set and the union of any collection of such sets is such a set.

b. Show that the identity mapping from X to the subspace $X^* \sim \{\omega\}$ is a homeomorphism.

c. Show that X^* is compact and Hausdorff.

13. Let X be a locally compact space and K a compact subset of it. Show that there is an open set $O \supset K$ such that $\bar{O}$ is compact. (Hint: For each point $x \varepsilon K$ there is an O_x containing x with $\bar{O}_x$ compact. Let O be the union of a finite number of these O_x which cover K.)

14. Let X be a locally compact Hausdorff space and K a compact set. Then there is a continuous real-valued function on X which is identically 1 on K and for which the set $O = \{x: f(x) \neq 0\}$ has compact closure. (Hint: Use 12(c), 13, and the Urysohn lemma.)

15. Show that the Alexandroff one point compactification of R^n is homeomorphic to the boundary of a sphere in R^{n+1}.

16. a. Let O be an open subset of a compact Hausdorff space. Then O is locally compact.

b. Let O be an open set in a compact Hausdorff space X. Then the mapping of X to the one point compactification of O which is the identity on O and takes each point in $X \sim O$ into ω is continuous.

17. A continuous mapping f from a topological space X to a topological space Y is called **proper** if the inverse image of every compact set is compact. Let X and Y be locally compact Hausdorff spaces, and f a continuous mapping of X into Y. Let X^* and Y^* be the one point compactifications of X and Y, and f^* the mapping of X^* into Y^* whose restriction to X is f and which takes the point at infinity in X^* into the point at infinity in Y^*. Then f is proper if and only if f^* is continuous.

18. a. Let X be a locally compact space. A subset F of X is closed if and only if $F \cap K$ is closed for each closed compact set K.

b. The above conclusion is true if X is a Hausdorff space satisfying the first axiom of countability instead of being locally compact.

6 THE STONE-WEIERSTRASS THEOREM

Let X be a compact Hausdorff space. We denote by $C(X)$ the set of all continuous real-valued functions on X. Since X is normal, it follows from Urysohn's lemma that there are enough functions in $C(X)$ to separate points; that is, given two distinct points x and y in X we can find an f in $C(X)$ such that $f(x) \neq f(y)$. The set $C(X)$ is a linear space, since any constant multiple of a continuous real-valued function is continuous and the sum of two continuous functions is continuous. The space $C(X)$ becomes a normed linear space if we define $\|f\| = \max |f(x)|$, and a metric space if we set $\rho(f, g) = \|f - g\|$. As a metric space $C(X)$ is complete.

The space $C(X)$ has also a ring structure: the product fg of two functions f and g in $C(X)$ is again in $C(X)$. A linear space A of functions in $C(X)$ is called an **algebra** if the product of any two elements in A is again in A. Thus A is an algebra if for any two functions f and g in A and any real numbers a and b we have $af + bg$ in A and fg in A. A family A of functions on X is said to separate points if given distinct points x and y of X there is an f in A such that $f(x) \neq f(y)$. In the present section we study the closed subalgebras of $C(X)$ and prove that if A is a subalgebra of $C(X)$ which separates points, contains the constant functions, and is closed, then $A = C(X)$.

The space $C(X)$ also has a lattice structure: If f and g are in $C(X)$ so is the function $f \wedge g$ defined by $(f \wedge g)(x) = \min [f(x), g(x)]$ and the function $f \vee g$ defined by $(f \vee g)(x) = \max [f(x), g(x)]$. A subset L of $C(X)$ is called a **lattice** if for every pair of functions f and g in L we also have $f \vee g$ and $f \wedge g$ in L. It is convenient to investigate subalgebras of $C(X)$ by first investigating lattices of functions. The following proposition can be thought of as a generalization of the Dini theorem:

20. Proposition: *Let L be a lattice of continuous real-valued functions on a compact space X, and suppose that the function h defined by*

$$h(x) = \inf_{f \in L} f(x)$$

is continuous. Then given $\epsilon > 0$, there is a g in L such that $0 \leq g(x) - h(x) < \epsilon$ for all x in X.

Proof: For each x in X there is a function f_x in L such that $f_x(x) < h(x) + \epsilon/3$. Since f_x and h are continuous, there is an open set O_x containing x such that

$$|f_x(y) - f_x(x)| < \epsilon/3 \text{ and } |h(y) - h(x)| < \epsilon/3$$

for all $y \in O_x$. Hence $f_x(y) - h(y) < \epsilon$ for all y in O_x. Now the sets O_x cover X, and by compactness there are a finite number of them, say $\{O_{x_1}, \ldots, O_{x_n}\}$, which cover X. Let $g = f_{x_1} \wedge f_{x_2} \wedge \cdots \wedge f_{x_n}$. Then $g \in L$, and given y in X we may choose i so that $y \in O_{x_i}$, whence

$$g(y) - h(y) \leq f_{x_i}(y) - h(y) < \epsilon. \quad \blacksquare$$

21. Proposition: *Let X be a compact space and L a lattice of continuous real-valued functions on X with the following properties:*

i. L separates points; that is, if $x \neq y$, there is an $f \in L$ with $f(x) \neq f(y)$.

ii. The constant functions belong to L.

iii. If $f \in L$, and c is any real number, then cf and $c + f$ also belong to L.

Then given any continuous real-valued function h on X and any $\epsilon > 0$, there is a function $g \in L$ such that for all $x \in X$

$$0 \leq g(x) - h(x) < \epsilon.$$

Before proving the proposition, we first establish two lemmas.

22. Lemma: *Let L be a family of real-valued functions on a compact space X which satisfies properties (i) and (iii) of Proposition 21. Then given any two real numbers a and b and any pair x and y of distinct points of X there is an $f \in L$ such that $f(x) = a$ and $f(y) = b$.*

Proof: Let g be a function in L such that $g(x) \neq g(y)$. Let

$$f = \frac{a - b}{g(x) - g(y)} g + \frac{bg(x) - ag(y)}{g(x) - g(y)}.$$

Then $f \in L$, by property (iii), and $f(x) = a, f(y) = b$. ▮

23. Lemma: *Let L be as in Proposition 21, a and b real numbers with $a \leq b$, F a closed subset of X, and p a point not in F. Then there is a function f in L such that $f \geq a$, $f(p) = a$, and $f(x) > b$ for all $x \in F$.*

Proof: By Lemma 22 we can choose for each $x \in F$ a function f_x such that $f_x(p) = a$ and $f_x(x) = b + 1$. Let $O_x = \{y: f_x(y) > b\}$. Then the sets $\{O_x\}$ cover F, and since F is compact, there are a finite number $\{O_{x_1}, \ldots, O_{x_n}\}$ which cover F. Let $f = f_{x_1} \vee \cdots \vee f_{x_n}$. Then $f \in L, f(p) = a$, and $f > b$ on L. If we replace f by $f \vee a$, then we also have $f \geq a$ on X. ▮

Proof of Proposition 21: Given $g \in C(X)$, let $L' = \{f: f \in L$ and $f \geq g\}$. Proposition 21 will follow from Proposition 20 if we can show that for each $p \in X$ we have $g(p) = \inf f(p)$, $f \in L'$. Choose a positive real number η. Since g is continuous, the set

$$F = \{x: g(x) \geq g(p) + \eta\}$$

is closed. Since X is compact, g is bounded on X say by M. By Lemma 23 we can find a function $f \in L$ such that $f \geq g(p) + \eta$,

$f(p) = g(p) + \eta$, and $f(x) > M$ on F. Since $g < g(p) + \eta$ on $\tilde{F}$, we have $g < f$ on X. Thus $f \in L'$, and $f(p) \le g(p) + \eta$. Since η was an arbitrary positive number, we have $g(p) = \inf f(p), f \in L'$. ∎

24. Lemma: *Given $\epsilon > 0$, there is a polynomial P in one variable such that for all $s \in [-1, 1]$ we have $|P(s) - |s|| < \varepsilon$.*

Proof: Let $\sum_{n=0}^{\infty} c_n t^n$ be the binomial series for $(1 - t)^{1/2}$. This series converges uniformly for t in the interval $[0, 1]$. Hence given $\epsilon > 0$, we can choose N so that for all $t \in [0, 1]$ we have $|(1 - t)^{1/2} - Q_N(t)| < \epsilon$, where $Q_N = \sum_{n=0}^{N} c_n t^n$. Let $P(s) = Q_N(1 - s^2)$. Then P is a polynomial in s, and $||s| - P(s)| < \epsilon$ for $s \in [-1, 1]$. ∎

25. Theorem (Stone-Weierstrass): *Let X be a compact space and A an algebra of continuous real-valued functions on X which separates the points of X and which contains the constant functions. Then given any continuous real-valued function f on X and any $\epsilon > 0$ there is a function g in A such that for all x in X we have $|g(x) - f(x)| < \epsilon$. In other words, A is a dense subset of $C(X)$.*

Proof: Let $\bar{A}$ denote the closure of A considered as a subset of $C(X)$. Thus $\bar{A}$ consists of those functions on X which are uniform limits of sequences of functions from A. It is easy to verify that $\bar{A}$ is itself an algebra of continuous real-valued functions on X. The theorem is equivalent to the statement that $\bar{A} = C(X)$. This will follow from Proposition 21 if we can show that $\bar{A}$ is a lattice. Let $f \in \bar{A}$, and $\|f\| \le 1$. Then given $\epsilon > 0$, $\||f| - P(f)\| < \epsilon$ where P is the polynomial given in Lemma 24. Since $\bar{A}$ is an algebra containing the constants, $P(f) \in \bar{A}$, and since $\bar{A}$ is a closed subset of $C(X)$, we have $|f| \in A$. If now f is any function in A, then $f/\|f\|$ has norm 1, and so $|f|/\|f\|$ and hence also $|f|$ belong to $\bar{A}$. Thus $\bar{A}$ contains the absolute value of each function which is in $\bar{A}$. But

$$f \vee g = \tfrac{1}{2}(f + g) + \tfrac{1}{2}|f - g|$$

and

$$f \wedge g = \tfrac{1}{2}(f + g) - \tfrac{1}{2}|f - g|.$$

Thus $\bar{A}$ is a lattice and must be $C(X)$ by Proposition 21. ∎

26. Corollary: *Every continuous function on a closed bounded set X in $\mathbf{R}^n$ can be uniformly approximated on X by a polynomial (in the coordinates).*

Proof: The set of all polynomials in the coordinate functions form an algebra containing the constants. It separates points, since given two distinct points in R^n, one of the coordinate functions takes different values on these points. Hence Theorem 25 applies. ▎

Problems

19. Let f be a continuous periodic real-valued function on $\mathbf{R}^1$ with period 2π; that is $f(x + 2\pi) = f(x)$. Show that given $\epsilon > 0$, there is a finite Fourier series φ, given by $\varphi(x) = a_0 + \sum_{n=1}^{N} (a_n \cos nx + b_n \sin nx)$, such that $|\varphi(x) - f(x)| < \epsilon$ for all x. (Hint: Note that periodic functions are really functions on the circumference of the unit circle, and that $\cos mx \cos nx = \frac{1}{2}[\cos (m + n)x - \cos (m - n)x]$, etc.)

20. Let A be an algebra of continuous real-valued functions on a compact space X, and assume that A separates the points of X. Then either $\bar{A} = C(X)$ or there is a point $p \in X$ and $\bar{A} = \{f: f \in C(X), f(p) = 0\}$.

21. Let $\mathscr{F}$ be a family of continuous real-valued functions on a compact Hausdorff space X, and suppose that $\mathscr{F}$ separates the points of X. Then every continuous real-valued function on X can be uniformly approximated by a polynomial in a finite number of functions of $\mathscr{F}$.

22. a. Let X be a topological space and A a set of real-valued continuous functions on X. Define $x \equiv y$ if $f(x) = f(y)$ for all $f \in A$. Show that $\equiv$ is an equivalence relation.

b. Let $\tilde{X}$ be the set of equivalence classes of $\equiv$ and φ the natural map of X into $\tilde{X}$. Show that for each $f \in A$ there is a unique real-valued function $\tilde{f}$ on $\tilde{X}$ such that $f = \tilde{f} \circ \varphi$.

c. Let $\tilde{X}$ have the weak topology generated by these $\tilde{f}$. Then φ is continuous.

d. If X is compact then so is $\tilde{X}$, and the functions $\tilde{f}$ in (b) are continuous.

e. Let X be a compact space and A a closed subalgebra of $C(X)$ containing the constant functions. Then there is a compact Hausdorff space $\tilde{X}$ and a mapping φ of X onto $\tilde{X}$ such that A is the set of all functions f of the form $\tilde{f} \circ \varphi$ with $\tilde{f} \in C(\tilde{X})$.

23. Let X and Y be compact spaces. Then for each continuous real-valued function f on $X \times Y$ and each $\epsilon > 0$, we can find continuous real-valued functions $g_1, \ldots, g_n$ on X and $h_1, \ldots, h_n$ on Y such that for each $\langle x, y \rangle \in X \times Y$ we have

$$|f(x, y) - \sum_{i=1}^{n} g_i(x)h_i(y)| < \epsilon.$$

24. The Weierstrass theorem, which states that a continuous function on a cube in $\mathbf{R}^n$ can be uniformly approximated by a polynomial, can be proved directly by giving an integral formula for the approximating polynomials.[1] Show that this special case implies the general Stone-Weierstrass theorem by showing that the functions of norm 1 in the algebra $\mathcal{A}$ give a mapping of X into the infinite dimensional cube $\mathsf{X} I_f : f \in \mathcal{A}, \|f\| = 1$. Use the Tietze extension theorem (Problem 8.23) and Problem 11 to show that each continuous function on the image of X can be approximated by a polynomial in (a finite number of) the coordinate functions.

The Stone-Weierstrass theorem gives precise information about approximation by functions in an algebra of continuous functions. A natural question is the nature of functions that can be approximated by a ring of real-valued continuous functions, that is to say when we no longer postulate the possibility of multiplying by arbitrary real numbers. The next three problems give some results in this direction.

25. Let I be the interval $[-1, 1]$ in $\mathbf{R}^1$ and f a continuous real-valued function on I such that $f(-1)$, $f(0)$, and $f(1)$ are integers and $f(1) = f(-1)$ mod 2. Then given $\epsilon > 0$, there is a polynomial P with integral coefficients such that $|f(x) - P(x)| < \epsilon$ for all $x \in I$. Hints:

a. Let φ be the polynomial defined by $\varphi(x) = x + x(1 - 2x)(1 - x)$. Then φ is a monotone increasing function whose fixed points are $0, \frac{1}{2}$, and 1.

b. Choose $\epsilon > 0$. Then some iterate φ_n of φ is a polynomial with integral coefficients which is monotone increasing on $[0, 1]$ and such that $|\varphi_n(x) - \frac{1}{2}| < \epsilon$ for $x \in [\epsilon, 1 - \epsilon]$.

c. Given a number α, $0 < \alpha < 1$, and any $\epsilon > 0$, then there is a polynomial ψ with integral coefficients (and no constant term) such that $0 \le \psi(x) \le 1$ in $[0, 1]$ and $|\psi(x) - \alpha| < \epsilon$ for all x in $[\epsilon, 1 - \epsilon]$.

[1] See for example Courant-Hilbert, *Mathematische Physik*, Bd. I, p. 55–7.

d. Let P be a polynomial with integral coefficients, and suppose that $P(-1) = P(0) = P(1) = 0$. Let β be any real number. Then for each $\epsilon > 0$, βP can be uniformly approximated to within ϵ on $[-1, 1]$ by a polynomial having integral coefficients and no constant term.

e. Reduce the statement of the problem to (d) and the Stone-Weierstrass theorem.

26. a. Let X be a set and R a ring of real-valued functions on X. Let $\bar{R}$ be the ring of all real-valued functions which can be uniformly approximated by functions in R. Then if $f \in \bar{R}$, and $\sup_X |f(x)| < 1$, then $cf \in \bar{R}$ for each real number c.

b. Let X be a compact Hausdorff space and R a ring of continuous real-valued functions on X such that $1 \in R$, and for each pair of distinct points x and y there is a function f in R such that $f(x) \neq f(y)$, and $|f(z)| < 1$ for all $z \in X$. Then every continuous real-valued function on X can be uniformly approximated by functions in R.

27. a. The statement of Problem 25 can be improved slightly. Show, for example, that we may take the interval I to be $[-\sqrt{2}, \sqrt{2}]$. [The polynomial $x^2 - 1$ has absolute value at most 1 on I. Apply Problem 26(b).]

b. Show that we cannot take I in Problem 25 to be $[-2, 2]$. (Hint: If P is a polynomial with integral coefficients,

$$\frac{1}{\pi}\int_{-2}^{2} P(x)(4 - x^2)^{1/2}\, dx \text{ is an integer.})$$

7 THE ASCOLI THEOREM

It is often useful in analysis to know conditions under which a sequence of functions has a subsequence which is convergent in some sense. The following notion plays a central role in such questions: a family $\mathfrak{F}$ of functions from a topological space X to a metric space $\langle Y, \sigma\rangle$ is called **equicontinuous** at the point $x \in X$ if given $\epsilon > 0$ there is an open set O containing x such that $\sigma[f(x), f(y)] < \epsilon$ for all y in O and all $f \in \mathfrak{F}$. The family is said to be equicontinuous on X if it is equicontinuous at each point x in X. We are going to show that if $\langle f_n\rangle$ is a sequence from an equicontinuous family of functions, and if at each point x of X there is a convergent subsequence of

$\langle f_n(x)\rangle$, then $\langle f_n\rangle$ has a subsequence which converges uniformly on each compact subset of X. We begin with several lemmas.

27. Lemma: *Let $\langle f_n\rangle$ be a sequence of mappings of a countable set D into a topological space Y such that for each $x \in D$ the closure of the set $\{f_n(x): 0 \leq n < \infty\}$ is sequentially compact. Then there is a subsequence $\langle f_{n_k}\rangle$ which converges for each x in D.*

Proof: Let $D = \{x_k\}$. By the sequential compactness of the closure of $\{f_n(x_1): 0 \leq n < \infty\}$ we can pick a subsequence $\langle f_{1n}\rangle$ of $\langle f_n\rangle$ such that $\langle f_{1n}(x)\rangle$ converges. We can now pick a subsequence $\langle f_{2n}\rangle$ of $\langle f_{1n}\rangle$ such that $\langle f_{2n}(x_2)\rangle$ converges. Continuing in this fashion we obtain a subsequence $\langle f_{jn}\rangle$ convergent on x_j. Consider the "diagonal" sequence $\langle f_{nn}\rangle$. We have $\langle f_{nn}\rangle_{n=j}^{\infty}$ a subsequence of $\langle f_{jn}\rangle$, and so $\langle f_{nn}(x_j)\rangle$ converges. ▎

28. Lemma: *Let $\langle f_n\rangle$ be an equicontinuous sequence of mappings from a topological space X to a complete metric space Y. If the sequences $\langle f_n(x)\rangle$ converge for each point x of a dense subset D of X, then $\langle f_n\rangle$ converges at each point of X, and the limit function is continuous.*

Proof: Given x in X and $\epsilon > 0$, we can find an open set O containing x such that $\sigma[f_n(x), f_n(y)] < \epsilon/3$ for all y in O. Since D is dense, there must be a point $y \in D \cap O$, and since $\langle f_n(y)\rangle$ converges, it must be a Cauchy sequence, and we may choose N so large that $\sigma[f_n(y), f_m(y)] < \epsilon/3$ for all $m, n \geq N$. Then

$$\begin{aligned}\sigma[f_n(x), f_m(x)] &\leq \sigma[f_n(x), f_n(y)] + \sigma[f_n(y), f_m(y)] + \sigma[f_m(x), f_m(y)]\\ &< \epsilon\end{aligned}$$

for all $m, n \geq N$. Thus $\langle f_n(x)\rangle$ is a Cauchy sequence, and converges by the completeness of Y.

Let $f(x) = \lim f_n(x)$. To see that f is continuous at x, let $\epsilon > 0$ be given. By equicontinuity there is an open set O containing x such that $\sigma[f_n(x), f_n(y)] < \epsilon$ for all n and all y in O. Hence for all y in O we have

$$\sigma[f(x), f(y)] = \lim \sigma[f_n(x), f_n(y)] \leq \epsilon,$$

and f is continuous at x. ▎

29. Lemma: *Let K be a compact topological space and $\langle f_n\rangle$ an equicontinuous sequence of functions to a metric space Y which converge* *at each point of K to a function f. Then $\langle f_n \rangle$ converges to f uniformly on K.*

Proof: Choose $\epsilon > 0$. By equicontinuity each x in K is contained in an open set O_x such that $\sigma[f_n(x), f_n(y)] < \epsilon/3$ for all y in O and all n. From this it follows that also $\sigma[f(x), f(y)] \le \epsilon/3$ for all y in O. By the compactness of K there is a finite collection $\{O_{x_1}, \ldots, O_{x_k}\}$ of these sets which covers K. Choose N so large that for all $n \ge N$ we have $\sigma[f_n(x_i), f(x_i)] < \epsilon/3$ for each x_i corresponding to this finite collection. Then for any y in K there is an $i \le k$ such that $y \in O_{x_i}$. Hence

$$\sigma[f_n(y), f(y)] \le \sigma[f_n(y), f_n(x_i)] + \sigma[f_n(x_i), f(x_i)] + \sigma[f(y), f(x_i)] < \epsilon$$

for $n \ge N$. Thus $\langle f_n \rangle$ converges to f uniformly on K. ▌

These three lemmas taken together imply the following theorem:

30. Theorem (Ascoli): *Let $\mathfrak{F}$ be an equicontinuous family of functions from a separable metric space X to a metric space Y. Let $\langle f_n \rangle$ be a sequence in $\mathfrak{F}$ such that for each x in X the closure of the set $\{f_n(x): 0 \le n < \infty\}$ is compact. Then there is a subsequence $\langle f_{n_k} \rangle$ which converges pointwise to a continuous function f, and the convergence is uniform on each compact subset of X.*

31. Corollary: *Let $\mathfrak{F}$ be an equicontinuous family of real-valued functions on a separable metric space X. Then each sequence $\langle f_n \rangle$ in $\mathfrak{F}$ which is bounded at each point (of a dense subset) has a subsequence $\langle f_{n_k} \rangle$ which converges pointwise to a continuous function, the convergence being uniform on each compact subset of X.*

Problems

28. The set of all functions from X to Y is precisely the product of X copies of Y and is often denoted by Y^X. The product topology in Y^X is called the topology of pointwise convergence.

a. Show that a sequence $\langle f_n \rangle$ of mappings of X into Y converges to f in the topology of pointwise convergence if and only if $\langle f_n(x) \rangle$ converges to $f(x)$ for each x in X.

b. Let $\mathfrak{F}$ be a family of equicontinuous functions from a topological space X to a metric space Y. Then the closure $\bar{\mathfrak{F}}$ of $\mathfrak{F}$ in the topology of pointwise convergence is also equicontinuous.

29. Let X be a space which is either locally compact, or Hausdorff and satisfies the first axiom of countability. Let $\langle f_n \rangle$ be a sequence of continuous functions from X to a metric space Y which converge to a function f uniformly on each compact subset K of X. Then f is continuous. (Hint: Use Problem 18.)

30. Let X be a separable, locally compact metric space, and $\langle Y, \sigma \rangle$ any metric space. Show that:

a. There is a countable collection $\{O_n\}$ of open subsets of X such that $\bar{O}_n$ is compact and $X = \bigcup O_n$.

b. The set of functions from X into Y becomes a metric space if we define

$$\sigma^*(f, g) = \sum 2^{-n} \sigma_n^*(f, g),$$

where

$$\sigma_n^*(f, g) = \sup_{\bar{O}_n} \frac{\sigma[f(x), g(x)]}{1 + \sigma[f(x), g(x)]}.$$

c. The sequence $\langle f_n \rangle$ converges to f uniformly on compact subsets of X if and only if $\sigma^*(f, f_n) \to 0$.

31. Let X and Y be metric spaces. A sequence $\langle f_n \rangle$ of mappings from X to Y is said to converge continuously to f at x if for each sequence $\langle x_n \rangle$ such that $x = \lim x_n$ we have $f(x) = \lim f_n(x_n)$. We say $\langle f_n \rangle$ converges continuously to f if it converges continuously at each x in X.

a. Show that if each f_n is continuous at x and if $\langle f_n \rangle$ converges continuously to f at x, then f is continuous on X.

b. Show that $\langle f_n \rangle$ converges continuously to f if and only if $\langle f_n \rangle$ converges to f uniformly on each compact subset of X.

32. A real-valued function f on $[0, 1]$ is said to be Hölder continuous of order α if there is a constant C such that $|f(x) - f(y)| \leq C|x - y|^\alpha$. Define $\|f\|_\alpha = \max|f(x)| + \sup \dfrac{|f(x) - f(y)|}{|x - y|^\alpha}$.

Show that for $0 < \alpha \leq 1$, the set of functions with $\|f\|_\alpha \leq 1$ is a compact subset of $C[0, 1]$.

10 Banach Spaces

1 INTRODUCTION

We are going to study a class of spaces which are endowed with both a topological and an algebraic structure. A set X of elements is called a **vector space** (or linear space, or linear vector space) over the reals if we have a function $+$ on $X \times X$ to X and a function $\cdot$ on $R^1 \times X$ to X which satisfy the following conditions:

1. $x + y = y + x$.
2. $(x + y) + z = x + (y + z)$.
3. There is a vector θ in X such that $x + \theta = x$ for all x in X.
4. $\lambda(x + y) = \lambda x + \lambda y$; $\lambda \in \mathbf{R}^1$, $x, y \in X$.
5. $(\lambda + \mu)x = \lambda x + \mu x$; $\lambda, \mu \in \mathbf{R}^1$, $x \in X$.
6. $\lambda(\mu x) = (\lambda\mu)x$; $\lambda, \mu \in \mathbf{R}^1$, $x \in X$.
7. $0 \cdot x = \theta$, $1 \cdot x = x$.

We call $+$ addition and $\cdot$ multiplication by scalars. It should be noted that the element θ defined in (3) is unique, for if θ' also has this property, then $\theta = \theta + \theta' = \theta' + \theta = \theta'$. The element $(-1)x$ is called the negative of x and written $-x$. We have $x + (-x) = 1 \cdot x + (-1)x = (1 - 1)x = 0 \cdot x = \theta$.

A nonnegative real-valued function $\| \ \|$ defined on a vector space is called a **norm** if

1. $\|x\| = 0 \Leftrightarrow x = \theta$.
2. $\|x + y\| \leq \|x\| + \|y\|$.
3. $\|\alpha x\| = |\alpha| \, \|x\|$.

A normed vector space becomes a metric space if we define a metric

ρ by $\rho(x, y) = \|x - y\|$. When we speak about metric properties in a normed space we are referring to this metric.

If a normed vector space is complete in this metric, it is called a Banach space. Examples of Banach spaces were given in Chapter 6. Another example is $C(X)$ the space of all continuous real-valued functions on a compact space X. We restate here Proposition 6.4, and note that the proof given in Chapter 6 is valid in any normed vector space.

1. Proposition: *A normed vector space is complete if and only if every absolutely summable sequence is summable.*

A nonempty subset S of a vector space X is a **subspace** or **linear manifold** if $\lambda_1 x_1 + \lambda_2 x_2$ belongs to S whenever x_1 and x_2 do. If S is also closed as a subset of X, then it is called a closed linear manifold. The intersection of any family of linear manifolds is a linear manifold. Hence, given a set A in X, there is always a smallest linear manifold containing A. We often denote this manifold by $\{A\}$.

If A is any set in X, we use $A + x$ to denote the set of all elements z of the form $z = x + y$, $y \in A$. The set $A + x$ is called the translate of A by x. The set λA is the set of all elements of the form λx with $x \in A$, and $A + B$ is the set of all elements of the form $x + y$ with x in A and y in B.

Problems

1. Show that if $x_n \to x$, then $\|x_n\| \to \|x\|$.

2. Two norms $\| \ \|_1$ and $\| \ \|_2$ are called equivalent if there is a positive constant K such that $K^{-1} \|x\|_1 \leq \|x\|_2 \leq K \|x\|_1$. If the norms are equivalent, then the metrics derived from them are uniformly equivalent. Show that the metrics introduced in Problem 7.10(b) for $\mathbf{R}^n$ are derived from norms for $\mathbf{R}^n$ and these norms are all equivalent.

3. Show that $+$ is a continuous function from $X \times X$ into X and that $\cdot$ is a continuous function from $R^1 \times X$ into X.

4. Show that a nonempty set M is a linear manifold if and only if $M + M = M$ and $\lambda M = M$ for each λ.

5. a. Prove that the intersection of a family of linear manifolds is a manifold.
   b. Prove that there is a smallest linear manifold $\{A\}$ containing a given set A.

c. Show that $\{A\}$ consists of all finite linear combinations of the form $\lambda_1 x_1 + \cdots + \lambda_n x_n$ with $x_i \in A$.

6. a. If M and N are linear manifolds so is $M + N$, and $M + N = \{M \cup N\}$.

b. If M is a linear manifold so is $\bar{M}$.

7. Show that the set P of all polynomials on [0, 1] is a linear manifold in $C[0, 1]$. Is it closed? Give an example of a closed linear manifold in $C[0, 1]$.

8. A linear manifold M is said to be finite dimensional if there are a finite number of elements $x_1, \cdots, x_n$ such that $M = \{x_1, \cdots, x_n\}$. Prove that every finite dimensional linear manifold in a normed vector space X must be closed.

9. Let S be the spheroid of radius one centered at θ, that is $S = \{x\colon \|x\| < 1\}$. Prove that S is open and that

$$\bar{S} = \{x\colon \|x\| \leq 1\}.$$

We call S the open unit sphere (or ball), and $\bar{S}$ the unit sphere (or ball).

10. A nonnegative real-valued function $\| \ \|$ defined on a vector space X is called a **pseudonorm** if $\|x + y\| \leq \|x\| + \|y\|$ and $\|\alpha x\| = |\alpha|\, \|x\|$. Show that the relation $x \equiv y$ defined by $\|x - y\| = 0$ is an equivalence relation compatible with addition and multiplication by scalars, and that if $x \equiv y$ then $\|x\| = \|y\|$. Let X' be the set of equivalence classes of X under $\equiv$. Then X' becomes a normed vector space if we define $\alpha x' + \beta y'$ as the (unique) equivalence class which contains $\alpha x + \beta y$ for $x \in x'$ and $y \in y'$ and define $\|x'\| = \|x\|$ for $x \in x'$. The mapping φ of X onto X' which takes each element of X into the equivalence class to which it belongs is a homomorphism (called the natural homomorphism) of X onto X'. What is the kernel of φ? Illustrate this procedure with the L^p spaces on [0, 1].

11. Let X be a normed linear space (with norm $\| \ \|$) and M a linear manifold in X. Show that $\|x\|_1 = \inf_{m \in M} \|x - m\|$ defines a pseudonorm on X. Let X' be the normed linear space derived from X and the pseudonorm $\| \ \|_1$ using the process described in Problem 10. The natural map φ of X onto X' has kernel $\bar{M}$. Prove that φ takes open sets into open sets. The space X' is usually denoted by $X/\bar{M}$ and called the quotient space of X modulo $\bar{M}$.

12. Show that, if X is complete and M is a closed linear manifold of X, then X/M is also complete. (Hint: Use Proposition 1.)

2 LINEAR OPERATORS

A mapping A of a vector space X into a vector space Y is called a linear mapping or a linear operator if

$$A(\alpha_1 x_1 + \alpha_2 x_2) = \alpha_1 A x_1 + \alpha_2 A x_2$$

for all x_1, x_2 in X and all real α_1, α_2. If X and Y are normed vector spaces, we call a linear operator A bounded if there is a constant M such that for all x we have $\|Ax\| \le M \|x\|$. We call the least such M the norm of A and denote it by $\|A\|$. Thus

$$\|A\| = \sup_{\substack{x \varepsilon X \\ x \neq 0}} \frac{\|Ax\|}{\|x\|}.$$

Since $A(\alpha x) = \alpha A x$, we have also

$$\|A\| = \sup_{\|x\|=1} \|Ax\| = \sup_{\|x\| \le 1} \|Ax\|.$$

The following proposition relates the notions of boundedness and continuity for linear operators:

2. Proposition: *A bounded linear operator is uniformly continuous. If a linear operator is continuous at one point, it is bounded.*

Proof: Suppose A is bounded. Then

$$\|Ax_1 - Ax_2\| \le \|A\| \cdot \|x_1 - x_2\| < \epsilon$$

for all x_1 and x_2 in X with $\|x_1 - x_2\| < \epsilon / \|A\|$. Thus A is uniformly continuous.

Suppose now that A is a linear operator which is continuous at x_0. Then there is a $\delta > 0$ such that $\|Ax - Ax_0\| < 1$ for all x such that $\|x - x_0\| < \delta$. For any z in X, set $w = \eta z / \|z\|$, where $0 < \eta < \delta$. Then

$$\frac{\eta}{\|z\|} Az = Aw = A(w + x_0) - A(x_0),$$

and

$$\frac{\eta}{\|z\|} \|Az\| \le \|A(w + x_0) - A(x_0)\| < 1,$$

since $\|w + x_0 - x_0\| = \|w\| = \eta < \delta$. Consequently, $\|Az\| \le \eta^{-1} \|z\|$, and A is bounded. ❙

3. Proposition: *The space $\mathcal{B}$ of all bounded linear operators from a normed vector space X to a Banach space Y is itself a Banach space.*

Proof: If A and B are in $\mathcal{B}$, we define $\alpha A + \beta B$ by $(\alpha A + \beta B)x = \alpha Ax + \beta Bx$, it is easily seen to be a linear operator. Now

$$\|\lambda A\| = \sup_{\|x\|=1} \|\lambda Ax\| = |\lambda| \sup_{\|x\|=1} \|Ax\| = |\lambda| \, \|A\|,$$

and

$$\|A + B\| = \sup_{\|x\|=1} \|Ax + Bx\| \leq \sup_{\|x\|=1} \|Ax\| + \|Bx\| \leq \|A\| + \|B\|.$$

Thus any linear combination of two bounded linear operators is again a bounded linear operator. If $\|A\| = 0$, then

$$\|Ax\| \leq \|A\| \cdot \|x\| = 0,$$

and so $Ax = \theta$. Thus $\|A\| = 0$ only for the operator 0 which maps every x into θ. Thus $\| \;\|$ satisfies all the requirements of a norm and we have only to show that if Y is complete so is $\mathcal{B}$.

Let $\langle A_n \rangle$ be a Cauchy sequence from $\mathcal{B}$. For each $x \in X$ we have $\|A_n x - A_m x\| < \|A_n - A_m\| \cdot \|x\|$, and so $\langle A_n x \rangle$ is a Cauchy sequence in Y, and so must converge to an element y in Y. Call this element Ax. It follows from the definition of Ax that $A(\lambda x) = \lambda Ax$ and $A(x_1 + x_2) = Ax_1 + Ax_2$.

In order to show that the linear operator A is bounded, we observe that, given $\epsilon > 0$, there is an N such that for all $m, n \geq N$ we have $\|A_n - A_m\| < \epsilon$. Hence $\|A_n\| \leq \|A_N\| + \epsilon$ for all $n \geq N$, and so

$$\|Ax\| = \lim \|A_n x\| < (\|A_N\| + \epsilon) \, \|x\|.$$

Thus A is bounded. For each x in X we have

$$\begin{aligned} \|A_n x - Ax\| &= \lim_{m \to \infty} \|A_n x - A_m x\| \\ &\leq \lim_{m \to \infty} \|A_n - A_m\| \, \|x\| \\ &\leq \epsilon \, \|x\| \end{aligned}$$

for all $n \geq N$. Thus for $n \geq N$,

$$\|A_n - A\| = \sup_{\|x\|=1} \|(A_n - A)x\| \leq \epsilon.$$

Thus $A_n \to A$ and $\mathcal{B}$ is complete. ▍

Problems

13. Show that if $A_n \to A$ and $x_n \to x$ then $A_n x_n \to Ax$.

14. The kernel of an operator A is the set $\{x : Ax = \theta\}$. Prove that the kernel of a linear operator is a linear manifold and that the kernel of a continuous operator is closed.

15. a. Let X be a normed linear space and M a closed linear manifold. Then the natural homomorphism φ of X onto X/M has norm 1.

b. Let X and Y be normed linear spaces and A a bounded linear operator from X into Y whose kernel is M. Then there is a unique bounded linear operator B from X/M into Y such that $A = B \circ \varphi$. Moreover $\|A\| = \|B\|$.

16. Let X be a metric space, and let Y be the space consisting of those real-valued functions f on X which vanish at a fixed point $x_0 \in X$ and satisfy $|f(x) - f(y)| \leq M\rho(x, y)$ for some M (depending on f). Define $\|f\| = \sup \dfrac{|f(x) - f(y)|}{\rho(x, y)}$. Then Y is a normed linear space. For each $x \in X$, the functional F_x defined by $F_x(f) = f(x)$ is a bounded linear functional on Y, and $\|F_x - F_y\| = \rho(x, y)$. Thus X is isometric to a subset of the space Y^* of bounded linear operators from Y to $\mathbf{R}^1$. Since Y^* is complete by Proposition 3, the closure of this subset gives a completion of Y, and we have another proof of Theorem 7.9.

3 LINEAR FUNCTIONALS AND THE HAHN-BANACH THEOREM

A linear functional on a vector space X is a linear operator from X to the space $\mathbf{R}^1$ of real numbers. Thus a linear functional is a real-valued function f on X such that $f(\alpha x + \beta y) = \alpha f(x) + \beta f(y)$. The first question with which we shall be concerned is that of extending a linear functional from a subspace to the whole space X in such a manner that various properties of the functional are preserved. The principal result in this direction is the following:

4. Theorem (Hahn-Banach): *Let p be a real-valued function defined on the vector space X satisfying $p(x + y) \leq p(x) + p(y)$ and $p(\alpha x) = \alpha p(x)$ for each $\alpha \geq 0$. Suppose that f is a linear functional defined on a subspace S and that $f(s) \leq p(s)$ for all s in S. Then there* *is a linear functional F defined on X such that $F(x) \leq p(x)$ for all x, and $F(s) = f(s)$ for all s in S.*

Proof: Consider all linear functionals g defined on a subspace of X and satisfying $g(x) \leq p(x)$ whenever $g(x)$ is defined. This set is partially ordered by setting $g_1 \prec g_2$ if g_2 is an extension of g_1, that is if the domain of g_1 is contained in the domain of g_2 and $g_1 = g_2$ on the domain of g_1.

By the Hausdorff maximal principle there is a maximal linearly ordered subfamily $\{g_\alpha\}$ which contains the given functional f. We define a functional F on the union of the domains of the g_α by setting $F(x) = g_\alpha(x)$ if x is in the domain of g_α. Since $\{g_\alpha\}$ is linearly ordered, this definition is independent of the g_α chosen. The domain of F is a subspace and F is a linear functional, for if x and y are in the domain of F, then $x \in$ domain g_α and $y \in$ domain g_β for some α, β. By the linear ordering of $\{g_\alpha\}$, we have either $g_\alpha \prec g_\beta$ or $g_\beta \prec g_\alpha$, say the former. Then x and y are in the domain of g_β, and so $\lambda x + \mu y$ is in the domain of g_β and so in the domain of F, and $F(\lambda x + \mu y) = g_\beta(\lambda x + \mu y) = \lambda g_\beta(x) + \mu g_\beta(y) = \lambda F(x) + \mu F(y)$. Thus F is an extension of f. Moreover, F is a maximal extension. For if G is any extension of F, $g_\alpha \prec F \prec G$ implies that G must belong to $\{g_\alpha\}$ by the maximality of $\{g_\alpha\}$. Hence $G \prec F$, and so $G = F$.

It remains only to show that F is defined for all $x \in X$. Since F is maximal, this will follow if we can show that each g which is defined on a proper subspace T of X and satisfies $g(t) \leq p(t)$ has a proper extension h.

Let y be an element in $X \sim T$. We shall show that g may be extended to the subspace U spanned by T and y, that is, to the subspace consisting of elements of the form $\lambda y + t$ with $t \in T$. If h is an extension of g, we must have

$$h(\lambda y + t) = \lambda h(y) + h(t) = \lambda h(y) + g(t),$$

and so h is defined as soon as we specify $h(y)$.

For t_1, $t_2 \in T$ we have

$$g(t_1) + g(t_2) = g(t_1 + t_2) \leq p(t_1 + t_2) \leq p(t_1 - y) + p(t_2 + y).$$

Hence

$$-p(t_1 - y) + g(t_1) \leq p(t_2 + y) - g(t_2),$$

and so

$$\sup_{t \varepsilon T} [-p(t - y) + g(t)] \leq \inf_{t \varepsilon T} [p(t + y) - g(t)].$$

Define $h(y) = \alpha$, where α is a real number such that

$$\sup [-p(t - y) + g(t)] \leq \alpha \leq \inf [p(t + y) - g(t)] .$$

We must now show that

$$h(\lambda y + t) = \lambda\alpha + g(t) \leq p(\lambda y + t).$$

If $\lambda > 0$, then

$$\begin{aligned} \lambda\alpha + g(t) &= \lambda[\alpha + g(t/\lambda)] \\ &\leq \lambda[\{p(t/\lambda + y) - g(t/\lambda)\} + g(t/\lambda)] \\ &= \lambda p(t/\lambda + y) = p(t + \lambda y). \end{aligned}$$

If $\lambda = -\mu < 0$, then

$$\begin{aligned} -\alpha\mu + g(t) &= \mu(-\alpha + g(t/\mu)) \\ &\leq \mu(\{p(t/\mu - y) - g(t/\mu)\} + g(t/\mu)) \\ &= \mu p(t/\mu - y) = p(t - \mu y). \end{aligned}$$

Thus $h(\lambda y + t) \leq p(\lambda y + t)$ for all λ, and h is a proper extension of g. ∎

The Hahn-Banach theorem has a wide range of applications, many of them involving a clever choice of the subadditive function p. Propositions 6, 7, and Theorem 19 are applications of this sort. The following proposition is a generalization of the Hahn-Banach theorem which is useful in certain applications (cf. Problems 20 and 21). By an Abelian semigroup of linear operators on a vector space X we mean a collection G of linear operators from X to X such that if A and B are in G, then $AB = BA$ and AB is in G.

5. Proposition: *Let X, S, p, and f be as in Theorem* 4, *and let G be an Abelian semigroup of linear operators on X such that for every A in G we have $p(Ax) \leq p(x)$ for all x in X, while for each s in S we have As in S and $f(As) = f(s)$. Then there is an extension F of f to a linear functional on X such that $F(x) \leq p(x)$ and $F(Ax) = F(x)$ for all x in X.*

Proof: Define a function q on X by setting

$$q(x) = \inf \frac{1}{n} p(A_1x + \cdots + A_nx)$$

where the inf is taken over all finite sequences $\langle A_1, \ldots, A_n \rangle$ of G. We clearly have $q(x) \leq p(x)$ and $q(\alpha x) = \alpha q(x)$ for $\alpha \geq 0$. For any x and y in X and any $\epsilon > 0$, we can choose $\langle A_1, \ldots, A_n \rangle$ and $\langle B_1, \ldots, B_m \rangle$ so that

$$\frac{1}{n} p(A_1 x + \cdots + A_n x) < q(x) + \epsilon$$

and

$$\frac{1}{m} p(B_1 y + \cdots + B_m y) < q(y) + \epsilon.$$

Then

$$\begin{aligned} q(x + y) &\leq \frac{1}{nm} p\left(\sum_{i=1}^{n} \sum_{j=1}^{m} A_i B_j (x + y)\right) \\ &\leq \frac{1}{nm} p\left(\sum_{j=1}^{m} B_j \left(\sum_{i=1}^{n} A_i x\right)\right) + \frac{1}{nm} p\left(\sum_{i=1}^{n} A_i \left(\sum_{j=1}^{m} B_j y\right)\right) \\ &\leq \frac{1}{n} p\left(\sum_{i=1}^{n} A_i x\right) + \frac{1}{m} p\left(\sum_{j=1}^{m} B_j y\right) \\ &< q(x) + q(y) + 2\epsilon. \end{aligned}$$

Since ϵ is arbitrary, $q(x + y) \leq q(x) + q(y)$.

For s in S,

$$f(s) = \frac{1}{n} f(A_1 s + \cdots + A_n s) \leq \frac{1}{n} p(A_1 s + \cdots + A_n s).$$

Hence $f(s) \leq q(s)$, and we may apply Theorem 4 with p replaced by q to obtain an extension F of f to all X such that $F(x) \leq q(x) \leq p(x)$. It remains only to show that $F(Ax) = F(x)$. Now

$$\begin{aligned} q(x - Ax) &\leq \frac{1}{n} p((x - Ax) + A(x - Ax) + \cdots + A^n(x - Ax)) \\ &= \frac{1}{n} p(x - A^{n+1}x) \leq \frac{1}{n} [p(x) + p(-x)]. \end{aligned}$$

Thus $q(x - Ax) \leq 0$. Since

$$F(x) - F(Ax) = F(x - Ax) \leq q(x - Ax) \leq 0,$$

we have $F(x) \leq F(Ax)$, and applying this to $-x$, we get $F(x) = F(Ax)$. ∎

6. Proposition: *Let x be an element in a normed vector space X. Then there is a bounded linear functional f on X such that $f(x) = \|f\| \, \|x\|$.*

Proof: Let S be the subspace consisting of all multiples of x, and define f on S by $f(\lambda x) = \lambda \|x\|$, and set $p(y) = \|y\|$. Then by the Hahn-Banach theorem there is an extension of f to be a linear functional on X such that $f(y) \leq \|y\|$. Since $f(-y) \leq \|y\|$, we have $\|f\| \leq 1$. Also $f(x) = \|x\| \leq \|f\| \cdot \|x\|$. Thus $\|f\| = 1$ and $f(x) = \|f\| \cdot \|x\|$. ∎

7. Proposition: *Let T be a linear subspace of a normed linear space X and y an element of X whose distance to T is at least δ, i.e. an element such that $\|y - t\| \geq \delta$ for all $t \in T$. Then there is a bounded linear functional f on X with $\|f\| \leq 1, f(y) = \delta$, and such that $f(t) = 0$ for all t in T.*

Proof: Let S be the subspace spanned by T and y, that is the subspace consisting of all elements of the form $\alpha y + t$ with $t \in T$. Define $f(\alpha y + t) = \alpha\delta$. Then f is a linear functional on S, and since $\|\alpha y + t\| = |\alpha| \cdot \|y + t/\alpha\| \geq \alpha\delta$, we have $f(s) \leq \|s\|$ on S. By the Hahn-Banach theorem we may extend f to all of X so that $f(x) \leq \|x\|$. But this implies $\|f\| \leq 1$. By the definition of f on S, we have $f(t) = 0$ for $t \in T$ and $f(y) = \delta$. ∎

The space of bounded linear functionals on a normed space X is called the **dual** (or conjugate) of X and is denoted by X^*. Since $\mathbf{R}^1$ is complete, the dual X^* of any normed space X is a Banach space by Proposition 3. Two normed vector spaces are said to be isometrically isomorphic if there is a one-to-one linear mapping of one of them onto the other which preserves norms. From an abstract point of view, isometrically isomorphic spaces are identical, the isomorphism merely amounting to a renaming of the elements. In Chapter 6 we saw that the dual of L^p was (isometrically isomorphic) to L^q for $1 \leq p < \infty$ and that there was a natural representation of the bounded linear functionals on L^p by elements of L^q.

We are now in a position to show that a similar representation does not hold for bounded linear functionals on $L^\infty[0, 1]$. We note that $C[0, 1]$ is a closed subspace of $L^\infty[0, 1]$. Let f be that linear functional on $C[0, 1]$ which assigns to each x in $C[0, 1]$ the value $x(0)$ of x at 0. It has norm 1 on C, and so can be extended to a bounded linear functional F on $L^\infty[0, 1]$. Now there is no y in $L^1[0, 1]$ such that $F(x) = \int_0^1 xy\, dt$ for all x in C, for let $\langle x_n \rangle$ be a sequence of continuous functions on [0, 1] which are bounded by 1, have $x_n(0) = 1$ and such that $x_n(t) \to 0$ for all $t \neq 0$. Then for each $y \in L^1$, $\int x_n y \to 0$, while $F(x_n) = 1$.

If we consider the dual X^{**} of X^*, then to each x in X there corresponds an element φx in X^{**} defined by $(\varphi x)(f) = f(x)$. We have $\|\varphi x\| = \sup_{\|f\|=1} f(x)$. Since $f(x) \leq \|f\| \, \|x\|$, we have $\|\varphi x\| \leq \|x\|$, while by Proposition 6 we have an f of norm 1 with $f(x) = \|x\|$. Hence $\|\varphi x\| = \|x\|$. Since φ is clearly a linear mapping, φ is an isometric isomorphism of X onto some linear subspace $\varphi[X]$ of X^{**}. The mapping φ is called the natural isomorphism of X into X^{**}, and if $\varphi[X] = X^{**}$ we say that X is reflexive. Thus L^p for $1 < p < \infty$ is reflexive, while L^∞ and L^1 are not.

By Proposition 3, the space X^{**} is complete, and so the closure $\overline{\varphi[X]}$ in X^{**} must be complete by Proposition 7.14. Thus each normed vector space is isometrically isomorphic to a dense subset of a Banach space.

Before closing this section, we add a word about the Hahn-Banach theorem for complex vector spaces. A complex vector space is a vector space in which we allow multiplication by complex scalars. We have the following extension of Theorem 4 to the complex case:

8. Theorem: *Let X be a complex vector space, S a linear subspace, p a real-valued function on X such that $p(x + y) \leq p(x) + p(y)$ and $p(\alpha x) = |\alpha| \, p(x)$. Let f be a (complex) linear functional on S such that $|f(s)| \leq p(s)$ for all s in S. Then there is a linear functional F defined on X such that $F(s) = f(s)$ for s in S and $|F(x)| \leq p(x)$ for all x in X.*

Proof: We first note that X can be considered as a real vector space if we simply ignore the possibility of multiplying by complex constants. A mapping F from X to the complex numbers which is linear in the real sense is linear in the complex sense if and only if $F(ix) = iF(x)$ for each x. On S define g and h by taking $g(s)$ to be the real part of $f(s)$ and $h(s)$ the imaginary part. Then g and h are linear in the real sense and $f = g + ih$. Since f is linear in the complex sense, $g(is) + ih(is) = f(is) = if(s) = ig(s) - h(s)$, and we see that $h(s) = -g(is)$.

Since $g(s) \leq |f(s)| \leq p(s)$, we can extend g to a functional G on X which is linear in the real sense and satisfies $G(x) \leq p(x)$. Let

$F(x) = G(x) - iG(ix)$. Then $F(s) = f(s)$ for s in S. Since $F(ix) = G(ix) - iG(-x) = i[G(x) - iG(ix)]$, we have F linear in the complex sense. For any x, choose ω to be a complex number such that $|\omega| = 1$ and $\omega F(x) = |F(x)|$. Then $|F(x)| = \omega F(x) = F(\omega x) \leq p(\omega x) = p(x)$. ∎

Problems

17. Show that a linear functional f on a normed linear space is bounded if and only if its kernel is closed. (The kernel of f is $\{x : f(x) = 0\}$.)

18. Let T be a linear subspace of a normed linear space X, and y a given element of X. Show that $\inf_{t \in T} \|y - t\| = \sup \{f(y) : \|f\| = 1, f(t) = 0 \text{ all } t \in T\}$.

19. Prove Proposition 7 by taking S to be the subspace consisting of multiples of y, $f(\lambda y) = \lambda\delta$, and $p(x) = \inf_{t \in T} \|x - t\|$.

20. Let l^∞ be the space of all bounded sequences. Use Proposition 5 to show that there is a linear functional F on l^∞ with the following properties:

i. $\underline{\lim}\ \xi_n \leq F[\langle \xi_n \rangle] \leq \overline{\lim}\ \xi_n$.

ii. $F[\langle \xi_n + \eta_n \rangle] = F[\langle \xi_n \rangle] + F[\langle \eta_n \rangle]$.

iii. $F[\langle \alpha\xi_n \rangle] = \alpha F[\langle \xi_n \rangle]$.

iv. If $\eta_n = \xi_{n+1}$, then $F[\langle \eta_n \rangle] = F[\langle \xi_n \rangle]$.

The functional F is called a *Banach limit* and is often denoted by LIM.

21. Use Proposition 5 to show that there is a set function μ defined for all bounded sets of $\mathbf{R}^1$ such that

i. If $A \cap B = \varnothing$, $\mu(A \cup B) = \mu A + \mu B$.

ii. $\mu(A + t) = \mu A$.

iii. If $A \subset B$, $\mu A \leq \mu B$.

iv. If A is Lebesgue measurable, then μA is the Lebesgue measure of A.

(Hint: It is easier to work with integrals than sets.)

22. Let X be a vector space and P a subset of X such that $x, y \in P$ implies $x + y \in P$ and $\alpha x \in P$ for $\alpha > 0$. Define a partial order in X by defining $x \leq y$ to mean $y - x \in P$. A linear functional f on X is said to be positive (with respect to P) if $f(x) \geq 0$ for all $x \in P$. Let S be any subspace of X with the property that for each $x \in X$ there is an $s \in S$ with $x \leq s$. Then each positive linear functional on S can be extended to a positive linear functional on X. (Hint: The transfinite part of the proof is the same as that for the Hahn-Banach theorem. The possibility of extending a functional to a space containing one more element is even simpler than for the Hahn-Banach theorem.)

23. Let f be a mapping of the unit sphere $S = \{x : \|x\| \leq 1\}$ into $\mathbf{R}^1$ such that $f(\alpha x + \beta y) = \alpha f(x) + \beta f(y)$ whenever x, y and $\alpha x + \beta y$ are in S. Show that f may be extended to all of X so that it is a linear functional.

4 THE CLOSED GRAPH THEOREM

A continuous linear transformation A of a Banach space X onto a Banach space Y is called a *homomorphism* if it is an open mapping; that is, if it takes open sets into open sets. Thus a one-to-one homomorphism of X onto Y is an isomorphism, that is it has a continuous inverse. In this section we shall show that all continuous linear transformations are homomorphisms and use this result to prove the continuity of a number of transformations. We begin by establishing a lemma.

9. Lemma: *Let A be a continuous linear transformation of the Banach space X onto the Banach space Y. Then the image by A of the unit sphere in X contains a sphere about the origin in Y.*

Proof: Let $S_n = \{x : \|x\| < 1/2^n\}$. Since A is onto and

$$X = \bigcup_{k=1}^{\infty} kS_1,$$

we have

$$Y = \bigcup_{k=1}^{\infty} kA(S_1).$$

But Y is a complete metric space, and so is not of first category in itself. Consequently $A(S_1)$ cannot be nowhere dense, and $\overline{A(S_1)}$ contains some sphere, say

$$\{y : \|y - p\| < \eta\}.$$

Then $\overline{A(S_1)} - p$ contains the sphere

$$\{y : \|y\| < \eta\}.$$

But

$$\overline{A(S_1)} - p \subset \overline{A(S_1)} - \overline{A(S_1)} \subset 2\overline{A(S_1)} = \overline{A(S_0)}\ .$$

Thus $\overline{A(S_0)}$ contains a sphere about the origin of radius η and so by the linearity of A, $\overline{A(S_n)}$ contains a sphere about the origin of radius $\eta/2^n$.

We now proceed to show that $A(S_0)$ contains a sphere of radius $\eta/2$ about the origin. Let y be an arbitrary point of Y with $\|y\| < \eta/2$. Since $y \in \overline{A(S_1)}$, we can choose $x_1 \in S_1$ such that

$$\|y - A(x_1)\| < \eta/4.$$

Similarly, we may choose $x_2 \in S_2$ such that

$$\|y - A(x_1) - A(x_2)\| < \eta/8,$$

and we continue so that we choose $x_n \in S_n$ with

$$\left\| y - \sum_{k=1}^{n} A(x_k) \right\| < \eta/2^{n+1}.$$

Since $\|x_k\| < 1/2^k$, $\sum_{k=1}^{\infty} x_k$ is absolutely convergent and $x = \sum_{k=1}^{\infty} x_k$ belongs to S_0. Moreover,

$$A(x) = A\left(\sum_{k=1}^{\infty} x_k \right) = \sum_{k=1}^{\infty} A(x_k) = y.$$

Thus $y \in A(S_0)$ and so

$$\{y : \|y\| < \eta/2\} \subset A(S_0). \ \blacksquare$$

10. Proposition: *A continuous linear transformation A of a Banach space X onto a Banach space Y is a homomorphism. Thus in particular, if A is one-to-one, it is an isomorphism.*

Proof: Let O be an arbitrary open set of X, and y any point of $A[O]$. Then there is some $x \in O$ such that $y = A(x)$. Since O is open there is a sphere S containing x and contained in O. But Lemma 9 states that $A(S - x)$ must contain a sphere about the origin or that $A(S)$ must contain a sphere about y. Thus y is contained in a sphere which is contained in $A[O]$, and so $A[O]$ is open. $\blacksquare$

11. Proposition: *Let X be a linear vector space which is complete in each of the norms* $\| \ \|$ *and* $|||\ |||$, *and suppose there is a constant C such that*

$$\|x\| \le C\,|||x|||$$

for all $x \in X$. *Then the norms are equivalent. That is to say there is a second constant* C' *such that*

$$|||x||| \le C'\,\|x\|$$

for all $x \in X$.

Proof: The identity map of $(X, |||\ |||)$ onto $(X, \|\ \|)$ is a one-to-one continuous linear transformation and so must be an isomorphism by Proposition 10. Therefore the inverse mapping must be bounded. ▌

12. Theorem (Closed Graph Theorem): *Let A be a linear transformation on a Banach space X to a Banach space Y. Suppose that A has the property that whenever $\langle x_n \rangle$ is a sequence in X which converges to some point x and $\langle Ax_n \rangle$ converges in Y to a point y then $y = Ax$. Then A is continuous.*

Proof: Define a new norm in X by

$$|||x||| = \|x\| + \|Ax\|.$$

Then X is complete in the norm $|||\ |||$. For if $|||x_p - x_q||| \to 0$, then $\|x_p - x_q\| \to 0$ and $\|Ax_p - Ax_q\| \to 0$. Hence by the completeness of X and Y we have $x \in X$ and $y \in Y$ such that $\|x_p - x\| \to 0$ and $\|Ax_p - y\| \to 0$. By the hypothesis of our theorem $y = Ax$. Hence $|||x_p - x||| \to 0$, and X is complete with respect to $|||\ |||$. But now Proposition 11 applies, and there is a C' such that

$$\|x\| + \|Ax\| \leq C' \|x\|.$$

Thus

$$\|Ax\| \leq C' \|x\|,$$

and A is bounded. ▌

The graph of a mapping of X into Y is just the set of all $\langle x, Ax \rangle$ in $X \times Y$. The hypothesis of Theorem 12 merely states that the graph of A is closed.

Another consequence of the theory of category is the following proposition which is known as the principle of uniform boundedness.

13. Proposition: *Let X be a Banach space and $\mathfrak{F}$ a family of bounded linear operators from X to a normed space Y. Suppose that for each x in X there is a constant M_x such that $\|Tx\| \leq M_x$ for all T in $\mathfrak{F}$. Then the operators in $\mathfrak{F}$ are uniformly bounded; that is there is a constant M such that $\|T\| \leq M$ for all T in $\mathfrak{F}$.*

Proof: For each T the function f defined by $f(x) = \|Tx\|$ is a real-valued continuous function on X. Since the family of these functions is bounded at each x in X and X is complete, there is by Theorem 7.17 an open set O in X on which these functions are uniformly bounded. Thus there is a constant M' such that $\|Tx\| \leq M'$

for all $x \in O$. Let y be a point in O. Since O is open, there is a sphere $S = \{x : \|x - y\| < \delta\}$ of some radius δ centered at y and contained in O. If $\|z\| \leq \delta$, then $Tz = T(y + z) - Ty$ with $y + z$ in $S \subset O$. Hence $\|Tz\| \leq \|T(y + z)\| + \|Ty\| \leq M' + M_y$. Consequently $\|T\| \leq \dfrac{M' + M_y}{\delta}$ for all T in $\mathfrak{F}$. ▎

Problem

24. Let $\langle T_n \rangle$ be a sequence of continuous linear operators on a Banach space X to a normed vector space Y, and suppose that for each x in X the sequence $\langle T_n x \rangle$ converges to a value Tx. Then T is a bounded linear operator.

*5 WEAK TOPOLOGIES

In addition to the metric topology induced by the norm in a Banach space, there are other topologies in a vector space that are important for applications. If X is any vector space and $\mathfrak{F}$ a collection of linear functionals on X, we consider the weakest topology $\mathscr{T}$ for X such that each f in $\mathfrak{F}$ is continuous (cf. Problem 8.23). This topology is called the weak topology generated by $\mathfrak{F}$, and we can show that in this topology addition is a continuous mapping of $X \times X$ into X and multiplication by scalars is a continuous mapping of $\mathbf{R}^1 \times X$ into X. (Problems 26 and 33). This topology will be Hausdorff if there are enough functions in $\mathfrak{F}$ to separate the points of X. A base at θ for $\mathscr{T}$ is given by the sets $\{x : |f_i(x)| < \epsilon, i = 1, \ldots, n\}$ where $\{f_1, \ldots, f_n\}$ is a finite subset of $\mathfrak{F}$. A base for $\mathscr{T}$ is obtained by taking all possible translates of such sets. A sequence (or net) $\langle x_n \rangle$ converges to x in this topology if and only if $f(x_n) \to f(x)$ for each $f \in \mathfrak{F}$.

If X is a normed vector space and the functionals in $\mathfrak{F}$ are all continuous (that is, if $\mathfrak{F} \subset X^*$), then the weak topology generated by $\mathfrak{F}$ is weaker (has fewer open sets) than the norm topology of X. We usually call the metric topology generated by the norm the strong topology of X and the weak topology on X generated by X^* *the* weak topology of X. Thus we speak of strongly closed and strongly open sets when referring to the strong topology and weakly open and weakly closed sets for the weak topology. Every weakly closed set is strongly closed but not conversely. Every strongly convergent sequence (or net) is weakly convergent. While not every strongly closed set is weakly closed, we do have the following proposition, a generalization of which is given by Proposition 22.

14. Proposition: *A linear manifold M is weakly closed if and only if it is strongly closed.*

Proof: Since every weakly closed set is strongly closed, we have only to show that if M is strongly closed it is also weakly closed. Suppose M is strongly closed and x is a point not on M. We must show that x is not a point of closure of M in the weak topology. Since x is not a point of closure of M in the strong (metric) topology we have $\inf_{s \in M} \|x - s\| \geq \delta > 0$. Hence by Proposition 7 there is a continuous linear functional f which vanishes on M and does not vanish at x. Now $\{y: f(y) \neq 0\}$ is an open set in the weak topology which contains x but does not meet M. Hence x is not a weak point of closure of M. ▌

If we apply the notion of weak topology to the dual X^* of a normed space X we see that the weak topology of X^* is the weakest topology for X^* such that all of the functionals in X^{**} are continuous. The weak topology for X^* turns out to be less useful than the weak topology for X^* generated by X (or more precisely, by $\varphi[X]$ where φ is the natural imbedding of X into X^{**}). This topology is called the weak* topology for X^* and is even weaker than the weak topology. Thus a weak* closed subset of X^* is weakly closed, and weak convergence implies weak* convergence. A base at θ for the weak* topology is given by sets of the form $\{f: |f(x_i)| < \epsilon, i = 1, \ldots, n\}$ where $\{x_1, \ldots, x_n\}$ is a finite subset of X. If X is reflexive, then the weak and weak* topologies of X^* coincide. Some of the importance of the weak* topology stems from the following theorem:

15. Theorem (Alaoglu): *The unit sphere* $S^* = \{f: \|f\| \leq 1\}$ *of* X^* *is compact in the weak* topology.*

Proof: If $f \in S^*$, then $|f(x)| \leq \|x\|$, and so $f(x) \in [-\|x\|, \|x\|]$. Let $I_x = [-\|x\|, \|x\|]$. Then each $f \in S^*$ corresponds to a point in $P = \times_{x \in X} I_x$, since the latter is by definitions the set of all functions

f on X such that $f(x) \in I_x$. Thus we may think of S^* as a subset of P, and the definition of the topology for P shows that the topology S^* inherits as a subspace of P is the weak* topology of S^*. Since P is compact by the Tychonoff theorem, S^* will be compact if it is a closed subset of P. Let f be a point of closure of S^* in P. Then f is a mapping of X into $\mathbf{R}$. Since $|g(x)| \leq \|x\|$ for $g \in S^*$, and evaluation at x is a continuous function on P, we have $|f(x)| \leq \|x\|$. Let x, y, and z be three points of X such that $z = \alpha x + \beta y$. For each $\epsilon > 0$ the set $N = \{g \in P\colon |g(x) - f(x)| < \epsilon, |g(y) - f(y)| < \epsilon$, and $|g(z) - f(z)| < \epsilon\}$ is an open subset of P containing f. Since f is a point of closure of S^*, we can find a g in $S^* \cap N$. Since this g is linear (being in S^*) we have $g(z) = \alpha g(x) + \beta g(y)$. Hence it follows that $|f(z) - \alpha f(x) - \beta f(y)| < \epsilon(1 + |\alpha| + |\beta|)$. This inequality holding for each positive ϵ, we have $f(z) = \alpha f(x) + \beta f(y)$, and f is linear on X. Thus f is in S^*, and so S^* is closed. ▌

16. Corollary: *In a reflexive Banach space the unit sphere is compact in the weak topology.*

Problems

25. a. Show that if $x_n \to x$ weakly then $\langle \|x_n\| \rangle$ is bounded.

b. Let $\langle x_n \rangle$ be a sequence in l^p, $1 < p < \infty$, and let $x_n = \langle \xi_{m,n} \rangle_{m=1}^{\infty}$. Show that $\langle x_n \rangle$ converges weakly to $x = \langle \xi_m \rangle$ if and only if $\langle \|x_n\| \rangle$ is bounded and for each m we have $\xi_{m,n} \to \xi_m$.

c. Let $\langle x_n \rangle$ be a sequence in $L^p[0, 1]$, $1 \leq p < \infty$. Show that $\langle x_n \rangle$ converges weakly to x if $\langle \|x_n\| \rangle$ is bounded and $\langle x_n \rangle$ converges to x in measure (cf. Problem 6.16).

d. In l^p, $1 < p < \infty$, let x_n be that sequence whose nth term is one and whose remaining terms are zero. Then $\langle x_n \rangle$ does not converge in the strong topology, but $x_n \to 0$ in the weak topology.

e. Let $\langle x_n \rangle$ be as in (d), and define $y_{n,m} = x_n + n x_m$. Then the set $F = \{y_{n,m}\colon m > n\}$ is strongly closed. (Hint: The distance between any two points of F is at least 1. Hence F contains no nonconstant sequences which converge in the strong topology.)

f. The set F in (*e*) has θ as a weak closure point. However, there is no sequence $\langle z_n \rangle$ from F which converges weakly to zero.

26. a. Let $\mathscr{T}$ be a topology for a vector space X. Then the mapping f

defined by $f(x) = x + y$ is continuous for each y if and only if the translate $O - y$ of each open set O is open. Thus if addition is continuous in each variable separately and $\mathcal{B}$ is a base at θ, then $\{N + x: N \in \mathcal{B})$ is a base at x.

b. Addition is continuous from $X \times X$ to X in the topology $\mathcal{T}$ if and only if each translate of an open set is open and, given any open set O containing θ, there is an open set O' containing θ such that $O' + O' \subset O$.

c. The function f defined by $f(x) = \lambda x$ is continuous iff $\lambda^{-1}O$ is open for each open set O.

27. Let X be a vector space and $\mathcal{B}$ a family of sets containing θ. The translates of sets in $\mathcal{B}$ will be the base for a topology on X if (*a*) for each O_1 and O_2 in $\mathcal{B}$ there is an O_3 in $\mathcal{B}$ such that $O_3 \subset O_1 \cap O_2$, and (b) for each O in $\mathcal{B}$ and $x \in O$ there is an O' in $\mathcal{B}$ such that $x + O' \subset O$. (You must show that given O_1 and O_2 in $\mathcal{B}$ and $z \in (O_1 + x) \cap (O_2 + y)$ there is an O_3 in $\mathcal{B}$ such that $z + O_3 \subset (O_1 + x) \cap (O_2 + y)$.)

28. a. Let S be a bounded subset of a normed space X. Let $\mathcal{F}$ be a set of functionals in X^* and let $\mathcal{F}_0$ be a dense subset of $\mathcal{F}$ (dense in the sense of the norm topology on X^*). Then $\mathcal{F}$ and $\mathcal{F}_0$ may generate different weak topologies for X, but these topologies are the same on S, i.e. S inherits the same topology from each.

b. Let S^* be the unit sphere in the dual X^* of a separable Banach space X. Then the weak* topology on S^* is metrizable. (*Caution:* This does not mean the weak* topology on X^* is metrizable!)

*6 CONVEXITY

A subset K of a vector space X is said to be **convex** if, whenever it contains x and y, it also contains $\lambda x + (1 - \lambda)y$ for $0 \le \lambda \le 1$. The set $\{z: z = \lambda x + (1 - \lambda)y \text{ for } 0 \le \lambda \le 1\}$ is called the line segment joining x and y. The points x and y are its endpoints, and a z for which $0 < \lambda < 1$ is called an interior point of the segment. Thus a set K is convex iff whenever it contains x and y it contains the line segment joining x and y. Every linear manifold is convex, and the unit ball in a normed space is convex. The following lemma gives some basic properties of convex sets. Further properties are given in Problems 29, 30, and 31. The proof of the lemma is straightforward and is omitted.

17. Lemma: *If K_1 and K_2 are convex sets, so also are the sets $K_1 \cap K_2, \lambda K_1$, and $K_1 + K_2$.*

A point x_0 is said to be an internal point of a set K if the intersection with K of each line through x_0 contains an open interval about x_0. Thus x_0 is internal to K if, given $x \in X$, there is an $\epsilon > 0$ such that $x_0 + \lambda x \in K$ for all λ with $|\lambda| < \epsilon$. Let K be a convex set which contains θ as an internal point. Then we define the support function p of K (with respect to θ) by $p(x) = \inf \{\lambda: \lambda^{-1}x \in K, \lambda > 0\}$. We have the following properties for this support function:

18. Lemma: *If K is a convex set containing θ as an internal point, then the support function p has the following properties:*

i. $p(\lambda x) = \lambda p(x)$ *for* $\lambda \geq 0$.
ii. $p(x + y) \leq p(x) + p(y)$.
iii. $\{x: p(x) < 1\} \subset K \subset \{x : p(x) \leq 1\}$.

Proof: The first and third properties follow immediately from the definition of p. To prove the second, suppose that $\lambda^{-1}x$ and $\mu^{-1}y$ belong to K. Then

$$(\lambda + \mu)^{-1}(x + y) = \lambda(\lambda + \mu)^{-1}(\lambda^{-1}x) + \mu(\lambda + \mu)^{-1}(\mu^{-1}y)$$

belongs to K, since K is convex. Thus $p(x + y) \leq \lambda + \mu$, and taking infima over all admissible λ and μ we obtain $p(x + y) \leq p(x) + p(y)$. ▌

Two convex sets K_1 and K_2 are said to be **separated** by a linear functional f if there is a real number α such that $f(x) \leq \alpha$ on K_1 and $f(x) \geq \alpha$ on K_2.

19. Theorem: *Let K_1 and K_2 be two disjoint convex sets in a vector space X, and suppose that one of them has an internal point. Then there is a nonzero linear functional f which separates K_1 and K_2.*

Proof: Let x_1 be an internal point of K_1. Then $K_1 - K_2$ is convex, and the point $x_0 = x_1 - x_2$ is an internal point of $K_1 - K_2$ for any x_2 in K_2. Let $K = K_1 - K_2 - x_0$. Then K is a convex set containing θ as an internal point. Since K_1 and K_2 are disjoint, $\theta \notin K_1 - K_2$, and so $-x_0 \notin K$.

Let p be the support function of K (with respect to θ). Then $p(-x_0) \geq 1$. Let S be the one-dimensional subspace of X consisting of all multiples of x_0. On S define f by $f(\alpha x_0) = -\alpha$. Then $f(s) \leq p(s)$, and p satisfies the condition of the Hahn-Banach theorem by Lemma 18. Thus we may extend f to a linear functional defined on all of X so that $f(x) \leq p(x)$ for all x. Thus if $x \in K$, we have $f(x) \leq 1$.

Let $x \in K_1$ and $y \in K_2$. Then $x - y - x_0 \in K$, and we have

$$f(x) - f(y) - f(x_0) = f(x - y - x_0) \leq 1.$$

Since $f(x_0) = -1$, we have $f(x) \leq f(y)$. This being true for each $x \in K_1$ and each y in K_2, we have $\sup_{x \in K_1} f(x) \leq \inf_{y \in K_2} f(y)$. Thus f separates K_1 and K_2, and f is a nonzero functional since $f(x_0) = -1$. ❙

A topological vector space is a vector space X together with a Hausdorff topology for X such that addition is a continuous mapping of $X \times X$ into X and multiplication by scalars is a continuous mapping of $\mathbf{R}^1 \times X$ into X. A topological vector space is called **locally convex** if we can find a base for the topology consisting of convex sets. The following lemma is useful:

20. Lemma: *Let O be an open set in a topological vector space. Then each point of O is internal.*

Proof: Let $x_0 \in O$. The mapping $\varphi(\lambda) = x_0 + \lambda x$ is a continuous function of λ for each x. Hence $\varphi^{-1}[O]$ must be an open set of real numbers containing 0, and so $x_0 + \lambda x$ belongs to O for all sufficiently small λ. ❙

The following proposition gives a convenient criterion for insuring that a given topology $\mathcal{T}$ for a vector space X will make X into a topological vector space. Suggestions for its proof are given in Problem 33.

21. Proposition: *Let $\mathcal{N}$ be a family of convex sets in a vector space, and suppose that the intersection of the sets of $\mathcal{N}$ contains only the origin θ of X. Then the following conditions are sufficient for the translates of sets in $\mathcal{N}$ to form a base for a topology which makes X into a locally convex topological vector space:*

i. If $N \in \mathcal{N}$, each point of N is internal.
ii. If N_1 and N_2 are in $\mathcal{N}$, there is an N_3 in $\mathcal{N}$ with $N_3 \subset N_1 \cap N_2$.
iii. If N is in $\mathcal{N}$, then $-N = N$, and for each $\lambda > 0$ there is an N_1 in $\mathcal{N}$ with $N_1 \subset \lambda N$.

Moreover, in each locally convex topological vector space there is a base $\mathcal{N}$ *at* θ *which satisfies these conditions.*

It follows from this proposition that the weak topology on a vector space X which is generated by a family of linear functionals makes X into a locally convex topological vector space, provided there are enough functionals in the family to separate the points of X. Also a normed vector space is a locally convex topological vector space.

22. Proposition: *Let* X *be a locally convex topological vector space and* F *a closed convex subset. Let* x_0 *be a point of* X *not in* F. *Then there is a continuous linear functional* f *on* X *such that*

$$f(x_0) < \inf_{x \in F} f(x).$$

Proof: By translating by $-x_0$, we reduce the proposition to the case that $x_0 = \theta$. Since θ is not a point of closure of F, there is a convex open set N which contains θ but does not meet F. Let $O = N \cap (-N)$. Then O is an open convex set containing θ and disjoint from F, and $-O = O$. Since θ is an internal point of O by Lemma 20, there is by Theorem 19 a nonzero linear functional f such that $\sup_{x \in O} f(x) \le \inf_{y \in F} f(y) = \alpha$. Thus $f(x) \le \alpha$ for x in O, and since $x \in O$ implies $-x \in O$, we have $-f(x) \le \alpha$ on O, whence $|f(x)| \le \alpha$ on O. Thus for each $\epsilon > 0$, we have $|f(x)| < \epsilon$ on the set $O' = (\epsilon\alpha^{-1})O$. But O' is an open set containing θ, and so f is continuous at θ. Since f is linear and continuous at θ, it is continuous everywhere.

It remains only to show that $\alpha > 0$. Since f is a nonzero functional, there is an x such that $f(x) > 0$. Since θ is an internal point of O, we can choose $\lambda > 0$ so that λx is in O. Then

$$0 < \lambda f(x) = f(\lambda x) \le \alpha . \ \blacksquare$$

23. Corollary: *Let* K *be a convex set in a locally convex topological space. Then* K *is strongly closed if and only if it is weakly closed.*

24. Corollary: *Let* x *and* y *be distinct points of a locally compact topological vector space* X. *Then there is a continuous linear functional* f *such that* $f(x) \neq f(y)$.

Let K be a convex subset of a vector space X. A point x in K is called an **extreme** point if it is not an interior point of any line segment lying in K. Thus x is extreme iff whenever $x = \lambda y + (1 - \lambda)z$ with $0 < \lambda < 1$, we have $y \notin K$ or $z \notin K$. We are going to show that every compact convex set has extreme points, but we first consider some preliminary notions. A subset S of a convex set K is called a supporting set of K if it is closed and convex and has the property that if an interior point of a line segment in K belongs to S then the entire line segment belongs to S. Thus an extreme point is a supporting set consisting of exactly one point.

25. Lemma: *Let f be a continuous linear functional on a closed convex set K. Then the set S of points where f assumes its maximum on K is a supporting set of K.*

Proof: The set S is convex, for if $f(x) = m$ and $f(y) = m$, then $f(\lambda x + (1 - \lambda)y) = m$. If the line segment joining x to y is in K and f assumes its maximum m at the point $z = \lambda x + (1 - \lambda)y$. Then $m = \lambda f(x) + (1 - \lambda)f(y)$, and since $f(x)$ and $f(y)$ are not greater than m, we must have $f(x) = f(y) = m$. But this implies that $f(\mu x + (1 - \mu)y) = m$, and so the entire line segment joining x to y is in S. ▎

The intersection of all convex sets containing a set E is a convex set which contains E and which is contained in every convex set containing E. This set is called the **convex hull** of E. The intersection of all closed convex sets containing E is a closed convex set which contains E and which is contained in every closed convex set containing E. This set is called the **closed convex hull** of E.

26. Theorem (Krein-Milman): *Let K be a compact convex set in a locally convex topological vector space X. Then K is the closed convex hull of its extreme points.*

Proof (Kelley): We assume that K is not empty. It follows from the definition of supporting sets that the intersection of a collection of supporting sets of K is a supporting set of K and that if S is a supporting set of K and T a supporting set of S then T is a supporting set of K.

Given any nonempty supporting set S of K, the family of all nonempty supporting sets of K is partially ordered by inclusion, and by the Hausdorff maximal principle there is a maximal linearly ordered family $\mathcal{S}$ of nonempty supporting sets containing S. Since K is compact, the intersection T of all members of $\mathcal{S}$ is nonempty, and hence is itself a nonempty supporting set of K. It is, moreover, a minimal nonempty supporting set, for if T properly contained a supporting set the family $\mathcal{S}$ would not be maximal. Thus any supporting set contains a minimal nonempty supporting set. Now a minimal nonempty supporting set can contain only one point. For if a supporting set S contains the distinct points x and y, there is a continuous linear functional f such that $f(x) > f(y)$. Then the subset of S where f attains its maximum is by Lemma 25 a supporting subset of S and hence of K. Since K is compact it is a nonempty supporting subset of K which does not contain y.

If a supporting set consists of just one point, that point must be extreme. Hence we have shown that every nonempty supporting set contains an extreme point.

Since the subset of K where a linear functional assumes its maximum is a nonempty supporting set, we conclude that the maximum of a continuous linear functional on K is equal to its maximum on the set E of extreme points of K. Let C be the closed convex hull of the extreme points of K, and suppose $x \notin C$. By Proposition 22 there is a continuous linear functional f such that $f(x) > \max_{y \in C} f(y) = \max_{y \in K} f(y)$. Thus $x \notin K$, and we have $K \subset C$. Hence $K = C$. ∎

Problems

29. Let A be a linear operator from the vector space X to the vector space Y. Then the image of each convex set (or linear manifold) in X is a convex set (or linear manifold) in Y and the inverse image of a convex set (or linear manifold) in Y is a convex set (or linear manifold) in X. Give an example to show that a nonconvex set may have a convex image.

30. Show that the closure of a convex set K in a topological vector space is convex.

31. **a.** Show that in $\mathbf{R}^n$ each internal point of a convex set is an interior point.

b. Give an example of a set in the plane which has an internal point that is not an interior point.

32. Let K be a convex set containing θ, and suppose that x is an internal point of K. Then for some $\lambda > 0$ the set $x + \lambda K$ is contained in K. (Hint: Choose $\lambda > 0$ so that $(1 - \lambda)^{-1}x$ is in K.)

33. Prove Proposition 21 by the following steps:

a. Use Problems 27 and 32 to show that the translates of sets in $\mathcal{N}$ form a base for some topology $\mathcal{T}$ on x. This topology is clearly Hausdorff.

b. In this topology addition is continuous from $X \times X$ to X. (Use Problem 26, and note that if O is a convex set containing θ, then $\frac{1}{2}O + \frac{1}{2}O = O$.)

c. Multiplication is a continuous mapping of $\mathbf{R}^1 \times X$ into X. (Let O be an element of $\mathcal{N}$ so that $O + \lambda_0 x_0$ is an arbitrary element of the base at $\lambda_0 x_0$. Let p be the support function for O. Then $p(\lambda x - \lambda_0 x_0) < 1$ if $|\lambda - \lambda_0| < [2p(x_0)]^{-1}$ and $x \in \alpha O + x_0$, where $\alpha < (2\lambda_0 + [p(x_0)]^{-1})^{-1}$.)

34. a. Prove that a linear mapping of a topological vector space X into a topological vector space Y is continuous everywhere if it is continuous at one point.

b. Show that a linear functional f on a topological vector space is continuous iff the set $\{x: f(x) > 0\}$ contains an open set.

35. ***The Finite Topology.*** A subset O of a topological vector space is called finitely open if each $x \in O$ is an internal point of some convex set contained in O.

a. Show that the finitely open sets of X form a topology for X (called the finite topology) and that X becomes a locally convex topological vector space in this topology. A base at θ is given by the family of all finitely open convex sets containing θ.

b. Let X be a vector space with the finite topology and A a linear mapping of X into a locally convex topological vector space Y. Then A is continuous. (Show that if Ax is an internal point of a convex set K in Y then x is an internal point of $A^{-1}[K]$, and use Problem 31.)

c. The finite topology for X is the strongest locally convex topology for X.

d. Let X be a finite dimensional locally convex topological vector space. Then the topology of X is the finite topology. Hence every n-dimensional locally convex topological vector space is isomorphic to $\mathbf{R}^n$.

e. A convex set O in a vector space X is open in this topology if and only if the intersection of each translate of O with each finite dimensional linear manifold M in X is an open subset of M.

f. Every finite dimensional linear manifold in a locally convex topological vector space is closed.

36. a. In $L^p[0, 1]$, $1 < p < \infty$, every x with $\|x\| = 1$ is an extreme point of the unit sphere $S = \{x\colon \|x\| \le 1\}$.

b. In $L^\infty[0, 1]$ the extreme points of the unit sphere are those x such that $|x(t)| = 1$ a.e.

c. The unit sphere in $L^1[0, 1]$ has no extreme points.

d. $L^1[0, 1]$ is not the dual of any normed linear space.

e. What are the extreme points of the unit sphere in l^p?

f. What are the extreme points of the unit sphere in $C(X)$, X a compact Hausdorff space? Show that $C[0, 1]$ is not the dual of any normed linear space.

37. Let X be the vector space of all measurable real-valued functions on $[0, 1]$ with addition and multiplication by scalars defined in the usual way. Define $\sigma(x) = \displaystyle\int_0^1 \frac{|x(t)|}{1 + |x(t)|}\,dt.$

a. We have $\sigma(x + y) \le \sigma(x) + \sigma(y)$. Hence if we define $\rho(x, y) = \sigma(x - y)$, ρ is a metric for X.

b. In this metric $x_n \to x$ if and only if $x_n \to x$ in measure.

c. X is a complete metric space (cf. Problem 4.19).

d. Addition is a continuous mapping of $X \times X$ into X.

e. Multiplication is a continuous mapping of $\mathbf{R}^1 \times X$ into X. Since X is a metric space, it suffices to prove that if $x_n \to x$ and $\lambda_n \to \lambda$ then $\lambda_n x_n \to \lambda x$. This follows from the Bounded Convergence theorem for convergence in measure.)

f. Show that the set of step functions is dense in X.

g. There is no nonzero continuous linear functional on X. (Show that there is an n such that $f(x) = 0$ whenever x is the characteristic function of an interval of length less than n. Hence $f(x) = 0$ for all step functions x.)

h. The space X is a topological vector space which is not locally convex.

i. Let s be the space of all sequences of real numbers, and define $\sigma(\langle\xi_\nu\rangle) = \sum \dfrac{2^{-\nu}\,|\xi_\nu|}{1 + |\xi_\nu|}$. Prove the analogues of (a), (c), (d) and (e). What is the most general continuous linear functional on s?

7 HILBERT SPACE

By a Hilbert space we mean a Banach space in which there is defined a function (x, y) on $H \times H$ to $\mathbf{R}^1$ with the following properties:[1]

i. $(\alpha_1 x_1 + \alpha_2 x_2, y) = \alpha_1(x_1, y) + \alpha_2(x_2, y)$.
ii. $(x, y) = (y, x)$.
iii. $(x, x) = \|x\|^2$.

We call (x, y) the inner product of x and y. Two examples are immediate: one is the space $\mathbf{R}^n$ with

$$(x, y) = \sum_{i=1}^{n} x_i y_i;$$

the other is the space L^2 with

$$(x, y) = \int x(t)\, y(t)\, dt.$$

Since $\|x\| \geq 0$ with equality only for $x = \theta$, we have

$$0 \leq \|x - \lambda y\|^2 = (x - \lambda y, x - \lambda y)$$
$$= (x, x) - 2\lambda(x, y) + \lambda^2(y, y).$$

If $\lambda > 0$, we have

$$2(x, y) \leq \lambda^{-1}\|x\|^2 + \lambda\|y\|^2.$$

Setting $\lambda = \|x\|/\|y\|$, we obtain

$$(x, y) \leq \|x\| \cdot \|y\|,$$

and we see that equality can only occur when $y = \theta$ or $x = \lambda y$ for some $\lambda \geq 0$. This inequality is variously known as the Schwarz, Cauchy-Schwarz, or Cauchy-Buniakowsky-Schwarz inequality. A consequence of this inequality is that the linear functional f defined by $f(x) = (x, y)$ is bounded by $\|y\|$, and from this it follows that (x, y) is a continuous function from $H \times H$ to $\mathbf{R}^1$.

We say that two elements x and y of H are *orthogonal* if $(x, y) = 0$. We write $x \perp y$ to mean x and y are orthogonal. A set $\mathcal{S}$ in H is called an *orthogonal system* if any two different elements φ and ψ of $\mathcal{S}$ are orthogonal, that is, $(\varphi, \psi) = 0$. An orthogonal system $\mathcal{S}$ is

[1] We have defined here a real Hilbert space. In analysis it is generally more convenient to deal with a complex Hilbert space, that is, one in which the scalars are complex numbers, the inner product is complex-valued, and (ii) is replaced by (ii′): $(x, y) = \overline{(y, x)}$

called *orthonormal* if $\|\varphi\| = 1$ for each φ in $\mathcal{S}$. Any two elements of an orthonormal system are at distance $\sqrt{2}$ from each other. Hence if H is separable, every orthonormal system in H must be countable.

Henceforth we shall deal only with separable Hilbert spaces. Thus each orthonormal system may be expressed as a sequence $\langle\varphi_\nu\rangle$, which may be finite or infinite. We define the Fourier coefficients (with respect to $\langle\varphi_\nu\rangle$) of an element x in H to be $a_\nu = (x, \varphi_\nu)$. For any n we have[2]

$$0 \le \|x - \sum_{\nu=1}^{n} a_\nu\varphi_\nu\|^2 = \|x\|^2 - 2\sum_{\nu=1}^{n} a_\nu(x, \varphi_\nu) + \sum_{\nu=1}^{n}\sum_{\mu=1}^{n} a_\nu a_\mu(\varphi_\nu, \varphi_\mu)$$
$$= \|x\|^2 - \sum_{\nu=1}^{n} a_\nu^2.$$

Thus

$$\sum_{\nu=1}^{n} a_\nu^2 \le \|x\|^2$$

and since n was arbitrary, we have Bessel's inequality:

$$\sum_{\nu=1}^{\infty} a_\nu^2 \le \|x\|^2.$$

On the other hand let $\langle a_\nu\rangle$ be any sequence of real numbers with $\sum_{\nu=1}^{\infty} a_\nu^2 < \infty$. Then the sequence

$$z_n = \sum_{\nu=1}^{n} a_\nu\varphi_\nu$$

is a Cauchy sequence, since for $m \ge n$

$$z_m - z_n = \sum_{\nu=n}^{m} a_\nu\varphi_\nu,$$

and we have

$$\|z_m - z_n\|^2 = \sum_{\nu=n}^{m} a_\nu^2$$

which must tend to zero since $\Sigma\, a_\nu^2$ converges. By the completeness of H there is an element y such that $y = \lim z_n$, and we write

$$y = \sum_{\nu=1}^{\infty} a_\nu\varphi_\nu.$$

[2] If there are only a finite number N of elements in $\langle\varphi_\nu\rangle$, we adopt the convention that $\sum_{\nu=1}^{n}$ means $\sum_{\nu=1}^{N}$ for $N \le n \le \infty$.

Since the inner product is continuous, we have

$$(y, \varphi_\nu) = \lim (z_n, \varphi_\nu) = a_\nu.$$

We have thus shown that for any x there is a y of the form $y = \sum_{\nu=1}^{\infty} a_\nu\varphi_\nu$ which has the same Fourier coefficients as x.

When does this y equal x? If we look at $y - x$, we see that all of its Fourier coefficients are zero. Hence $y = x$ if the orthonormal system $\langle\varphi_\nu\rangle$ has the property that if $(z, \varphi_\nu) = 0$ for all ν then $z = \theta$. An orthonormal system with this property is called complete (or total). A complete orthonormal system is clearly a maximal one, while if $\langle\varphi_\nu\rangle$ is a maximal orthonormal system, it must be complete. For, if $(z, \varphi_\nu) = 0$ all ν and $z \neq \theta$, then $z/\|z\|$ can be added to $\langle\varphi_\nu\rangle$. The Hausdorff maximal principle implies the existence of a maximal orthonormal system. We have thus established the following proposition:

27. Proposition: *In a separable Hilbert space every orthonormal system is countable and there is a complete orthonormal system. If $\langle\varphi_\nu\rangle$ is any complete orthonormal system and x any element of H, we have*

$$x = \sum_{\nu=1}^{\infty} a_\nu\varphi_\nu,$$

where $a_\nu = (x, \varphi_\nu)$. Moreover $\|x\|^2 = \sum_{\nu=1}^{\infty} a_\nu^2$.

In a separable Hilbert space there are two alternatives: either every complete orthonormal system has an infinite number of elements or else there is a complete orthonormal system with a finite number N of elements. In the latter case such a system is a basis (in the vector space sense) of H by Proposition 27. Hence H is a finite dimensional vector space, and any system of $N + 1$ elements is linearly dependent. Consequently, every orthonormal system can have at most N elements in it. From this it follows that every complete orthonormal system must have N elements. We have thus proved that in a separable Hilbert space H every complete orthonormal system has the same number of elements. We call this number the dimension of H. (Thus if H has a countably infinite complete orthonormal system we say $\dim H = \aleph_0$.)

An isomorphism Φ of a Hilbert space H onto a Hilbert space H' is a linear mapping of H onto H' such that $(\Phi x, \Phi y) = (x, y)$. Thus an isomorphism between Hilbert spaces is an isometry. Each n-dimensional Hilbert space is isomorphic to R^n, since the mapping defined by $\Phi(x) = \langle a_1, \dots, a_n \rangle$ where $a_\nu = (x, \varphi_\nu)$ is an isomorphism. Similarly every $\aleph_0$-dimensional Hilbert space is isomorphic to l^2. Since $L^2[0, \pi]$ is separable and $\{\cos \nu t\}$ is an infinite orthogonal system, we see that the dimension of L^2 is $\aleph_0$, and so L^2 is isomorphic to l^2.

28. Proposition: *Let f be a bounded linear functional on the Hilbert space H. Then there is a $y \in H$ such that $f(x) = (x, y)$ for all x. Moreover $\|f\| = \|y\|$.*

Proof: (We consider only the case of separable H. For nonseparable H see Problem 40). Let $\langle \varphi_\nu \rangle$ be a complete orthonormal system for H, and set $b_\nu = f(\varphi_\nu)$. Then for each n we have

$$\sum_{\nu=1}^{n} b_\nu^2 = f\left(\sum_{\nu=1}^{n} b_\nu \varphi_\nu\right) \le \|f\| \cdot \left\|\sum_{\nu=1}^{n} b_\nu \varphi_\nu\right\|$$
$$\le \|f\| \left[\sum_{\nu=1}^{n} b_\nu^2\right]^{1/2}.$$

Thus $\sum_{\nu=1}^{n} b_\nu^2 \le \|f\|^2$, and so $\sum_{\nu=1}^{\infty} b_\nu^2 \le \|f\|^2 < \infty$. Hence there is an element $y = \sum_{\nu=1}^{\infty} b_\nu \varphi_\nu$. We have $\|y\| \le \|f\|$.

Let x be any element of H. Then $\sum_{\nu=1}^{n} a_\nu \varphi_\nu \to x$, and so

$$f(x) = \lim f\left(\sum_{\nu=1}^{n} a_\nu \varphi_\nu\right) = \lim \sum_{\nu=1}^{n} a_\nu b_\nu$$
$$= \sum_{\nu=1}^{\infty} a_\nu b_\nu$$
$$= (x, y).$$

By the Schwarz inequality $\|f\| \le \|y\|$. ∎

Problems

38. Show that the inner product is continuous, i.e. that if $x_n \to x$ and $y_n \to y$, then $(x_n, y_n) \to (x, y)$.

39. a. Show that $\{\cos \nu t, \sin \nu t\}$ is (when suitably normalized) a complete orthonormal system for $L^2[0, 2\pi]$ (cf. Problems 6.14 and 9.19).

b. Every function in $L^2[0, 2\pi]$ is the limit in mean (of order 2) of its Fourier series (cf. Section 6.3).

40. a. Show that for each x in a nonseparable Hilbert space there are only a countable number of nonzero Fourier coefficients (with respect to a fixed orthonormal system).

b. Show that Proposition 27 is still valid in a nonseparable Hilbert space except that every complete orthonormal system is uncountable.

c. Show that Proposition 28 is still valid in a nonseparable Hilbert space.

d. Show that if H is any infinite dimensional Hilbert space then the number $\mathbf{n}$ of elements in a complete orthonormal system in H is the smallest cardinal $\mathbf{n}$ such that there is a dense subset of H with $\mathbf{n}$ elements. Hence every complete orthonormal system in H has the same number of elements. We call this number the dimension of H.

e. Show that two Hilbert spaces are isomorphic if and only if they have the same dimension.

f. Show that there is a Hilbert space of each dimension.

41. Let P be a subset of H. By the orthogonal complement $P^\perp$ of P we mean the set $\{y : y \perp x \text{ all } x \in P\}$.

a. Show that $P^\perp$ is always a closed linear manifold.

b. Show that $P^{\perp\perp}$ is the smallest closed linear manifold containing P.

c. Let M be a closed linear manifold. Then each $x \in H$ can be written uniquely in the form $x = y + z$ with $y \in M$ and $z \in M^\perp$. Moreover, $\|x\|^2 = \|y\|^2 + \|z\|^2$.

42. Let $\langle x_n \rangle$ be a bounded sequence of elements in a separable Hilbert space. Then $\langle x_n \rangle$ contains a subsequence which converges weakly.

Epilogue to Part II

In Chapters 7, 8, and 9 we have considered various aspects of general topology. For a more detailed treatment of this subject Kelley [11] is an excellent reference, and you will find there further references to the literature. In addition to the topics which we have discussed briefly, there is a chapter on uniform spaces which generalize the metric spaces and the topology of linear spaces so that the notions of completeness and uniform continuity are meaningful. For deeper properties of metric spaces and Borel sets Kuratowski [12] is good. Topology (as opposed to general or point set topology) is largely concerned with homeomorphisms and their invariants. The construction of these invariants leads to combinatorial or algebraic topology. For an elementary introduction see Hocking and Young [9].

In Chapter 10 we discussed briefly some of the geometrical aspects of Banach spaces, and topological linear spaces were touched upon to the extent needed for the weak and weak* topologies in Banach spaces. The Theorems (Hahn-Banach, closed graph, uniform boundedness, Alaoglu, Krein-Milman) are some of the most useful general tools at the disposal of the analyst. Useful theorems which we did not mention here are the fixed-point theorems of Schauder and Leray. A thorough catalogue of the "geometrical" properties of such spaces is given in Day [2] which also includes an excellent guide to the literature. The book by Banach is very readable, although it suffers from the fact that general topology was not in existence at the time it was written and the weak topological notions are treated entirely in terms of sequential convergence.

A central topic in modern analysis which we have not mentioned here is the theory of linear operators on a Banach or Hilbert space. Discussion of these from various points of view may be found in Dunford-Schwartz [3], Hille-Phillips [7], Riesz-Nagy [14], and Taylor [16].

Part Three

GENERAL MEASURE AND INTEGRATION THEORY

11 Measure and Integration

1 MEASURE SPACES

The purpose of the present chapter is to abstract the most important properties of Lebesgue measure and Lebesgue integration. We shall do this by giving certain axioms which Lebesgue measure satisfies and base our integration theory on these axioms. As a consequence our theory will be valid for every system satisfying the given axioms.

We begin by recalling that a σ-algebra $\mathfrak{B}$ is a family of subsets of a given set X which contains $\varnothing$ and is closed with respect to complements and with respect to countable unions. By a set function μ we mean a function which assigns an extended real number to certain sets. With this in mind we make the following definitions:

Definition: *By a measurable space we mean a couple* $(X, \mathfrak{B})$ *consisting of a set* X *and a* σ*-algebra* $\mathfrak{B}$ *of subsets of* X. *A subset* A *of* X *is called measurable (or measurable with respect to* $\mathfrak{B}$*) if* $A \in \mathfrak{B}$.

Definition: *By a measure* μ *on a measurable space* $(X, \mathfrak{B})$ *we mean a nonnegative set function defined for all sets of* $\mathfrak{B}$ *and satisfying* $\mu(\varnothing) = 0$, *and*

$$\mu\left(\bigcup_{i=1}^{\infty} E_i\right) = \sum_{i=1}^{\infty} \mu E_i$$

for any sequence E_i *of disjoint measurable sets. By a measure space* $(X, \mathfrak{B}, \mu)$ *we mean a measurable space* $(X, \mathfrak{B})$ *together with a measure* μ *defined on* $\mathfrak{B}$.

This second property of μ is often referred to by saying that μ is countably additive. We also have that μ is "finitely additive," that is,

$$\mu\left(\bigcup_{i=1}^{N} E_i\right) = \sum_{i=1}^{N} \mu E_i ,$$

for disjoint sets E_i belonging to $\mathcal{B}$, since we may use (ii) with $E_i = \varnothing$ for $i > N$.[1]

One example of a measure space is $(\mathbf{R}, \mathcal{M}, m)$, where $\mathbf{R}$ is the set of real numbers, $\mathcal{M}$ the Lebesgue measurable sets of real numbers and m Lebesgue measure. Another measure space results if we replace $\mathbf{R}$ by the interval $[0, 1]$ and $\mathcal{M}$ by the measurable subsets of $[0, 1]$. A third example is $(\mathbf{R}, \mathcal{B}, m)$ where $\mathcal{B}$ is the class of Borel sets and m is again Lebesgue measure. Another example is given by Problem 3.4. A slightly bizarre example is the following: Let X be any uncountable set, $\mathcal{B}$ the family of those subsets which are either countable or the complement of a countable set. Then $\mathcal{B}$ is a σ-algebra and we can define a measure on it by setting $\mu A = 0$ for each countable set and $\mu B = 1$ for each set whose complement is countable.

Two further properties of measures are given by the following propositions:

1. Proposition: *If $A \in \mathcal{B}$, $B \in \mathcal{B}$, and $A \subset B$, then*

$$\mu A \leq \mu B.$$

Proof: Since

$$B = A \cup [B \sim A]$$

is a disjoint union, we have

$$\mu B = \mu A + \mu(B \sim A) \geq \mu A. \ \blacksquare$$

2. Proposition: *If $E_i \in \mathcal{B}$, $\mu E_1 < \infty$ and $E_i \supset E_{i+1}$, then*

$$\mu\left(\bigcap_{i=1}^{\infty} E_i\right) = \lim_{n\to\infty} \mu E_n.$$

Proof: Set $E = \bigcap_{i=1}^{\infty} E_i$. Then

$$E_1 = E \cup \bigcup_{i=1}^{\infty} (E_i \sim E_{i+1}),$$

and this is a disjoint union. Hence

$$\mu E_1 = \mu E + \sum_{i=1}^{\infty} \mu(E_i \sim E_{i+1}).$$

[1] A set function μ defined on an algebra of sets and satisfying $\mu(\varnothing) = 0$ and $\mu(A \cup B) = \mu A + \mu B$ for disjoint sets A and B in the algebra is called a finitely additive measure. Since our definition (and the usual usage) requires a measure to be countably additive, it follows that a finitely additive measure is not in general a measure, though every measure is, of course, a finitely additive measure.

Since

$$E_i = E_{i+1} \cup (E_i \sim E_{i+1})$$

is a disjoint union, we have

$$\mu(E_i \sim E_{i+1}) = \mu E_i - \mu E_{i+1}.$$

Hence

$$\begin{aligned} \mu E_1 &= \mu E + \sum_{i=1}^{\infty} (\mu E_i - \mu E_{i+1}) \\ &= \mu E + \lim_{n\to\infty} \sum_{i=1}^{n-1} (\mu E_i - \mu E_{i+1}) \\ &= \mu E + \mu E_1 - \lim \mu E_n, \end{aligned}$$

whence the proposition follows. ▎

3. Proposition: *If $E_i \in \mathcal{B}$ then*

$$\mu\left(\bigcup_{i=1}^{\infty} E_i\right) \leq \sum_{i=1}^{\infty} \mu E_i.$$

Proof: Let $G_n = E_n \sim \left[\bigcup_{i=1}^{n-1} E_i\right]$. Then $G_n \subset E_n$ and the sets G_n are disjoint. Hence

$$\mu G_n \leq \mu E_n$$

while

$$\mu E = \sum_{n=1}^{\infty} \mu G_n \leq \sum_{n=1}^{\infty} \mu E_n. \text{ ▎}$$

A measure μ is called **finite** if $\mu(X) < \infty$. It is called **σ-finite** if there is a sequence $\langle X_n \rangle$ of sets in $\mathcal{B}$ such that

$$X = \bigcup_{n=1}^{\infty} X_n$$

and $\mu X_n < \infty$. By virtue of Proposition 1.2 we may always take $\langle X_n \rangle$ to be a disjoint sequence of sets. Lebesgue measure on [0, 1] is an example of a finite measure, while Lebesgue measure on $(-\infty, \infty)$ is an example of a σ-finite measure. The counting measure on an uncountable set is a measure which is not σ-finite. Other examples are given in Problem 24.

A set E is said to be of **finite measure** if $E \in \mathcal{B}$ and $\mu E < \infty$. A set E is said to be of **σ-finite measure** if E is the union of a countable collection of measurable sets of finite measure. Any measurable set contained in a set of σ-finite measure is itself of σ-finite measure, and the union of a countable collection of sets of σ-finite measure is again of σ-finite measure. If μ is σ-finite, then every measurable set is of σ-finite measure.

A measure space $(X, \mathcal{B}, \mu)$ is said to be **complete** if $\mathcal{B}$ contains all subsets of sets of measure zero, i.e. if $B \in \mathcal{B}$, $\mu B = 0$, and $A \subset B$ imply $A \in \mathcal{B}$. Thus Lebesgue measure is complete, while Lebesgue measure restricted to the σ-algebra of Borel sets is not complete. The following proposition, whose proof is left to the reader (Problem 2), shows that each measure space can be completed by the addition of subsets of sets of measure zero. The measure space $(X, \mathcal{B}_0, \mu_0)$ given in the proposition is called the completion of $(X, \mathcal{B}, \mu)$.

4. Proposition: *If $(X, \mathcal{B}, \mu)$ is a measure space, then we can find a complete measure space $(X, \mathcal{B}_0, \mu_0)$ such that*

i. $\mathcal{B} \subset \mathcal{B}_0$
ii. $E \in \mathcal{B} \Rightarrow \mu E = \mu_0 E$
iii. $E \in \mathcal{B}_0 \Leftrightarrow E = A \cup B$ *where* $B \in \mathcal{B}$ *and* $A \subset C$, $C \in \mathcal{B}$, $\mu C = 0$.

If $(X, \mathcal{B}, \mu)$ is a measure space, and $Y \in \mathcal{B}$, then we can form a new measure space $(Y, \mathcal{B}_Y, \mu_Y)$ by letting $\mathcal{B}_Y$ consist of those sets of $\mathcal{B}$ which are contained in Y and defining $\mu_Y E = \mu E$ for $E \in \mathcal{B}_Y$. The measure μ_Y is called the restriction of μ to Y, and in cases where no confusion is likely to arise we shall often write μ for μ_Y.

Problems

1. a. Show that $\mu(E_1 \triangle E_2) = 0$ implies $\mu E_1 = \mu E_2$ provided that E_1 and $E_2 \in \mathcal{B}$.

b. Show that if μ is complete then $E_1 \in \mathcal{B}$ and $\mu(E_1 \triangle E_2) = 0$ imply $E_2 \in \mathcal{B}$.

2. Prove Proposition 4. (First show that the family $\mathcal{B}_0$ defined by (iii) is a σ-algebra. If $E \in \mathcal{B}_0$, show that μA is the same for all sets $A \in \mathcal{B}$ such that $E = A \cup B$ with B a subset of a set of measure zero. Use this fact to define μ_0 and show μ_0 is a measure.)

3. Verify that we do actually get a measure space when we restrict μ to a measurable set Y.

4. Let $\{(X_\alpha, \mathcal{B}_\alpha, \mu_\alpha)\}$ be a collection of measure spaces, and suppose that the sets $\{X_\alpha\}$ are disjoint. Then we can form a new measure space (called their union) by letting $X = \bigcup X_\alpha$, $\mathcal{B} = \{B: (\alpha)[B \cap X_\alpha \in \mathcal{B}_\alpha]\}$, and defining $\mu(B) = \sum \mu_\alpha(B \cap X_\alpha)$.

a. Show that $\mathcal{B}$ is a σ-algebra.

b. Show that μ is a measure.

c. Show that μ is σ-finite if and only if all but a countable number of the μ_α are zero and the remainder are σ-finite.

5. Let $(X, \mathcal{B}, \mu)$ be a measure space. The set $E \in \mathcal{B}$ is called an atom if $\mu E > 0$ and for each measurable set $A \subset E$ either $\mu A = 0$ or $\mu(E \sim A) = 0$.

a. Show that Lebesgue measure has no atoms.

b. In a measure space $(X, \mathcal{B}, \mu)$ let E be a measurable set with $\mu E = \infty$. Then either E contains measurable sets of arbitrarily large finite measure, or else E contains a set each subset of which has either measure 0 or ∞. (Hint: If there are not sets of arbitrarily large finite measure, let λ be the supremum of the measures of the sets of finite measure, and let $\{A_n\}$ be a sequence of measurable subsets of E such that $\mu A_n \to \lambda$. Then the set $E \sim [\bigcup A_n]$ must be such a set.) Note that such a set need not be an atom.

6. Let $\{A_n\}$ be a countable collection of measurable sets. Then

$$\mu\left(\bigcup_{k=1}^{\infty} A_k\right) = \lim_{n\to\infty} \mu\left(\bigcup_{k=1}^{n} A_k\right).$$

2 MEASURABLE FUNCTIONS

The concept of a measurable function on an abstract measurable space is almost identical with that for functions of a real variable. Consequently only statements of the relevant definitions and theorems are given here, and the reader is left with the task of verifying that the proofs given in Section 5 of Chapter 3 hold for the corresponding theorems here. Throughout this section we assume that a fixed measurable space $(X, \mathcal{B})$ is given.

5. Proposition: *Let f be an extended real-valued function defined on X. Then the following statements are equivalent:*

i. $\{x: f(x) < \alpha\} \in \mathcal{B}$ *for each* α
ii. $\{x: f(x) \leq \alpha\} \in \mathcal{B}$ *for each* α
iii. $\{x: f(x) > \alpha\} \in \mathcal{B}$ *for each* α
iv. $\{x: f(x) \geq \alpha\} \in \mathcal{B}$ *for each* α.

(See Proposition 3.18.)

Definition: *The extended real-valued function f defined on X is called measurable (or measurable with respect to $\mathcal{B}$) if any one of the statements of Proposition 5 holds.*

6. Theorem: *If c is a constant and the functions f and g are measurable, then so are the functions $f + c$, cf, $f + g$, $f \cdot g$, and $f \vee g$. Moreover, if $\langle f_n \rangle$ is a sequence of measurable functions then* $\sup f_n$, $\inf f_n$, $\overline{\lim} f_n$, *and* $\underline{\lim} f_n$ *are all measurable.*
(See Theorems 3.19 and 3.20.)

7. Proposition: *If μ is a complete measure and f is a measurable function, then $f = g$* a.e. *implies g is measurable.*
(See Proposition 3.21.)

Problem

7. Prove Proposition 7, and show that it is false if the word 'complete' is omitted.

3 INTEGRATION

Since the definitions and proofs of Chapter 4 depend on only those properties of Lebesgue measure which are also true for any complete measure in an abstract measure space, we may carry them over to this case. In this section, we shall assume that we are dealing with a ***complete*** measure. This is not a severe restriction since a given measure may always be completed, but if we do not impose the requirement that our measure is complete, we would have to deal with the fact that the measurability of a function may be destroyed by changing its values on a set of measure zero.

In this section the principal theorems are merely stated, and the reader is left the task of verifying that the proofs given in Chapter 4 apply here.

By a simple function we mean as before a finite linear combination

$$\varphi(x) = \sum_{i=1}^{n} c_i \chi_{E_i}(x)$$

of characteristic functions of measurable sets E_i. If E is a set of finite measure, then we define

$$\int_E \varphi \, d\mu = \sum_{i=1}^{n} c_i \mu(E_i \cap E),$$

and it is easily seen that the value of this integral is independent of the representation of φ which we use. For a bounded measurable function f and a set E of finite measure we have as before

$$\sup_{\varphi \leq f} \int_E \varphi \, d\mu = \inf_{\psi \geq f} \int_E \psi \, d\mu$$

for all simple functions φ and ψ. We define this common value to be

$$\int_E f \, d\mu,$$

and the usual properties of this integral hold.

In Chapter 4 we defined the integral of a nonnegative measurable function f to be the supremum of $\int g \, d\mu$ as g ranged over all bounded measurable functions which vanished outside a set of finite measure. Unfortunatcly, this definition is not quite suitable in the case of general measures, for if $\mathfrak{B} = \{X, \varnothing\}$ and $\mu\varnothing = 0$, $\mu X = \infty$, then we certainly want $\int 1 \, d\mu = \infty$. But the only measurable function g which vanishes outside a set of finite measure is $g \equiv 0$, and hence $\sup \int g \, d\mu = 0$. In order to avoid this difficulty, we first note that the integral of a nonnegative simple function is well defined and make the following definition:

Definition: *Let f be a nonnegative extended real-valued measurable function on the measure space $(X, \mathfrak{B}, \mu)$. Then $\int f \, d\mu$ is the supremum of the integrals $\int \varphi \, d\mu$ as φ ranges over all simple functions with $0 \leq \varphi \leq f$.*

We observe that this definition agrees with our earlier definition of $\int f \, d\mu$ for the case when f is a bounded measurable function which vanishes except on a set of finite measure. The following proposition relates this definition to the one used in Chapter 4.

8. Proposition: *Let f be a nonnegative measurable function on the measure space $(X, \mathfrak{B}, \mu)$. Then $\int f \, d\mu < \infty$ only if $\{x: f(x) > 0\}$ is of σ-finite measure and $\mu\{x: f(x) = \infty\} = 0$. If $\{x: f(x) > 0\}$ is of σ-finite measure, then*

$$\int f \, d\mu = \sup \int g \, d\mu$$

as g runs over all bounded measurable functions with $g \leq f$, and g vanishing outside a set of finite measure.

Proof: If $\int f\,d\mu < \infty$, then clearly $\mu\{x: f(x) = \infty\} = 0$. If $E_n = \{x: f(x) > \frac{1}{n}\}$, then $\mu E_n = \int \chi_{E_n}\,d\mu \le n \int f\,d\mu < \infty$. Hence E_n is a set of finite measure and $\{x: f(x) > 0\} = \bigcup E_n$ is a set of σ-finite measure.

Let us now suppose that $\{x: f(x) \ne 0\}$ is of σ-finite measure. If g is a bounded measurable function which vanishes outside a set of finite measure and $g \le f$, then $\int f\,d\mu \ge \int g\,d\mu$, and so

$$\int f\,d\mu \ge \sup \int g\,d\mu$$

as g runs over all such functions. Now if φ is a nonnegative simple function and $\int \varphi\,d\mu < \infty$, then φ vanishes outside a set of finite measure. Hence if there is no non-negative simple function $\varphi \le f$ with $\int \varphi\,d\mu = \infty$, we have

$$\int f\,d\mu = \sup_{\varphi \le f} \int \varphi\,d\mu \le \sup_{g \le f} \int g\,d\mu$$

for g bounded and vanishing outside a set of finite measure. If on the other hand there is a simple $\varphi = \sum_{j=1}^{n} c_j \chi_{E_j}$ with $\varphi \le f$ and $\int \varphi\,d\mu = \infty$, then $\int f\,d\mu = \infty$, and at least one set E_i has infinite measure. Since $E_i \subset \{x: f(x) > 0\}$, it must be of σ-finite measure; that is, it must be the union of a countable collection $\{A_k\}$ of sets of finite measure. Let φ_n be the characteristic function of $\bigcup_{k=1}^{n} A_k$. Then $c_i\varphi_n$ is a bounded function which vanishes outside the set $\bigcup_{k=1}^{n} A_k$ of finite measure and $c_i\varphi_n \le f$. But

$$\int c_i\varphi_n\,d\mu = c_i\mu\left(\bigcup_{k=1}^{n} A_k\right),$$

and so

$$\lim_{n\to\infty} \int c_i\varphi_n\,d\mu = c_i\mu E_i = \infty$$

by Problem 6. Thus

$$\sup_{g \le f} \int g\,d\mu = \infty = \int f\,d\mu. \quad \blacksquare$$

9. Proposition: *If f and g are nonnegative measurable functions and E a measurable set, then*

i. $\int_E cf = c\int_E f$

ii. $\int_E (f+g) = \int_E f + \int_E g$

iii. $\int_E f \geq 0$ *with equality only if* $f = 0$ a.e.

Proof: Parts (i) and (iii) are proved as in Proposition 4.7. If $\{x: f(x) + g(x) > 0\}$ is a set of σ-finite measure, we use Proposition 8 to proceed as in Proposition 4.7. If $\{x: f(x) + g(x) > 0\}$ is not of σ-finite measure, then either $\{x: f(x) > 0\}$ or $\{x: g(x) > 0\}$ is not of σ-finite measure. Hence by Proposition 8 we have $\int (f+g) = \infty$ and either $\int f = \infty$ or $\int g = \infty$. ∎

The following proposition is often useful in extending results about simple functions which vanish outside sets of finite measure to more general functions. The proof is left as a problem (Problem 9).

10. Proposition: *Let $(X, \mathcal{B}, \mu)$ be a σ-finite measure space and f a nonnegative measurable function. Then there is a monotone increasing sequence $\langle\varphi_n\rangle$ of simple functions, each vanishing outside a set of finite measure, such that $f = \lim \varphi_n$ at each point of X.*

If f is a nonnegative integrable function, then by Proposition 8 the set $E = \{x: f(x) > 0\}$ is of σ-finite measure, and Proposition 10 gives us the following corollary:

11. Corollary: *Let f be a nonnegative function with $\int f < \infty$. Then there is an increasing sequence $\langle\varphi_n\rangle$ of simple functions, each of which vanishes outside a set of finite measure, such that $f = \lim \varphi_n$ at each point of X.*

12. Theorem (Fatou's Lemma): *If $\langle f_n\rangle$ is a sequence of nonnegative measurable functions and $f_n(x) \to f(x)$ almost everywhere on a set E, then*

$$\int_E f \leq \underline{\lim} \int_E f_n.$$

Proof: If $\underline{\lim} \int f_n = \infty$, there is nothing to prove. If $\underline{\lim} \int f_n < \infty$, we may (by passing to a subsequence if necessary) suppose that

$\int f_n < \infty$ for each n. Hence the set $E_n = \{x: f_n(x) > 0\}$ is σ-finite and so is the set $F = \bigcup E_n$. Since $f = 0$ on $E \sim F$, f vanishes outside a set of σ-finite measure, and Proposition 8 allows us to apply the proof given for Theorem 4.8. ❙

A nonnegative function f is called **integrable** (over a measurable set E with respect to μ) if it is measurable and

$$\int_E f\,d\mu < \infty.$$

An arbitrary function f is said to be integrable if both f^+ and f^- are integrable. In this case we define

$$\int_E f = \int_E f^+ - \int_E f^-.$$

13. Proposition: *If f and g are integrable functions and E is a measurable set, then*

i. $\int_E (c_1 f + c_2 g) = c_1 \int_E f + c_2 \int_E g;$

ii. if $|h| \leq |f|$ and h is measurable then h is integrable;

iii. if $f \geq g$ a.e., *then* $\int f \geq \int g.$

14. Theorem (Lebesgue Convergence Theorem): *Let g be integrable over E, and suppose that $\langle f_n \rangle$ is a sequence of measurable functions such that on E*

$$|f_n(x)| \leq g(x)$$

and such that almost everywhere on E

$$f_n(x) \to f(x).$$

Then

$$\int_E f = \lim \int_E f_n.$$

15. Theorem (Monotone Convergence Theorem): *Let $\langle f_n \rangle$ be a nondecreasing sequence of nonnegative measurable functions which converge pointwise to f. Then*

$$\int_E f = \lim \int_E f_n.$$

16. Corollary: *Let $\langle f_n \rangle$ be a sequence of nonnegative measurable functions. Then*

$$\int \sum_{n=1}^{\infty} f_n = \sum_{n=1}^{\infty} \int f_n.$$

As a further application of the Lebesgue and monotone convergence theorems we have the following corollary:

17. Proposition: *Let f be a measurable function defined on the measurable set E, and suppose either that f is integrable over E or that f is nonnegative on E. If E is the union of a disjoint sequence $\langle E_k \rangle$ of measurable sets we have*

$$\int_E f = \sum_{k=1}^{\infty} \int_{E_k} f.$$

Proof: Let $f_n = f \cdot \chi_{E_k}$. Then $\sum_{k=1}^{n} f_k(x)$ converges to $f(x)$ for each $x \in E$. If f is nonnegative the conclusion of the proposition follows by the monotone convergence theorem. If f is integrable over E, the conclusion follows from the Lebesgue convergence theorem since

$$\left| \sum_{k=1}^{n} f_k \right| \leq |f|. \blacksquare$$

Problems

8. Suppose that μ is not complete, but that we define a bounded function f to be integrable over a set E of finite measure if

$$\sup_{\varphi \leq f} \int_E \varphi \, d\mu = \inf_{\psi \geq f} \int_E \psi \, d\mu$$

for all simple functions φ and ψ. Show that f is integrable if and only if it is measurable with respect to the completion of μ.

9. Prove Proposition 10. (Since μ is σ-finite, there is an increasing sequence $\langle X_n \rangle$ of measurable sets of finite measure whose union is X. For each pair $\langle n, k \rangle$ of integers let $E_{n,k} = \left\{ x \in X_n : \frac{k}{n} \leq f(x) < \frac{k+1}{n} \right\}$. Let $\varphi_n = \frac{1}{n} \sum_{k=0}^{n^2} k \chi_{E_{n,k}}$. Then $\langle \varphi_n \rangle$ is almost the required sequence.)

10. a. By $L^p(\mu)$, $1 \leq p < \infty$, we mean the space of all measurable functions f on $(X, \mathfrak{B}, \mu)$ such that

$$\int_X |f|^p \, d\mu < \infty.$$

We identify functions which are equal almost everywhere and define

$$\|f\|_p = \left\{\int |f|^p \, d\mu\right\}^{1/p}.$$

Show that the Hölder inequality

$$\int_X |fg| \, d\mu \le \|f\|_p \, \|g\|_q, \quad \frac{1}{p} + \frac{1}{q} = 1$$

holds for $1 < p < \infty$.

b. Show that the Hölder inequality holds for $p = 1$ if we define

$$\|f\|_\infty = \text{ess sup} \, |f|.$$

We use $L^\infty(\mu)$ to denote the space of all bounded measurable functions on $(X, \mathcal{B})$.

c. Show that the spaces $L^p(\mu)$ are Banach spaces.

d. Show that both $L^p[0, 1]$, and l^p are special cases of $L^p(\mu)$.

11. Let $\langle f_n \rangle$ be a sequence of measurable functions. We say that f_n **converges in measure** to f if given $\epsilon > 0$, there is an N such that

$$\mu\{x\colon |f_n(x) - f(x)| > \epsilon\} < \epsilon$$

for $n \ge N$. We say that $\langle f_n \rangle$ is a Cauchy sequence in measure if given $\epsilon > 0$, there is an N such that

$$\mu\{x\colon |f_n(x) - f_m(x)| > \epsilon\} < \epsilon$$

for $m, n \ge N$.

Show that a necessary and sufficient condition that a sequence $\langle f_n \rangle$ of measurable functions converge in measure to some function f is that it be a Cauchy sequence in measure. If $\langle f_n \rangle$ converges to f in measure, then there is a subsequence f_{n_ν} which converges to f almost everywhere, and hence almost everywhere convergence may be replaced by convergence in measure in the convergence theorems.

12. Let f be an integrable function on the measure space $(X, \mathcal{B}, \mu)$. Show that given $\epsilon > 0$, there is a $\delta > 0$ such that for each measurable set E with $\mu E < \delta$ we have

$$\left|\int_E f\right| < \epsilon.$$

4 SIGNED MEASURES

In this section we consider some of the possibilities which may arise if a measure is allowed to take on both positive and negative values.

We first note that if μ_1 and μ_2 are two measures defined on the same measurable space $(X, \mathcal{B})$ then we may define a new measure μ_3 on $(X, \mathcal{B})$ by setting

$$\mu_3(E) = c_1\mu_1(E) + c_2\mu_2(E) \qquad c_1, c_2 \geq 0.$$

What happens if we try to define a measure by

$$\nu E = \mu_1 E - \mu_2 E?$$

The first thing that may occur is that ν is not always nonnegative and this leads to the consideration of signed measures which we shall define later. A more serious difficulty comes from the fact that ν is not defined when $\mu_1 E = \mu_2 E = \infty$. For this reason we should have either μ_1 or μ_2 finite. With these considerations in mind we make the following definition:

Definition: *By a signed measure on the measurable space* $(X, \mathcal{B})$ *we mean an extended real-valued set function* ν *defined for the sets of* $\mathcal{B}$ *which satisfies:*

i. ν *assumes at most one of the values* $+\infty, -\infty$
ii. $\nu(\varnothing) = 0$
iii. $\nu\left(\bigcup_{i=1}^{\infty} E_i\right) = \sum_{i=1}^{\infty} \nu E_i$ *for any sequence* E_i *of disjoint measurable sets, the equality taken to mean that the series on the right converges absolutely if* $\nu(\bigcup E_i)$ *is finite and that it properly diverges otherwise.*

Thus a measure is a special case of a signed measure, but a signed measure is not in general a measure. We say that a set A is a **positive set** with respect to a signed measure ν if A is measurable and for every measurable subset E of A we have $\nu E \geq 0$. Every measurable subset of a positive set is again positive, and if we take the restriction of ν to a positive set we obtain a measure. Similarly, a set B is called a negative set if it is measurable and every measurable subset of it has nonpositive ν measure. A set which is both positive and negative with respect to ν is called a **null set.** A measurable set is a null set if and only if every measurable subset of it has ν measure zero. The reader should carefully note the distinction between a null set and a set of measure zero; while every null set must have measure zero, a set of measure zero may well be a union of two sets whose measures are not zero but are negatives of each other. Similarly, a positive set is not to be confused with a set which merely has positive measure.

We have the following lemmas concerning positive sets. Similar statements hold of course for negative sets.

18. Lemma: *Every measurable subset of a positive set is itself positive. The union of a countable collection of positive sets is positive.*

Proof: The first statement is trivially true by the definition of a positive set. To prove the second statement, let A be the union of a sequence $\langle A_n \rangle$ of positive sets. If E is any measurable subset of A, set

$$E_n = E \cap A_n \cap \tilde{A}_{n-1} \cap \cdots \cap \tilde{A}_1.$$

Then E_n is a measurable subset of A_n and so $\nu E_n \geq 0$. Since the E_n are disjoint and $E = \bigcup E_n$, we have

$$\nu E = \sum_{n=1}^{\infty} \nu E_n \geq 0.$$

Thus A is a positive set. ∎

19. Lemma: *Let E be a measurable set such that $0 < \nu E < \infty$. Then there is a positive set A contained in E with $\nu A > 0$.*

Proof: Either E itself is a positive set or it contains sets of negative measure. In the latter case let n_1 be the smallest positive integer such that there is a measurable set $E_1 \subset E$ with

$$\nu E_1 < -\frac{1}{n_1}.$$

Proceeding inductively, let n_k be the smallest positive integer for which there is a measurable set E_k such that

$$E_k \subset E \sim \left[\bigcup_{j=1}^{k-1} E_j\right]$$

and

$$\nu E_k < -\frac{1}{n_k}.$$

If we set

$$A = E \sim \bigcup_{k=1}^{\infty} E_k,$$

then

$$E = A \cup \left[\bigcup_{k=1}^{\infty} E_k\right].$$

Since this is a disjoint union, we have

$$\nu E = \nu A + \sum_{k=1}^{\infty} \nu E_k$$

with the series on the right absolutely convergent since νE is finite. Thus $\sum \frac{1}{n_k}$ converges, and we have $n_k \to \infty$. Since $\nu E_k \leq 0$ and $\nu E > 0$, we must have $\nu A > 0$.

To show that A is a positive set, let $\epsilon > 0$ be given. Since $n_k \to \infty$, we may choose k so large that $(n_k - 1)^{-1} < \epsilon$. Since

$$A \subset E \sim \left[\bigcup_{j=1}^{k} E_j\right],$$

A can contain no measurable sets with measure less than $-(n_k - 1)^{-1}$ which is greater than $-\epsilon$. Thus A contains no measurable sets of measure less than $-\epsilon$. Since ϵ is an arbitrary positive number, it follows that A can contain no sets of negative measure and so must be a positive set. ▌

20. Proposition (The Hahn Decomposition Theorem): *Let ν be a signed measure on the measurable space $(X, \mathcal{B})$. Then there is a positive set A and a negative set B such that $X = A \cup B$, and we may take $A \cap B = \varnothing$.*

Proof: Without loss of generality we may assume that $+\infty$ is the infinite value omitted by ν. Let λ be the supremum of νA over all sets A which are positive with respect to ν. Since the empty set is positive, $\lambda \geq 0$. Let $\langle A_i \rangle$ be a sequence of positive sets such that

$$\lambda = \lim_{i \to \infty} \nu A_i,$$

and set

$$A = \bigcup_{i=1}^{\infty} A_i.$$

By Lemma 18 the set A is itself a positive set, and so $\lambda \geq \nu A$. But $A \sim A_i \subset A$ and so $\nu(A \sim A_i) \geq 0$. Thus

$$\nu A = \nu A_i + \nu(A \sim A_i) \geq \nu A_i.$$

Hence $\nu A \geq \lambda$, and so $\nu A = \lambda$, and $\lambda < \infty$.

Let $B = \sim A$, and suppose E is a positive subset of B. Then E and A are disjoint and $E \cup A$ is a positive set.
Hence

$$\lambda \geq \nu(E \cup A) = \nu E + \nu A = \nu E + \lambda,$$

whence $\nu E = 0$, since $0 \leq \lambda < \infty$. Thus B contains no positive subsets of positive measure and hence no subsets of positive measure by Lemma 19. Consequently B is a negative set. ❙

A decomposition of X into two disjoint sets A and B such that A is positive for ν and B negative is called a **Hahn decomposition** for ν. Proposition 20 states the existence of a Hahn decomposition for each signed measure. Unfortunately, a Hahn decomposition is not unique.

If $\{A, B\}$ is a Hahn decomposition for ν, then we may define two measures ν^+ and ν^- such that $\nu = \nu^+ - \nu^-$ by setting

$$\nu^+(E) = \nu(E \cap A)$$

and

$$\nu^-(E) = -\nu(E \cap B).$$

Two measures ν_1 and ν_2 on $(X, \mathcal{B})$ are said to be mutually singular (in symbols $\nu_1 \perp \nu_2$) if there are disjoint measurable sets A and B with $X = A \cup B$ such that $\nu_1(A) = \nu_2(B) = 0$. Thus the measures ν^+ and ν^- defined above are mutually singular. We have thus established the existence part of the following proposition. The uniqueness part is left to the reader.

21. Proposition: *Let ν be a signed measure on the measurable space $(X, \mathcal{B})$. Then there are two mutually singular measures ν^+ and ν^- on $(X, \mathcal{B})$ such that $\nu = \nu^+ - \nu^-$. Moreover, there is only one such pair of mutually singular measures.*

The decomposition of ν given by the proposition is called the **Jordan decomposition** of ν. The measures ν^+ and ν^- are called the positive and negative parts (or variations) of ν. Since ν assumes at most one of the values $+\infty$ and $-\infty$, either ν^+ or ν^- must be finite. If they are both finite, we call ν a finite signed measure.

The measure $|\nu|$ defined by

$$|\nu|(E) = \nu^+E + \nu^-E$$

is called the absolute value or total variation of ν. A set E is positive for ν if $\nu^-E = 0$. It is a null set if $|\nu|(E) = 0$.

Problems

13. a. Give an example to show that the Hahn decomposition need not be unique.

b. Show that the Hahn decomposition is unique except for null sets.

14. Show that there is only one pair of mutually singular measures ν^+ and ν^- such that $\nu = \nu^+ - \nu^-$. [Hint: Show that any such pair determines a Hahn decomposition and apply the results of 13(*b*).]

15. Show that if E is any measurable set, then

$$-\nu^- E \leq \nu E \leq \nu^+ E$$

and

$$|\nu E| \leq |\nu| (E).$$

16. Show that if ν_1 and ν_2 are any two finite signed measures then so is $\alpha\nu_1 + \beta\nu_2$ where α and β are real numbers. Show that

$$|\alpha\nu| = |\alpha| \, |\nu|$$

and

$$|\nu_1 + \nu_2| \leq |\nu_1| + |\nu_2|,$$

where $\nu \leq \mu$ means $\nu E \leq \mu E$ for all measurable sets E.

17. We define integration with respect to a signed measure ν by defining

$$\int f \, d\nu = \int f \, d\nu^+ - \int f \, d\nu^-.$$

If $|f| \leq M$

$$\left| \int_E f \, d\nu \right| \leq M \, |\nu|(E).$$

5 THE RADON-NIKODYM THEOREM

Let $(X, \mathscr{B})$ be a fixed measurable space. If μ and ν are two measures defined on $(X, \mathscr{B})$, we say that μ and ν are **mutually singular** (and write $\mu \perp \nu$) if there are disjoint sets A and B in $\mathscr{B}$ such that $X = A \cup B$ and $\nu A = \mu B = 0$. Despite the fact that the notion of singularity is symmetric in ν and μ we sometimes say that ν is singular with respect to μ. The notion antithetical to singularity is absolute continuity: A measure ν is said to be **absolutely continuous** with respect to the measure μ if $\nu A = 0$ for each set A for which $\mu A = 0$.

We use the symbolism $\nu << \mu$ for ν absolutely continuous with respect to μ.

In the case of signed measures μ and ν, we say $\nu << \mu$ if $|\nu| << |\mu|$ and $\nu \perp \mu$ if $|\nu| \perp |\mu|$.

Whenever we are dealing with more than one measure on a measurable space $(X, \mathcal{B})$ the term 'almost everywhere' becomes ambiguous, and we must specify almost everywhere with respect to μ or almost everywhere with respect to ν, etc. These are abbreviated a.e. $[\mu]$ and a.e. $[\nu]$. If $\nu << \mu$ and a property holds a.e. $[\mu]$, then it holds a.e. $[\nu]$.

Let μ be a measure, and f a nonnegative measurable function on X. For E in $\mathcal{B}$, set

$$\nu E = \int_E f\, d\mu.$$

Then ν is a set function defined on $\mathcal{B}$, and it follows from Proposition 17 that ν is countably additive and hence a measure. The measure ν will be finite if and only if f is integrable. Since the integral over a set of μ-measure zero is zero, we have ν absolutely continuous with respect to μ. The next theorem shows that, subject to σ-finiteness restrictions, every absolutely continuous measure ν is obtained in this fashion.

22. Theorem (Radon-Nikodym): *Let $(X, \mathcal{B}, \mu)$ be a σ-finite measure space, and let ν be a measure defined on $\mathcal{B}$ which is absolutely continuous with respect to μ. Then there is a nonnegative measurable function f such that for each set E in $\mathcal{B}$ we have*

$$\nu E = \int_E f\, d\mu.$$

The function f is unique in the sense that if g is any measurable function with this property then $g = f$ a.e. $[\mu]$.

Proof: The extension from the finite to the σ-finite case is not difficult and is left to the reader. Thus we assume that μ is finite. The concept of the proof is fairly straightforward: If ν is defined by $\nu E = \int_E f\, d\mu$, then the sets $\{x: f(x) > \alpha\}$ and $\{x: f(x) \leq \alpha\}$ form a Hahn decomposition for the signed measure $\nu - \alpha\mu$. This suggests that the negative set in the Hahn decomposition of $\nu - \alpha\mu$ will be the set $B_\alpha = \{x: f(x) \leq \alpha\}$, and when we know these sets for each α we can construct f by $f(x) = \inf \{\alpha: x \in B_\alpha\}$. There is unfortunately one technical difficulty in this program: The Hahn decomposition is unique only to within sets of measure zero, and unless $\mu\{x\} > 0$, we can assign the point x to either of the two sets in a Hahn decomposition of $\nu - \alpha\mu$. We can avoid this difficulty if we consider only rational values for α and take a fixed decomposition for each rational α. We now begin the proof in earnest.

Since μ is finite, $\nu - \alpha\mu$ is a signed measure for each rational number α. For each nonnegative rational number α, let $\{A_\alpha, B_\alpha\}$ be a Hahn decomposition for $\nu - \alpha\mu$. If $t \geq \alpha$, then B_α is a negative set for the signed measure $\nu - t\mu$; for if E is a measurable subset of B_α, then $\nu E - t\mu E \leq \nu E - \alpha\mu E \leq 0$. Similarly, A_α is a positive set for each measure $\nu - t\mu$ with $t \leq \alpha$.

Let us set $A_\infty = \bigcap A_\alpha$. Then A_∞ is the intersection of a countable collection of measurable sets and so must be measurable. If E is any measurable subset of A_∞, we have $E \subset A_\alpha$ for each α, and so $(\nu - \alpha\mu)E \geq 0$, or $\alpha\mu E \leq \nu E$. But this can be true for each rational α only if $\mu E = 0$ or $\nu E = \infty$. Thus $\mu E > 0$ implies $\nu E = \infty$.

We define a nonnegative extended-real-valued function f by setting

$$f(x) = \inf \{\alpha: x \in B_\alpha\},$$

where we follow the usual convention of setting $f(x) = \infty$ if $x \notin \bigcup B_\alpha$. Thus $f(x) = \infty$ if $x \in A_\infty$. For each real number t we have

$$\{x: f(x) \leq t\} = \bigcap_{\beta > t} \bigcup_{\alpha < \beta} B_\alpha$$

where α and β range over rational numbers, and so f is a measurable function.

If $\alpha < \beta$, then B_α is a negative set for $\nu - \beta\mu$, and so by Lemma 18 the set $\bigcup_{\alpha<\beta} B_\alpha$ is also a negative set for $\nu - \beta\mu$. Thus if E is any measurable set on which $f \leq \gamma$, then for each $\beta > \gamma$ we have $E \subset \bigcup_{\alpha<\beta} B_\alpha$, and hence $\nu E - \beta\mu E \leq 0$. But this can be true for each $\beta > \gamma$ only if $\nu E \leq \gamma\mu E$. Since $\{x: f(x) \leq \alpha\} \supset B_\alpha$ for α rational, we have $\{x: f(x) > \alpha\} \subset \tilde{B}_\alpha = A_\alpha$. Consequently, if $f > \alpha$ on a measurable set E, we have $E \subset A_\alpha$ and hence $\nu E \geq \alpha\mu E$. Therefore if $E = \{x: \alpha < f(x) \leq \gamma\}$ then $\alpha\mu E \leq \nu E \leq \gamma\mu E$.

We are now going to show that for any measurable set E we have

$$\nu E = \int_E f\,d\mu.$$

If $\mu[E \cap A_\infty] > 0$, then $\nu[E \cap A_\infty] = \infty$ and $\nu E = \infty$. Also

$$\int_E f\,d\mu \geq \int_{E \cap A_\infty} f\,d\mu = \infty,$$

and so

$$\nu E = \int_E f\,d\mu.$$

Let us now suppose that $\mu[E \cap A_\infty] = 0$. Then the absolute continuity of ν with respect to μ implies that $\nu[E \cap A_\infty] = 0$. Choose a positive integer N, and set

$$E_k = \left\{x \in E\colon \frac{k-1}{N} < f(x) \leq \frac{k}{N}\right\}.$$

Then

$$\frac{k-1}{N}\,\mu E_k \leq \nu E_k \leq \frac{k}{N}\,\mu E_k. \tag{1}$$

Since E is the disjoint union of the sets E_k and $E \cap A_\infty$, while $\nu(E \cap A_\infty) = \mu(E \cap A_\infty) = 0$, we have

$$\nu E = \sum_{k=1}^{\infty} \nu E_k$$

and

$$\int_E f\,d\mu = \sum_{k=1}^{\infty} \int_{E_k} f\,d\mu.$$

By the mean value theorem

$$\frac{k-1}{N}\,\mu E_k \leq \int_{E_k} f\,d\mu \leq \frac{k}{N}\,\mu E_k. \tag{2}$$

From the inequalities (1) and (2) it follows that

$$-\frac{1}{N}\,\mu E_k \leq \int_{E_k} f\,d\mu - \nu E_k \leq \frac{1}{N}\,\mu E_k.$$

Summing over k, we have

$$-\frac{1}{N}\,\mu E \leq \int_E f\,d\mu - \nu E \leq \frac{1}{N}\,\mu E.$$

Since μE is finite and N is an arbitrary positive integer,

$$\nu E = \int_E f\,d\mu. \blacksquare$$

The function f given by Theorem 22 is called the **Radon-Nikodym derivative** of ν with respect to μ. It is sometimes denoted by $\left[\frac{d\nu}{d\mu}\right]$.

23. Proposition (Lebesgue Decomposition): *Let $(X, \mathcal{B}, \mu)$ be a σ-finite measure space and ν a σ-finite measure defined on $\mathcal{B}$. Then we can find a measure ν_0 which is singular with respect to μ and a measure ν_1 which is absolutely continuous with respect to μ such that $\nu = \nu_0 + \nu_1$. The measures ν_0 and ν_1 are unique.*

Proof: Since μ and ν are σ-finite measures, so is the measure $\lambda = \mu + \nu$. Since both μ and ν are absolutely continuous with respect to λ, the Radon-Nikodym theorem asserts the existence of nonnegative measurable functions f and g such that for each $E \in \mathcal{B}$

$$\mu E = \int_E f\,d\lambda, \qquad \nu E = \int_E g\,d\lambda.$$

Let $A = \{x: f(x) > 0\}$ and $B = \{x: f(x) = 0\}$. Then X is the disjoint union of A and B, while $\mu B = 0$. If we define ν_0 by

$$\nu_0 E = \nu(E \cap B),$$

we have $\nu_0(A) = 0$ and so $\nu_0 \perp \mu$. Let

$$\nu_1(E) = \nu(E \cap A) = \int_{E \cap A} g\,d\lambda.$$

Then $\nu = \nu_0 + \nu_1$, and we have only to show that $\nu_1 << \mu$. Let E be a set of μ-measure zero. Then

$$0 = \mu E = \int_E f\,d\lambda,$$

and $f = 0$ a.e. $[\lambda]$ on E. Since $f > 0$ on $A \cap E$, we must have $\lambda(A \cap E) = 0$. Hence $\nu(A \cap E) = 0$, and so $\nu_1(E) = \nu(A \cap E) = 0$. This establishes the proposition except for the uniqueness which is left to the reader. ∎

Problems

18. a. Show that the Radon-Nikodym theorem for finite measures μ implies the theorem for σ-finite measures μ. (Hint: Decompose X into a countable union of sets X_i of finite μ-measure and apply the Radon-Nikodym theorem to each X_i to obtain f. Show f to have the required properties.)

b. Show the uniqueness of the function f in the Radon-Nikodym theorem.

19. ***Radon-Nikodym Derivatives.*** Show that the Radon-Nikodym derivative $\left[\frac{d\nu}{d\mu}\right]$ has the following properties:

a. $\left[\frac{d(\nu_1 + \nu_2)}{d\mu}\right] = \left[\frac{d\nu_1}{d\mu}\right] + \left[\frac{d\nu_2}{d\mu}\right].$

b. If $\nu << \mu << \lambda$, then

$$\left[\frac{d\nu}{d\lambda}\right] = \left[\frac{d\nu}{d\mu}\right]\left[\frac{d\mu}{d\lambda}\right].$$

c. If $\nu << \mu$ and $\mu << \nu$, then

$$\left[\frac{d\nu}{d\mu}\right] = \left[\frac{d\mu}{d\nu}\right]^{-1}.$$

d. If $\nu << \mu$ and f is ν-integrable, then

$$\int f\,d\nu = \int f\left[\frac{d\nu}{d\mu}\right]d\mu.$$

20. a. Show that if ν is a signed measure such that $\nu \perp \mu$ and $\nu << \mu$, then $\nu = 0$.

b. Show that if ν_1 and ν_2 are singular with respect to μ then so is $c_1\nu_1 + c_2\nu_2$.

c. Show that if ν_1 and ν_2 are absolutely continuous with respect to μ so is $c_1\nu_1 + c_2\nu_2$.

d. Prove the uniqueness assertion in the Lebesgue decomposition.

21. Extend the Radon-Nikodym theorem to the case of signed measures.

22. ***Complex Measures:*** A set function ν which assigns a complex number νE to each E in a σ-algebra $\mathcal{B}$ is called a complex measure if

$\nu\varnothing = 0$ and for each countable disjoint union $\bigcup E_i$ of sets in $\mathcal{B}$ we have

$$\nu(\bigcup E_i) = \sum_{i=1}^{\infty} \nu E_i$$

with absolute convergence on the right.

a. Show that each complex measure may be expressed as $\nu = \mu_1 - \mu_2 + i\mu_3 - i\mu_4$ where μ_1, μ_2, μ_3, and μ_4 are finite measures.

b. Show that for each complex measure ν there is a measure μ and a complex-valued measurable function φ with $|\varphi| = 1$ such that for each set E in $\mathcal{B}$,

$$\nu E = \int_E \varphi \, d\mu.$$

(Hint: Apply the Radon-Nikodym theorem to the measures μ_i with respect to the measure $\mu_1 + \mu_2 + \mu_3 + \mu_4$.)

c. Show that the measure μ in (b) is unique and that φ is uniquely determined to within sets of μ measure zero.

23. ***Linear Functionals on $L^p(\mu)$.***

a. Let $(X, \mathcal{B}, \mu)$ be a σ-finite measure space. Show that for $1 \leq p < \infty$ each bounded linear functional F on $L^p(\mu)$ is given by

$$F[f] = \int fg \, d\mu$$

where g is in L^q, $\frac{1}{q} + \frac{1}{p} = 1$, and $\|F\| = \|g\|_q$. (Hint: Modify the proof of Theorem 6.8, using the Radon-Nikodym theorem.)

b. Show that the above result is still true if μ is not σ-finite provided $p > 1$. (Hint: Apply the previous result to each set of finite μ-measure and show that the g obtained is unique.)

24. ***Decomposable Measures.*** Let $(X, \mathcal{B}, \mu)$ be a measure space. A collection $\{X_\alpha\}$ of disjoint measurable subsets of X is called a decomposition for μ if $\mu X_\alpha < \infty$ for each α and if $\mu E = 0$ for every measurable set E such that $\mu(E \cap X_\alpha) = 0$ for all α. A measure μ is called decomposable if it has a decomposition. It is called completely decomposable if it has a decomposition $\{X_\alpha\}$ with the property that every set E with $E \cap X_\alpha$ measurable for each α is itself measurable. (Such a decomposition will be referred to as a complete decomposition.)

a. Show that every decomposable measure can be extended to a completely decomposable measure $\bar{\mu}$. If μ is a complete measure, then the measurable sets of $\bar{\mu}$ which are of finite measure are measurable sets for μ.

b. If $\{X_\alpha\}$ is a decomposition for μ, and if E is any measurable set, then $\mu E = \Sigma\, \mu(X_\alpha \cap E)$ where Σ is meant in the sense of Problem 2.19.

c. If $\{X_\alpha\}$ is a complete decomposition for μ, then f is measurable if and only if the restriction of f to X_α is measurable for each α. If f is a nonnegative measurable function of X, then

$$\int_X f\, d\mu = \sum_\alpha \int_{X_\alpha} f\, d\mu.$$

d. Let ν be absolutely continuous with respect to μ, and suppose that there is a collection $\{X_\alpha\}$ which is a decomposition for ν and a complete decomposition for μ. Then there is a nonnegative real-valued function f such that for every measurable set E we have

$$\nu E = \int_E f\, d\mu.$$

e. Show that the conclusion of (d) holds whenever μ is completely decomposable and ν is a σ-finite measure which is absolutely continuous with respect to μ.

f. Show that the conclusion of (d) holds whenever μ is completely decomposable and ν is absolutely continuous with respect to μ and satisfies $\nu E \le \mu E$ for all $E \in \mathcal{B}$.

g. Show that the conclusion of 23(a) still holds for $p = 1$ and μ a decomposable measure.

h. Let X be the unit square $\{(x, y)\colon 0 \le x \le 1,\ 0 \le y \le 1\}$, and let $\mathcal{B}$ be the family of all sets E for which $\{x\colon (x, y) \in E\}$ is Lebesgue measurable for each $y \in [0, 1]$ and $\{y\colon (x, y) \in E\}$ is Lebesgue measurable for each $x \in [0, 1]$. Then $\mathcal{B}$ is a σ-algebra. Let $\nu(E) = \sum_y m\{x\colon (x, y) \in E\}$ where m is Lebesgue measure. Then $(X, \mathcal{B}, \nu)$ is a measure space which is decomposable but not σ-finite.

i. Let X and $\mathcal{B}$ be as in (h), and define

$$\mu(E) = \sum_y m\{x\colon (x, y) \in E\} + \sum_x m\{y\colon (x, y) \in E\}.$$

Then μ is a measure and ν is absolutely continuous with respect to μ. However, there is no $f \in L^1(\mu)$ such that $\nu E = \int_E f\, d\mu$ for all E in $\mathcal{B}$. Thus the measure space $(X, \mathcal{B}, \mu)$ is not decomposable.

j. Let X, $\mathcal{B}$, μ and ν be as in (*h*) and (i). Show that $F(f) = \int f\,d\nu$ defines a bounded linear functional on $L^1(\mu)$, but that there is no g in $L^\infty(\mu)$ such that

$$F(f) = \int fg\,d\mu.$$

25. ***Alternate Proof of the Radon-Nikodym Theorem*:** We can give a proof of the Radon-Nikodym theorem which is independent of the Hahn decomposition theorem by using Proposition 10.28 which states that for each bounded linear functional F on a Hilbert space H there is a g in H such that $F(f) = (f, g)$ for all f in H. The details are outlined below:

a. Let μ and ν be finite measures on a measurable space $(X, \mathcal{B})$ and set $\lambda = \mu + \nu$. Define $F(f) = \int f\,d\mu$. Then F is a bounded linear functional on $L^2(\lambda)$.

b. The function $g \in L^2(\lambda)$ such that $F(f) = (f, g)$ satisfies $0 \le g \le 1$, and

$$\mu(E) = \int_E g\,d\lambda$$

$$\nu(E) = \int_E (1 - g)\,d\lambda.$$

c. If $\nu << \mu$, then $\lambda << \mu$ and $g = 0$ only on a set of μ-measure zero. In this case

$$\lambda(E) = \int_E g^{-1}\,d\mu.$$

(Hint: Consider, for a fixed n, the sets

$$E_k = \left\{x \in E\colon \frac{n}{k+1} < g(x) \le \frac{n}{k}\right\}.$$

Then

$$\frac{k}{n}\,\mu(E_k) \le \lambda(E_k) \le \frac{k+1}{n}\,\mu(E_k),$$

and, apart from a set of λ-measure zero, E is the disjoint union of the sets E_k.)

d. If $\nu << \mu$, then $(1 - g)g^{-1}$ is integrable with respect to μ and

$$\nu(E) = \int_E (1 - g)g^{-1}\,d\mu.$$

12 Measure and Outer Measure

In this chapter we first consider some of the ways in which a measure can be defined on a σ-algebra. In the case of Lebesgue measure we first defined measure on open sets and then defined outer measure from which we obtained the notion of measurable set and Lebesgue measure. Such a procedure is feasible in general. In the first section we discuss the process of deriving a measure from an outer measure, and in the second section we derive an outer measure from a measure which is defined only on an algebra of sets. The remainder of the chapter is devoted to some applications of this process.

OUTER MEASURE AND MEASURABILITY

By an outer measure μ^* we mean an extended-real-valued set function defined on all subsets of a space X and having the properties:

i. $\mu^* \varnothing = 0$;

ii. $A \subset B \Rightarrow \mu^* A \leq \mu^* B$;

iii. $E \subset \bigcup_{i=1}^{\infty} E_i \Rightarrow \mu^* E \leq \sum_{i=1}^{\infty} \mu^* E_i$.

The second property is called monotonicity and the third countable subadditivity. In view of (i) finite subadditivity follows from (iii). Because of (ii), property (iii) can be replaced by

iii'. $E = \bigcup_{i=1}^{\infty} E_i$, E_i disjoint $\Rightarrow \mu^* E \leq \sum_{i=1}^{\infty} \mu^* E_i$.

The outer measure μ^* is called finite if $\mu^* X < \infty$. It is called σ-finite if

$$X = \bigcup_{i=1}^{\infty} E_i, \quad \mu^* E_i < \infty.$$

In analogy to the case of Lebesgue measure we define a set E to be measurable with respect to μ^* if for every set A we have

$$\mu^*(A) = \mu^*(A \cap E) + \mu^*(A \cap \tilde{E}).$$

In view of the subadditivity of μ^* it is only necessary to show that

$$\mu^*(A) \geq \mu^*(A \cap E) + \mu^*(A \cap \tilde{E})$$

for every A in order to prove that E is measurable. Since this inequality is trivially true when $\mu^*A = \infty$, we need only establish it for sets A with μ^*A finite.

1. Theorem: *The class $\mathcal{B}$ of μ^*-measurable sets is a σ-algebra. If $\bar{\mu}$ is μ^* restricted to $\mathcal{B}$, then $\bar{\mu}$ is a complete measure on $\mathcal{B}$.*

Proof: Trivially the empty set is measurable. Since the definition of the measurability of E is symmetric in E and $\tilde{E}$ it follows that $\tilde{E}$ is measurable whenever E is.

Suppose now that E_1 and E_2 are measurable sets. Then since E_2 is measurable,

$$\mu^*(A) = \mu^*(A \cap E_2) + \mu^*(A \cap \tilde{E}_2),$$

and since E_1 is also measurable

$$\mu^*(A) = \mu^*(A \cap E_2) + \mu^*(A \cap \tilde{E}_2 \cap E_1) + \mu^*(A \cap \tilde{E}_1 \cap \tilde{E}_2).$$

Now

$$A \cap [E_1 \cup E_2] = [A \cap E_2] \cup [A \cap E_1 \cap \tilde{E}_2],$$

and so by subadditivity

$$\mu^*(A \cap [E_1 \cup E_2]) \leq \mu^*(A \cap E_2) + \mu^*(A \cap \tilde{E}_2 \cap E_1),$$

whence

$$\mu^*A \geq \mu^*(A \cap [E_1 \cup E_2]) + \mu^*(A \cap \tilde{E}_1 \cap \tilde{E}_2),$$

which means that $E_1 \cup E_2$ is measurable since

$$\sim(E_1 \cup E_2) = \tilde{E}_1 \cap \tilde{E}_2.$$

Thus the union of two measurable sets is measurable and so by induction the union of any finite number of measurable sets is measurable, and $\mathcal{B}$ is an algebra of sets.

Assume that $\langle E_i \rangle$ is a disjoint sequence of measurable sets and $E = \bigcup E_i$. Then, setting

$$G_n = \bigcup_{i=1}^{n} E_i.$$

We have G_n measurable and

$$\mu^*(A) = \mu^*(A \cap G_n) + \mu^*(A \cap \tilde{G}_n) \geq \mu^*(A \cap G_n) + \mu^*(A \cap \tilde{E}),$$

since $\tilde{E} \subset \tilde{G}_n$. Now $G_n \cap E_n = E_n$ and $G_n \cap \tilde{E}_n = G_{n-1}$. Since E_n is measurable, we have

$$\mu^*(A \cap G_n) = \mu^*(A \cap E_n) + \mu^*(A \cap G_{n-1})$$

and by induction

$$\mu^*(A \cap G_n) = \sum_{i=1}^{n} \mu^*(A \cap E_i).$$

Thus

$$\mu^*(A) \geq \mu^*(A \cap \tilde{E}) + \sum_{i=1}^{\infty} \mu^*(A \cap E_i) \geq \mu^*(A \cap \tilde{E}) + \mu^*(A \cap E),$$

since

$$A \cap E \subset \bigcup_{i=1}^{\infty} (A \cap E_i).$$

Thus E is measurable, and since the union of any sequence of sets of an algebra can be replaced by a disjoint union of sets of the algebra it follows that $\mathcal{B}$ is a σ-algebra.

We next demonstrate the finite additivity of $\bar{\mu}$. Let E_1 and E_2 be disjoint measurable sets. Then by the measurability of E_2

$$\begin{aligned}\bar{\mu}(E_1 \cup E_2) &= \mu^*(E_1 \cup E_2)\\ &= \mu^*([E_1 \cup E_2] \cap E_2) + \mu^*([E_1 \cup E_2] \cap \tilde{E}_2)\\ &= \mu^*E_2 + \mu^*E_1.\end{aligned}$$

Finite additivity follows by induction.

If now E is the disjoint union of the measurable sets $\{E_i\}$ then

$$\bar{\mu}(E) \geq \bar{\mu}\left(\bigcup_{i=1}^{n} E_i\right) = \sum_{i=1}^{n} \bar{\mu}(E_i),$$

and so

$$\bar{\mu}(E) \geq \sum_{i=1}^{\infty} \bar{\mu}(E_i).$$

But

$$\bar{\mu}(E) \leq \sum_{i=1}^{\infty} \bar{\mu}(E_i)$$

by the subadditivity of μ^*. Hence $\bar{\mu}$ is countably additive and thus a measure since $\bar{\mu}\varnothing = \mu^*\varnothing = 0$ and since μ^* is nonnegative. ∎

Problems

1. Prove that (iii′) and (ii) imply (iii) in the definition of outer measure.
2. Prove that an outer measure is nonnegative.
3. Prove the completeness of $\bar{\mu}$.

2 THE EXTENSION THEOREM

By a **measure on an algebra** we mean a nonnegative extended-real valued set function μ defined on an algebra $\mathcal{A}$ of sets such that

i. $\mu(\varnothing) = 0$;

ii. If $\langle A_i \rangle$ is a disjoint sequence of sets in $\mathcal{A}$ whose union is also in $\mathcal{A}$, then

$$\mu\left(\bigcup_{i=1}^{\infty} A_i\right) = \sum_{i=1}^{\infty} \mu A_i.$$

Thus a measure on an algebra $\mathcal{A}$ is a measure if and only if $\mathcal{A}$ is a σ-algebra. The purpose of this section is to show that if we start with a measure on an algebra $\mathcal{A}$ of sets we may extend it to be a measure defined on a σ-algebra $\mathcal{B}$ containing $\mathcal{A}$. We shall do this by using the measure on the algebra to construct an outer measure μ^* and show that the measure $\bar{\mu}$ induced by μ^* is the desired extension of μ. The process by which we construct μ^* from μ is analogous to that by which we constructed Lebesgue outer measure from the lengths of intervals: We define

$$\mu^* E = \inf \sum_{i=1}^{\infty} \mu A_i \tag{1}$$

where $\langle A_i \rangle$ ranges over all sequences from $\mathcal{A}$ such that $E \subset \bigcup_{i=1}^{\infty} A_i$. We first establish some lemmas concerning μ^*.

2. Lemma: *If $A \in \mathcal{A}$ and if $\langle A_i \rangle$ is any sequence of sets in $\mathcal{A}$ such that $A \subset \bigcup_{i=1}^{\infty} A_i$, then $\mu A \leq \sum_{i=1}^{\infty} \mu A_i$.*

Proof: Set

$$B_n = A \cap A_n \cap \tilde{A}_{n-1} \cap \cdots \cap \tilde{A}_1.$$

Then $B_n \in \mathcal{A}$ and $B_n \subset A_n$. But A is the disjoint union of the sequence $\langle B_n \rangle$, and so by countable additivity

$$\mu A = \sum_{n=1}^{\infty} \mu B_n \leq \sum_{n=1}^{\infty} \mu A_n. \blacksquare$$

3. Corollary: *If $A \in \mathcal{A}$, $\mu^* A = \mu A$.*

4. Lemma: *The set function μ^* is an outer measure.*

Proof: Since μ^* is clearly a monotone nonnegative set function defined for all sets and $\mu^* \varnothing = 0$, we have only to show that it is countably subadditive. Let $E \subset \bigcup_{i=1}^{\infty} E_i$. If $\mu^* E_i = \infty$ for any i, we have $\mu^* E \leq \Sigma\, \mu^* E_i = \infty$. If not, given $\epsilon > 0$, there is for each i a sequence $\langle A_{ij} \rangle_{j=1}^{\infty}$ of sets in $\mathcal{A}$ such that $E_i \subset \bigcup_{j=1}^{\infty} A_{ij}$ and

$$\sum_{i=1}^{\infty} \mu A_{ij} < \mu^* E_i + \epsilon/2^i$$

Then

$$\mu^* E \leq \sum_{ij} \mu A_{ij} < \sum_{i=1}^{\infty} \mu^* E_i + \epsilon.$$

Since ϵ was an arbitrary positive number,

$$\mu^* E \leq \sum_{i=1}^{\infty} \mu^* E_i,$$

and μ^* is subadditive. $\blacksquare$

5. Lemma: *If $A \in \mathcal{A}$, then A is measurable with respect to μ^*.*

Proof: Let E be an arbitrary set of finite outer measure and ϵ a positive number. Then there is a sequence $\langle A_i \rangle$ from $\mathcal{A}$ such that $E \subset \bigcup A_i$ and

$$\Sigma\, \mu A_i < \mu^* E + \epsilon.$$

By the additivity of μ on $\mathcal{A}$ we have

$$\mu(A_i) = \mu(A_i \cap A) + \mu(A_i \cap \tilde{A}).$$

Hence

$$\mu^* E + \epsilon > \sum_{i=1}^{\infty} \mu(A_i \cap A) + \sum_{i=1}^{\infty} \mu(A_i \cap \tilde{A})$$

$$> \mu^*(E \cap A) + \mu^*(E \cap \tilde{A}),$$

since

$$E \cap A \subset \bigcup (A_i \cap A)$$

and

$$E \cap \tilde{A} \subset \bigcup (A_i \cap \tilde{A}).$$

Thus, since ϵ was an arbitrary positive number,

$$\mu^*E \geq \mu^*(E \cap A) + \mu^*(E \cap \tilde{A}),$$

and A is measurable. ▌

The outer measure μ^* which we have defined is called the *outer measure induced by* μ. Combining the three lemmas we have the following theorem:

6. Theorem: *Let μ be a measure on an algebra $\mathcal{A}$. Then the set function μ^* defined by (1) is an outer measure and the measure $\bar{\mu}$ induced by μ^* is an extension of μ to a σ-algebra of sets which contains $\mathcal{A}$. If μ is finite (or σ-finite) so is $\bar{\mu}$.*

For a given algebra $\mathcal{A}$ of sets we use $\mathcal{A}_\sigma$ to denote those sets which are countable unions of sets of $\mathcal{A}$ and use $\mathcal{A}_{\sigma\delta}$ to denote those sets which are countable intersections of sets in $\mathcal{A}_\sigma$. Proposition 9 can be considered a generalization of the first principle of Littlewood.

7. Proposition: *Let μ be a measure on an algebra $\mathcal{A}$ and μ^* the outer measure induced by μ. Then given any set E, and any $\epsilon > 0$, there is a set $A \in \mathcal{A}_\sigma$ such that $E \subset A$ and*

$$\mu^*A \leq \mu^*E + \epsilon.$$

Proof: By the definition of μ^* there is a sequence $\langle A_i \rangle$ from $\mathcal{A}$ such that $E \subset \bigcup A_i$ and

$$\sum_{i=1}^{\infty} \mu A_i \leq \mu^*E + \epsilon .$$

Set $A = \bigcup A_i$. Then $\mu^*A \leq \Sigma\, \mu^*A_i = \Sigma\, \mu A_i$. ▌

8. Proposition: *Let μ be a measure on an algebra $\mathcal{A}$ and μ^* the outer measure induced by μ. Then given any set E with $\mu^*E < \infty$, there is a set A in $\mathcal{A}_{\sigma\delta}$ with $E \subset A$ and $\mu^*E = \mu^*A$.*

Proof: Given a positive integer n, there is a set A_n in $\mathcal{A}_\sigma$ such that $E \subset A_n$ and $\mu^*A_n < \mu^*E + \frac{1}{n}$. Let $A = \bigcap A_n$. Then $A \in \mathcal{A}_{\sigma\delta}$ and $E \subset A$. Since $A \subset A_n$, $\mu^*A \leq \mu^*A_n < \mu^*E + \frac{1}{n}$. Since n is arbitrary, $\mu^*A \leq \mu^*E$. But $E \subset A$, and so $\mu^*A \geq \mu^*E$ by monotonicity. Hence $\mu^*A = \mu^*E$. ▌

9. Proposition: *Let μ be a σ-finite measure on an algebra $\mathcal{A}$, and let μ^* be the outer measure generated by μ. A set E is μ^* measurable if and only if E is the proper difference $A \sim B$ of a set A in $\mathcal{A}_{\sigma\delta}$ and a set B with $\mu^*B = 0$. Each set B with $\mu^*B = 0$ is contained in a set C in $\mathcal{A}_{\sigma\delta}$ with $\mu^*C = 0$.*

Proof: The "if" part of the proposition follows from the fact that each set in $\mathcal{A}_{\sigma\delta}$ must be measurable, since the measurable sets form a σ-algebra, while each set of μ^*-measure zero must be measurable, since $\bar{\mu}$ is complete.

To prove the "only if" part of the proposition, let $X = \bigcup_{i=1}^{\infty} X_i$ where $X_i \in \mathcal{A}$ and $\mu X_i < \infty$. If E is measurable, then E is the disjoint union of the measurable sets $E_i = X_i \cap E$. By Proposition 7 we can find for each positive integer n a set A_{ni} in $\mathcal{A}_\sigma$ such that $E_i \subset A_{ni}$ and

$$\bar{\mu}A_{ni} \leq \bar{\mu}E_i + \frac{1}{n2^i}.$$

Set

$$A_n = \bigcup_{i=1}^{\infty} A_{ni}.$$

Then $E \subset A_n$, and $A_n \sim E \subset \bigcup_{i=1}^{\infty} [A_{ni} \sim E_i]$.

Hence

$$\bar{\mu}(A_n \sim E) \leq \sum_{i=1}^{\infty} \bar{\mu}(A_{ni} \sim E_i)$$

$$\leq \sum_{i=1}^{\infty} \frac{1}{n2^i} = \frac{1}{n}.$$

Since $A_n \in \mathcal{A}_\sigma$, the set $A = \bigcap_{n=1}^{\infty} A_n$ is in $\mathcal{A}_{\sigma\delta}$, and for each n

$$A \sim E \subset A_n \sim E.$$

Hence

$$\bar{\mu}(A \sim E) \leq \bar{\mu}(A_n \sim E) \leq \frac{1}{n}.$$

Since this holds for each positive integer n, we must have

$$\bar{\mu}(A \sim E) = 0. \blacksquare$$

The next proposition shows that if we consider sets in the smallest σ-algebra $\mathcal{B}$ containing $\mathcal{A}$, then the extension $\bar{\mu}$ is the only possible extension of μ on sets of finite outer measure. If also μ is σ-finite, then $\bar{\mu}$ is the only extension of μ to $\mathcal{B}$.

10. Proposition: *Let μ be a measure on an algebra $\mathcal{A}$, μ^* the induced outer measure, and μ_1 any extension of μ to the smallest σ-algebra $\mathcal{B}$ containing $\mathcal{A}$. If $\mu^*B < \infty$ for a set B in $\mathcal{B}$, then $\mu_1 B = \mu^*B$. If μ is a σ-finite measure then the extension of μ to $\mathcal{B}$ is unique.*

Proof: Since each set in $\mathcal{A}_\sigma$ can be expressed as a disjoint countable union of sets in $\mathcal{A}$, the measure μ_1 must be uniquely defined on $\mathcal{A}_\sigma$, that is, it must agree with $\bar{\mu}$ on $\mathcal{A}_\sigma$. Let B be any set in $\mathcal{B}$ with finite outer measure. Then by Proposition 7 there is an A in $\mathcal{A}_\sigma$ such that $B \subset A$ and

$$\mu^*A \leq \mu^*B + \epsilon.$$

Since $B \subset A$,

$$\mu_1 B \leq \mu_1 A = \mu^*A \leq \mu^*B + \epsilon.$$

Since ϵ is an arbitrary positive number, we have

$$\mu_1 B \leq \mu^*B$$

for each $B \in \mathcal{B}$.

Since the class of sets measurable with respect to μ^* is a σ-algebra containing $\mathcal{A}$, each B in $\mathcal{B}$ must be measurable. If B is measurable and A is in $\mathcal{A}_\sigma$ with $B \subset A$ and $\mu^*A \leq \mu^*B + \epsilon$, then

$$\mu^*A = \mu^*B + \mu^*(A \sim B),$$

and so

$$\mu^*(A \sim B) \leq \epsilon,$$

if $\mu^*B < \infty$. Hence

$$\begin{aligned} \mu^*B \leq \mu^*A &= \mu_1 A \\ &= \mu_1 B + \mu_1(A \sim B) \\ &\leq \mu_1 B + \epsilon. \end{aligned}$$

Since ϵ is arbitrary, we have

$$\mu^*B \leq \mu_1 B$$

and so

$$\mu^*B = \mu_1 B.$$

If μ is a σ-finite measure, let $\{X_i\}$ be a countable disjoint collection of sets in $\mathcal{A}$ with $X = \bigcup X_i$ and μX_i finite. If B is any set in $\mathcal{B}$, then

$$B = \bigcup (X_i \cap B)$$

and this is a countable disjoint union of sets in $\mathcal{B}$, and so we have

$$\mu_1 B = \sum \mu_1(X_i \cap B)$$

and

$$\bar{\mu} B = \sum \bar{\mu}(X_i \cap B).$$

Since $\mu^*(X_i \cap B) < \infty$, we have

$$\bar{\mu}(X_i \cap B) = \mu_1(X_i \cap B). \ \blacksquare$$

It is often convenient to start with a set function on a collection $\mathcal{C}$ of sets having less structure than an algebra of sets. We say that a collection $\mathcal{C}$ of subsets of X is a **semialgebra** of sets if the intersection of any two sets in $\mathcal{C}$ is again in $\mathcal{C}$ and the complement of any set in $\mathcal{C}$ is a finite disjoint union of sets in $\mathcal{C}$. If $\mathcal{C}$ is any semialgebra of sets, then the collection $\mathcal{A}$ consisting of the empty set and all finite disjoint unions of sets in $\mathcal{C}$ is an algebra of sets which is called the algebra generated by $\mathcal{C}$. If μ is a set function defined on $\mathcal{C}$, it is natural to attempt to define a finitely additive set function on $\mathcal{A}$ by setting $\mu A = \sum_{i=1}^{n} \mu E_i$ whenever A is the disjoint union of the sets E_i in $\mathcal{C}$. Since a set A in $\mathcal{A}$ may possibly be represented in several ways as a disjoint union of sets in $\mathcal{C}$, we must be certain that such a procedure leads to a unique value for μA. The following proposition gives conditions under which this procedure can be carried out and will give a measure on the algebra $\mathcal{A}$.

11. Proposition: *Let $\mathcal{C}$ be a semialgebra of sets and μ a non-negative set function defined on $\mathcal{C}$ with $\mu\varnothing = 0$ (if $\varnothing \in \mathcal{C}$). Then μ has a unique extension to a measure on the algebra $\mathcal{A}$ generated by $\mathcal{C}$ if the following conditions are satisfied:*

i. If a set C in $\mathcal{C}$ is the union of a finite disjoint collection $\{C_i\}$ of sets in $\mathcal{C}$, then $\mu C = \Sigma\, \mu C_i$.

ii. If a set C in $\mathcal{C}$ is the union of a countable disjoint collection $\{C_i\}$ of sets in $\mathcal{C}$, then $\mu C \leq \Sigma\, \mu C_i$.

Problems

4. Prove Proposition 11 by showing:

a. Condition (i) implies that, if A is the union of each of two finite disjoint collections $\{C_i\}$ and $\{D_j\}$ of sets in $\mathcal{C}$, then $\Sigma\, \mu C_i = \Sigma\, \mu D_j$. (Hint: $\mu C_i = \sum_j \mu(C_i \cap D_j)$.)

b. Condition (ii) implies that μ is countably additive on $\mathcal{A}$. (For finite additivity and monotonicity already imply the reverse inequality.)

5. Show that the last statement in Proposition 10 need not be true if μ is not σ-finite. (Construct an example by letting X be the set of rational numbers and $\mathcal{A}$ the algebra of finite unions of intervals of the form $(a, b]$ with $\mu(a, b] = \infty$ and $\mu\varnothing = 0$. The extension of μ to the smallest σ-algebra containing $\mathcal{A}$ is not unique.)

6. If we start with an outer measure μ^* on X and form the induced measure $\bar{\mu}$ on the μ^*-measurable sets, we can use $\bar{\mu}$ to induce an outer measure μ^+.

a. Show that for each set E we have $\mu^+E \geq \mu^*E$.

b. For a given set E we have $\mu^+E = \mu^*E$ if and only if there is a μ^*-measurable set $A \supset E$ with $\mu^*A = \mu^*E$.

c. An outer measure which satisfies the criterion in (b) for each set E is called a **regular** outer measure. Show that every outer measure induced by a measure on an algebra is regular.

d. Let X be a set consisting of two points. Construct an outer measure on X which is not regular.

7. Let μ be a finite measure on an algebra $\mathcal{A}$, and μ^* the induced outer measure. Show that a set E is measurable if and only if for each $\epsilon > 0$ there is a set $A \in \mathcal{A}_\delta$, $A \subset E$, such that $\mu^*(E \sim A) < \epsilon$.

*3 THE LEBESGUE-STIELTJES INTEGRAL

Let X be the set of real numbers and $\mathcal{B}$ the class of all Borel sets. A measure μ defined on $\mathcal{B}$ is called a **Borel measure** (on the real line). If μ is a finite Borel measure we associate to it a function F called its cumulative distribution function by setting

$$F(x) = \mu(-\infty, x]. \tag{2}$$

The function F is a real-valued monotone increasing function, and

$$\mu(a, b] = F(b) - F(a).$$

Since $(a, b]$ is the intersection of the sets $\left(a, b + \frac{1}{n}\right]$, Proposition 11.2 implies that

$$\mu(a, b] = \lim_{n\to\infty} \mu\left(a, b + \frac{1}{n}\right],$$

and so

$$F(b) = \lim_{n\to\infty} F\left(b + \frac{1}{n}\right) = F(b+).$$

Thus a cumulative distribution function is continuous on the right. Similarly

$$\begin{aligned}\mu\{b\} &= \lim_{n\to\infty} \mu\left(b - \frac{1}{n}, b\right] \\ &= \lim_{n\to\infty} F(b) - F\left(b - \frac{1}{n}\right) \\ &= F(b) - F(b-).\end{aligned}$$

Hence F is continuous at b if and only if the set $\{b\}$ consisting of b alone has measure zero. Since $\varnothing = \bigcap\, (-\infty, -n]$, we have

$$\lim_{n\to-\infty} F(n) = 0,$$

and hence

$$\lim_{x\to-\infty} F(x) = 0,$$

because of the monotonicity of F. We summarize these properties in the following lemma:

12. Lemma: *If μ is a finite Borel measure on the real line then its cumulative distribution function F is a monotone increasing bounded function which is continuous on the right. Moreover,* $\lim_{x\to-\infty} F(x) = 0$.

Suppose that we begin with a monotone increasing function F which is continuous on the right. Then we shall show that there is a unique Borel measure μ such that

$$\mu(a, b] = F(b) - F(a) \tag{3}$$

for all intervals of the form $(a, b]$, where we define $F(\infty) = \lim_{x\to\infty} F(x)$ and $F(-\infty) = \lim_{x\to-\infty} F(x)$. We begin with the following lemma, whose proof is left to the reader (Problem 8):

13. Lemma: *Let F be a monotone increasing function continuous on the right. If $(a, b] \subset \bigcup_{i=1}^{\infty} (a_i, b_i]$, then*

$$F(b) - F(a) \le \sum_{i=1}^{\infty} F(b_i) - F(a_i).$$

If we let $\mathcal{C}$ be the semialgebra consisting of all intervals of the form $(a, b]$ and set $\mu(a, b] = F(b) - F(a)$, then μ is easily seen to satisfy condition (i) of Proposition 11, and since Lemma 13 is precisely the second condition, we see that μ admits a unique extension to a measure on the algebra generated by $\mathcal{C}$. By Theorem 6 this μ can be extended to a σ-algebra containing $\mathcal{C}$. Since the class $\mathcal{B}$ of Borel sets is the smallest σ-algebra containing $\mathcal{C}$, we have an extension of μ to a Borel measure. The measure μ is σ-finite, since X is the union of the intervals $(n, n + 1]$ and each has finite measure. Hence Proposition 10 implies that the extension of μ to $\mathcal{B}$ is unique, and we have the following proposition:

14. Proposition: *Let F be a monotone increasing function which is continuous on the right. Then there is a unique Borel measure μ such that for all a and b we have*

$$\mu(a, b] = F(b) - F(a).$$

15. Corollary: *Each bounded monotone function which is continuous on the right is the cumulative distribution function of a unique finite Borel measure provided $F(-\infty) = 0$.*

If φ is a nonnegative Borel measurable function and F is a monotone increasing function which is continuous on the right we define the Lebesgue-Stieltjes integral of φ with respect to F as

$$\int \varphi\, dF = \int \varphi\, d\mu$$

where μ is the Borel measure having F as its cumulative distribution function. If φ is both positive and negative, we call it integrable with respect to F if $\int \varphi^+\, dF$ and $\int \varphi^-\, dF$ are both finite. In this case we set

$$\int \varphi\, dF = \int \varphi^+\, dF - \int \varphi^-\, dF.$$

If F is any monotone increasing function, then there is a unique function F^* which is monotone increasing, continuous on the right and agrees with F wherever F is continuous on the right (Problem 9). Then we can define the Lebesgue-Stieltjes integral of φ with respect to F by

$$\int \varphi\, dF = \int \varphi\, dF^*.$$

If F is a monotone function, continuous on the right, then

$$\int_a^b \varphi\, dF$$

agrees with the Riemann-Stieltjes integral whenever the latter is defined. The Lebesgue-Stieltjes integral is only defined when F is monotone [or more generally of bounded variation as in Problem 10(c)] while the Riemann-Stieltjes integral can exist when F is not of bounded variation, say when F is continuous and φ is of bounded variation.

Problems

8. Prove Lemma 13. (Choose $\epsilon > 0$. By the continuity on the right of F, choose $\eta_i > 0$ so that $F(b_i + \eta_i) < F(b_i) + \epsilon 2^{-i}$, and choose $\delta > 0$ so that $F(a + \delta) < F(a) + \epsilon$. Then the open intervals $(a_i, b_i + \eta_i)$ cover the closed interval $[a + \delta, b]$, and the proof proceeds like that of Proposition 3.1. A little extra care must be taken when $(a, b]$ is infinite.)

9. Let F be a monotone increasing function, and define

$$F^*(x) = \lim_{y \to x+} F(y).$$

Then F^* is a monotone increasing function which is continuous on the right and agrees with F wherever F is continuous on the right. We have $(F^*)^* = F^*$, and if F and G are monotone increasing functions which agree wherever they are both continuous, then $F^* = G^*$.

10. a. Show that each bounded function F of bounded variation gives rise to a finite signed Borel measure ν such that

$$\nu(a, b] = F(b+) - F(a+).$$

b. Compare Theorem 5.4 with the Jordan decomposition of ν.

c. Extend the definition of the Lebesgue-Stieltjes integral $\int \varphi dF$ to functions F of bounded variation.

11. a. Let F be the cumulative distribution function of the Borel measure ν, and assume that F is continuous. Then for any Borel set E we have $mE = \nu[F^{-1}(E)]$, with m Lebesgue measure. (Hint: This is true for intervals, and the uniqueness part of Proposition 10 can be used to conclude its truth in general.)

b. Generalize to the case of discontinuous cumulative distribution functions.

12. a. Show that a measure μ is absolutely continuous with respect to Lebesgue measure if and only if its cumulative distribution function is absolutely continuous.

b. If μ is absolutely continuous with respect to Lebesgue measure, then its Radon-Nikodym derivative is the derivative of its cumulative distribution function.

4 PRODUCT MEASURES

Let $(X, \mathcal{A}, \mu)$ and $(Y, \mathcal{B}, \nu)$ be two complete measure spaces, and consider the direct product $X \times Y$ of X and Y. If $A \subset X$ and $B \subset Y$, we call $A \times B$ a rectangle. If $A \in \mathcal{A}$ and $B \in \mathcal{B}$, we call $A \times B$ a measurable rectangle. The collection $\mathcal{R}$ of measurable rectangles is a semialgebra, since

$$(A \times B) \cap (C \times D) = (A \cap C) \times (B \cap D)$$

and

$$\sim(A \times B) = (\tilde{A} \times B) \cup (A \times \tilde{B}) \cup (\tilde{A} \times \tilde{B}).$$

If $A \times B$ is a measurable rectangle, we set

$$\lambda(A \times B) = \mu A \cdot \nu B.$$

16. Lemma: *Let $\{(A_i \times B_i)\}$ be a countable disjoint collection of measurable rectangles whose union is a measurable rectangle $A \times B$. Then*

$$\lambda(A \times B) = \sum \lambda(A_i \times B_i).$$

Proof: Fix a point $x \in A$. Then for each $y \in B$, the point $\langle x, y \rangle$ belongs to exactly one rectangle $A_i \times B_i$. Thus B is the disjoint union of those B_i such that x is in the corresponding A_i. Hence

$$\sum \nu B_i \cdot \chi_{A_i}(x) = \nu B \cdot \chi_A(x),$$

since ν is countably additive. Thus by the corollary of the Monotone Convergence Theorem (11.16), we have

$$\sum \int \nu B_i \cdot \chi_{A_i} \, d\mu = \int \nu(B) \cdot \chi_A \, d\mu,$$

or

$$\sum \nu B_i \cdot \mu A_i = \nu B \cdot \mu A. \quad \blacksquare$$

The lemma implies that λ satisfies the conditions of Proposition 11 and hence has a unique extension to a measure on the algebra $\mathcal{R}'$

consisting of all finite disjoint unions of sets in $\mathcal{R}$. Theorem 6 allows us to extend λ to be a complete measure on a σ-algebra $\mathcal{S}$ containing $\mathcal{R}$. This extended measure is called the product measure of μ and ν and is denoted by $\mu \times \nu$. If μ and ν are finite (or σ-finite) so is $\mu \times \nu$. If X and Y are the real line and μ and ν are both Lebesgue measure, then $\mu \times \nu$ is called two-dimensional Lebesgue measure for the plane.

The purpose of the next few lemmas is to describe the structure of the sets which are measurable with respect to the product measure $\mu \times \nu$. If E is any subset of $X \times Y$ and x a point of X, we define the *x cross-section* E_x by

$$E_x = \{y: \langle x, y\rangle \in E\},$$

and similarly for the y cross-section for ay in Y. The characteristic function of E_x is related to that of E by

$$\chi_{E_x}(y) = \chi_E(x, y).$$

17. Lemma: *Let x be a point of X and E a set in $\mathcal{R}_{\sigma\delta}$. Then E_x is a measurable subset of Y.*

Proof: The lemma is trivially true if E is in the class $\mathcal{R}$ of measurable rectangles. We next show it to be true for E in $\mathcal{R}_\sigma$. Let $E = \bigcup_{i=1}^{\infty} E_i$, where each E_i is a measurable rectangle. Then

$$\begin{aligned}\chi_{E_x}(y) &= \chi_E(x, y)\\ &= \sup_i \chi_{E_i}(x, y)\\ &= \sup_i \chi_{(E_i)_x}(y).\end{aligned}$$

Since each E_i is a measurable rectangle, $\chi_{(E_i)_x}(y)$ is a measurable function of y, and so χ_{E_x} must also be measurable, whence E_x is measurable.

Suppose now that $E = \bigcap_{i=1}^{\infty} E_i$ with $E_i \in \mathcal{R}_\sigma$. Then

$$\begin{aligned}\chi_{E_x}(y) &= \chi_E(x, y)\\ &= \inf_i \chi_{E_i}(x, y)\\ &= \inf_i \chi_{(E_i)_x}(y),\end{aligned}$$

and we see that χ_{E_x} is measurable. Thus E_x is measurable for any $E \in \mathcal{R}_{\sigma\delta}$. ∎

18. Lemma: *Let E be a set in $\mathcal{R}_{\sigma\delta}$ with $\mu \times \nu(E) < \infty$. Then the function g defined by*

$$g(x) = \nu E_x$$

is a measurable function of x and

$$\int g \, d\mu = \mu \times \nu(E).$$

Proof: The lemma is trivially true if E is a measurable rectangle. We first note that any set in $\mathcal{R}_\sigma$ is a disjoint union of measurable rectangles. Let $\langle E_i \rangle$ be a disjoint sequence of measurable rectangles, and let $E = \bigcup E_i$. Set

$$g_i(x) = \nu[(E_i)_x].$$

Then each g_i is a nonnegative measurable function, and

$$g = \sum g_i.$$

Thus g is measurable, and by the corollary of the Monotone Convergence Theorem (11.16), we have

$$\begin{aligned} \int g \, d\mu &= \sum \int g_i \, d\mu \\ &= \sum \mu \times \nu(E_i) \\ &= \mu \times \nu(E) \end{aligned}$$

Consequently, the lemma holds for $E \in \mathcal{R}_\sigma$.

Let E be a set of finite measure in $\mathcal{R}_{\sigma\delta}$. Then there is a sequence $\langle E_i \rangle$ of sets in $\mathcal{R}_\sigma$ such that $E_{i+1} \subset E_i$ and $E = \bigcap E_i$. It follows from Proposition 7 that we may take $\mu \times \nu E_1 < \infty$. Let $g_i(x) = \nu[(E_i)_x]$. Then $g(x) = \lim g_i(x)$, and so g is measurable. Since

$$\int g_1 \, d\mu = \mu \times \nu(E_1) < \infty,$$

we have $g_1(x) < \infty$ for almost all x. For an x with $g_1(x) < \infty$, we have $\langle (E_i)_x \rangle$ a decreasing sequence of measurable sets of finite measure whose intersection is E_x.

Thus by Proposition 11.2 we have

$$\begin{aligned} g(x) = \nu(E_x) &= \lim \nu[(E_i)_x] \\ &= \lim g_i(x). \end{aligned}$$

Hence

$$g_i \to g \qquad \text{a.e.,}$$

and so g is measurable. Since $0 \leq g_i \leq g_1$, the Lebesgue Convergence Theorem implies that

$$\begin{aligned}\int g\,d\mu &= \lim \int g_i\,d\mu \\ &= \lim \mu \times \nu(E_i) \\ &= \mu \times \nu(E),\end{aligned}$$

the last equality following from Proposition 11.2. ▎

19. Lemma: *Let E be a set for which $\mu \times \nu(E) = 0$. Then for almost all x we have $\nu(E_x) = 0$.*

Proof: By Proposition 8 there is a set F in $\mathcal{R}_{\sigma\delta}$ such that $E \subset F$ and $\mu \times \nu(F) = 0$. It follows from Lemma 18 that for almost all x we have $\nu(F_x) = 0$. But $E_x \subset F_x$, and so $\nu E_x = 0$ for almost all x since ν *is complete.* ▎

20. Proposition: *Let E be a measurable subset of $X \times Y$ such that $\mu \times \nu(E)$ is finite. Then for almost all x the set E_x is a measurable subset of Y. The function g defined by*

$$g(x) = \nu(E_x)$$

is a measurable function defined for almost all x and

$$\int g\,d\mu = \mu \times \nu(E).$$

Proof: By Proposition 8 there is a set F in $\mathcal{R}_{\sigma\delta}$ such that $E \subset F$ and $\mu \times \nu(F) = \mu \times \nu(E)$. Let $G = F \sim E$. Since E and F are measurable, so is G, and

$$\mu \times \nu(F) = \mu \times \nu(E) + \mu \times \nu(G).$$

Since $\mu \times \nu(E)$ is finite and equal to $\mu \times \nu(F)$, we have $\mu \times \nu(G) = 0$. Thus by Lemma 19 we have $\nu G_x = 0$ for almost all x. Hence

$$g(x) = \nu E_x = \nu F_x \qquad \text{a.e.},$$

and so g is a measurable function by Lemma 18. Again by Lemma 18

$$\begin{aligned}\int g\,d\mu &= \mu \times \nu(F) \\ &= \mu \times \nu(E).\end{aligned}$$ ▎

The following two theorems enable us to interchange the order of integration and to calculate integrals with respect to product measures by iteration.

21. Theorem (Fubini): *Let $(X, \mathcal{A}, \mu)$ and $(Y, \mathcal{B}, \nu)$ be two complete measure spaces and f an integrable function on $X \times Y$. Then*

i. *For almost all x the function f_x defined by $f_x(y) = f(x, y)$ is an integrable function on Y;*

i′. *for almost all y the function f_y defined by $f_y(x) = f(x, y)$ is an integrable function on X;*

ii. $\int_Y f(x, y)\, d\nu(y)$ *is an integrable function on X;*

ii′. $\int_X f(x, y)\, d\mu(x)$ *is an integrable function on Y;*

iii. $\int_X \left[\int_Y f\, d\nu\right] d\mu = \int_{X \times Y} f d(\mu \times \nu) = \int_Y \left[\int_X f\, d\mu\right] d\nu.$

Proof: Because of the symmetry between x and y it suffices to prove (i), (ii) and the first half of (iii). If the conclusion of the theorem holds for each of two functions, it also holds for their difference, and hence it is sufficient to consider the case when f is nonnegative. Proposition 20 asserts that the theorem is true if f is the characteristic function of a measurable set of finite measure, and hence the theorem must be true if f is a simple function which vanishes outside a set of finite measure. But Corollary 11.11 asserts that for each nonnegative integrable function f there is an increasing sequence $\langle \varphi_n \rangle$ of nonnegative simple functions such that $f = \lim \varphi_n$. Hence f_x is measurable. By the monotone convergence theorem

$$\int_Y f(x, y)\, d\nu(y) = \lim \int_Y \varphi_n(x, y)\, d\nu(y),$$

and so this integral is a measurable function of x. Again by the monotone convergence theorem

$$\begin{aligned} \int_X \left[\int_Y f\, d\nu\right] d\mu &= \lim \int_X \left[\int_Y \varphi_n\, d\nu\right] d\mu \\ &= \lim \int_{X \times Y} \varphi_n d(\mu \times \nu) \\ &= \int_{X \times Y} f d(\mu \times \nu). \quad \blacksquare \end{aligned}$$

In order to apply the Fubini Theorem, one must first verify that f is integrable with respect to $\mu \times \nu$, that is one must show that f is a measurable function on $X \times Y$ and that $\int |f| \, d(\mu \times \nu) < \infty$. The measurability of f on $X \times Y$ is sometimes difficult to establish, but in many cases we can establish it by topological considerations (cf. Problem 17). In the case when μ and ν are σ-finite, the integrability of f can be determined by iterated integration using the following theorem:

22. Theorem (Tonelli): *Let $(X, \mathcal{A}, \mu)$ and $(Y, \mathcal{B}, \nu)$ be two σ-finite measure spaces, and let f be a nonnegative measurable function on $X \times Y$. Then*

- **i.** *for almost all x the function f_x defined by $f_x(y) = f(x, y)$ is a measurable function on Y;*
- **i′.** *for almost all y the function f_y defined by $f_y(x) = f(x, y)$ is a measurable function on X;*
- **ii.** $\int_Y f(x, y) \, d\nu(y)$ *is a measurable function on X;*
- **ii′.** $\int_X f(x, y) \, d\mu(x)$ *is a measurable function on Y;*
- **iii.** $\int_X \left[\int_Y f \, d\nu \right] d\mu = \int_{X \times Y} f d(\mu \times \nu) = \int_Y \left[\int_X f \, d\mu \right] d\nu.$

Proof: For a nonnegative measurable function f the only point in the proof of Theorem 21 where the integrability of f was used was to infer the existence of an increasing sequence $\langle \varphi_n \rangle$ of simple functions each vanishing outside a set of finite measure such that $f = \lim \varphi_n$. But if μ and ν are σ-finite, then so is $\mu \times \nu$, and any nonnegative measurable function on $X \times Y$ can be so approximated by Proposition 11.10. ▌

Problems

13. Let $X = Y$ be the set of positive integers, $\mathcal{A} = \mathcal{B} = \mathcal{P}(X)$, and let $\nu = \mu$ be the measure defined by setting $\mu(E)$ equal to the number of points in E if E is finite and ∞ if E is an infinite set. (This measure is called the counting measure.) State the Fubini and Tonelli Theorems explicitly for this case.

14. Let $(X, \mathcal{A}, \mu)$ be any σ-finite measure space, and Y the set of positive integers with ν the counting measure (Problem 13). Then Theorem 22 and the corollary to Theorem 11.15 state the same conclusion. However, Theorem 11.15 is valid even if μ is not σ-finite, and hence the Tonelli Theorem is true without σ-finiteness if $(Y, \mathcal{B}, \nu)$ is this special measure space.

15. Use the following example to show that we cannot remove the hypothesis that f be nonnegative from the Tonelli Theorem or that f be integrable from the Fubini Theorem. Let $X = Y$ be the positive integers and $\mu = \nu$ be the counting measure. Let

$$\begin{aligned} f(x, y) &= 2 - 2^{-x} && \text{if } x = y \\ &= -2 + 2^{-x} && \text{if } x = y + 1 \\ &= 0 && \text{otherwise.} \end{aligned}$$

16. Use the following example to show that we cannot remove the hypothesis that f be integrable from the Fubini Theorem or that μ and ν are σ-finite from the Tonelli Theorem: Let $X = Y$ be the interval $[0, 1]$, with $\mathcal{A} = \mathcal{B}$ the class of Borel sets. Let μ be Lebesgue measure, and ν the counting measure. Then the diagonal $\Delta = \{\langle x, y\rangle \in X \times Y: x = y\}$ is measurable (is an $\mathcal{R}_{\sigma\delta}$ in fact) but its characteristic function fails to satisfy any of the equalities in condition (iii) of the Fubini and Tonelli Theorems.

17. Let $X = Y = [0, 1]$, and let $\mu = \nu$ be Lebesgue measure. Show that each open set in $X \times Y$ is measurable, and hence each Borel set in $X \times Y$ is measurable.

18. Let h and g be integrable functions on X and Y, and define $f(x, y) = h(x)g(y)$. Then f is integrable on $X \times Y$ and

$$\int_{X\times Y} f d(\mu \times \nu) = \int_X h\, d\mu \int_Y g\, d\nu.$$

Note: We do not need to assume that μ and ν are σ-finite.

*5 CARATHEODORY OUTER MEASURE

Let X be a set of points and Γ a set of real-valued functions on X. It is often of interest to know conditions under which an outer measure μ^* will have the property that every function in Γ will be measurable, and it is the purpose of the present section to prove the sufficiency of one criterion for this.

Two sets are said to be *separated by the function* φ if there are numbers a and b with $a > b$ such that φ is greater than a on one and less than b on the other. An outer measure μ^* will be called a **Carathéodory outer measure** (with respect to Γ) if it satisfies the following axiom:

iv. If A and B are two sets which are separated by some function in Γ, then $\mu^*(A \cup B) = \mu^* A + \mu^* B$.

23. Proposition: *If* μ^* *is a Carathéodory outer measure, then every function in* Γ *is* μ^**-measurable.*

Proof: Given the real number a and the function $\varphi \in \Gamma$, we must show that the set

$$E = \{x: \varphi(x) > a\}$$

is μ^*-measurable, or equivalently, that given any set A,

$$\mu^* A \geq \mu^*(A \cap E) + \mu^*(A \cap \tilde{E}).$$

Since this inequality is trivial if $\mu^* A = \infty$, we suppose $\mu^* A < \infty$.

We begin by setting $B = E \cap A$, $C = \tilde{E} \cap A$, and

$$B_n = \left\{x: (x \in B) \;\&\; \left(\varphi(x) > a + \frac{1}{n}\right)\right\}.$$

Defining $R_n = B_n \sim B_{n-1}$, we have

$$B = B_n \cup \left[\bigcup_{k=n+1}^{\infty} R_k\right].$$

Now on B_{n-2} we have $\varphi > a + 1/(n-2)$, while on R_n we have $\varphi \leq a + 1/(n-1)$. Thus φ separates R_n and B_{n-2} and hence separates R_{2k} and $\bigcup_{j=1}^{k-1} R_{2j}$, since this latter set is contained in B_{2k-2}. Consequently,

$$\mu^*\left[\bigcup_{j=1}^{k} R_{2j}\right] = \mu^* R_{2x} + \mu^*\left[\bigcup_{j=1}^{k-1} R_{2j}\right]$$
$$= \sum_{j=1}^{k} \mu^* R_{2j},$$

by induction. Since

$$\bigcup_{j=1}^{k} R_{2j} \subset B \subset A,$$

we have

$$\sum_{j=1}^{k} \mu^* R_{2j} \leq \mu^* A,$$

and so the series $\sum_{j=1}^{\infty} \mu^* R_{2j}$ converges. Similarly the series

$$\sum_{k=1}^{\infty} \mu^* R_{2j+1}$$

converges, and therefore also the series

$$\sum_{k=1}^{\infty} \mu^* R_k.$$

From this it follows that, given $\epsilon > 0$, we can choose n so large that

$$\sum_{k=n}^{\infty} \mu^* R_k < \epsilon.$$

Then by the subadditivity of μ^*

$$\mu^* B \leq \mu^* B_n + \sum_{k=n+1}^{\infty} \mu^* R_k$$

$$< \mu^* B_n + \epsilon,$$

or

$$\mu^* B_n > \mu^* B - \epsilon.$$

Now

$$\mu^* A \geq \mu^*(B_n \cup C)$$
$$= \mu^* B_n + \mu^* C$$

since φ separates B_n and C. Consequently,

$$\mu^* A \geq \mu^* B + \mu^* C - \epsilon.$$

Since ϵ is an arbitrary positive quantity

$$\mu^* A \geq \mu^* B + \mu^* C. \ \blacksquare$$

24. Proposition: *Let* (X, ρ) *be a metric space, and let* μ^* *be an outer measure on* X *with the property that* $\mu^*(A \cup B) = \mu^* A + \mu^* B$ *whenever* $\rho(A, B) > 0$. *Then every closed set (and hence every Borel set) is measurable with respect to* μ^*.

Problem

19. Prove Proposition 24. (Let Γ be the set of functions φ of the form $\varphi(x) = \rho(x, E)$. Show that μ^* satisfies (iv) with respect to Γ, and note that for a closed set F we have $F = \{x\colon \rho(x, F) \leq 0\}$.)

13 The Daniell Integral

1 INTRODUCTION

It is sometimes convenient to introduce integration directly without first going through the process of defining a measure. We are often confronted with an integral I defined on some class L of functions and we would like to enlarge the class L and extend I so that most of the usual properties of the Lebesgue integral, including the convergence theorems, hold.

For example we might take L to be the set of continuous functions on $(-\infty, \infty)$ each of which vanishes outside a finite interval and I to be the Riemann integral. Since the principal deficiency of the Riemann integral is the failure of the convergence theorems to hold, an extension for which they are valid is useful. This has been done by Daniell for this case and generalized by Stone, who has also clarified the structure of the extended integral. It is the purpose of the present chapter to describe this extension procedure and to show its connection with measure theory.

Let L be a family of real-valued functions on some set X, and suppose that L is a vector lattice, that is, that whenever the functions f and g are in L so also are the functions $\alpha f + \beta g$, $f \vee g$, and $f \wedge g$. Since $f \wedge g = f + g - (f \vee g)$ and $f \vee g = (f - g) \vee 0 + g$, we see that a vector space L of functions is a vector lattice if for each h in L we have $h \vee 0$ in L. Thus a vector space of functions is a vector lattice if it is closed under the operation $f \to f^+ = f \vee 0$. Since $|f| = f^+ + (-f)^+$, each vector lattice contains the absolute value of each function in the lattice. Conversely, if L is a vector space such that $|f|$ is in L for each f in L then L is a vector lattice, for $f^+ = \frac{1}{2}(f + |f|)$.

A linear functional I on L is said to be positive[1] if $I(\varphi) \geq 0$ for each nonnegative function φ in L. If I is positive and $\varphi \leq \psi$, then $I(\varphi) \leq I(\psi)$. A positive linear functional I on L is called a Daniell functional or a Daniell integral if the following condition is satisfied:

(D) If $\langle \varphi_n \rangle$ is an increasing sequence of functions in L, and if φ is a function in L such that[2] $\varphi \leq \lim \varphi_n$, then $I(\varphi) \leq \lim I(\varphi_n)$.

A second condition which is clearly equivalent is the following:

(D′) If $\langle u_n \rangle$ is a sequence of nonnegative functions in L, and if φ is a function in L such that $\varphi \leq \Sigma\, u_n$, then $I(\varphi) \leq \Sigma\, I(u_n)$.

One example of a Daniell integral is given by taking I to be integration with respect to a measure μ for which the functions in L are integrable. Another example is given by taking L to be all continuous functions on $(-\infty, \infty)$ each of which vanishes outside of some finite interval and by taking $I[\varphi]$ to be the Riemann integral of φ. [It takes a little proof to show that (D) holds in this case. See the argument in Section 5.]

Suppose that L, as in the last example above, is not closed under the process of taking limits of sequences from L. Can we extend L to a larger vector lattice which is closed in this respect and to which I can be extended? It is the purpose of the next section to show that it can always be done and that the extension of I has all the properties that we find in integration with respect to a measure. In Section 3 we will see that under mild restrictions this extension is in fact integration with respect to a suitable measure.

THE EXTENSION THEOREM

We begin by considering the class L_u consisting of all those extended real-valued functions on X each of which is a limit of a monotone increasing sequence of functions in L. It is clear that if f and g are in L_u, then so is the function $\alpha f + \beta g$ where α and β are nonnegative constants. If $\langle \varphi_n \rangle$ is an increasing sequence of functions from L then $\langle I(\varphi_n) \rangle$ must be an increasing sequence of real numbers and so must have a limit (which may be ∞). It is tempting to try to define $\lim I(\varphi_n)$

[1] Properly speaking, we should call I "nonnegative," but the use of "positive" in this connection seems to be standard.

[2] Here, of course, lim means pointwise limit.

as the value of I for the function f which is the pointwise limit of the sequence $\langle\varphi_n\rangle$. In order to do this we need to know that this value depends only on the function f and not on the choice of the increasing sequence $\langle\varphi_n\rangle$ whose limit is f. That this is so is guaranteed by the following lemma:

1. Lemma: *If $\langle\varphi_n\rangle$ and $\langle\psi_m\rangle$ are increasing sequences from L and if $\lim \varphi_n \le \lim \psi_m$, then $\lim I(\varphi_n) \le \lim I(\psi_m)$.*

Proof: For fixed n, we have $\varphi_n \le \lim \varphi_n \le \lim \psi_m$, and so $I(\varphi_n) \le \lim I(\psi_m)$ by (D). Hence $\lim I(\varphi_n) \le \lim I(\psi_m)$. ∎

Thus we can extend the functional I to be an extended real-valued functional on L_u with the property that $I(f) \le I(g)$ for $f \le g$ and $I(\alpha f + \beta g) = \alpha I(f) + \beta I(g)$ for positive constants α and β and functions f and g in L_u. It is clear that L_u is a lattice, for if $\varphi_n \uparrow f$ and $\psi_n \uparrow g$, then $\varphi_n \wedge \psi_n \uparrow f \wedge g$ and $\varphi_n \vee \psi_n \uparrow f \vee g$.

2. Lemma: *A nonnegative function f belongs to L_u if and only if there is a sequence $\langle\psi_\nu\rangle$ of nonnegative functions in L such that $f = \sum_{\nu=1}^{\infty} \psi_\nu$. In this case $I(f) = \sum_{\nu=1}^{\infty} I(\psi_\nu)$.*

Proof: The "if" part is trivial. On the other hand let f be nonnegative and $\varphi_n \uparrow f$ with $\varphi_n \in L$. By replacing φ_n by $\varphi_n \vee 0$, we may assume that each φ_n is nonnegative. Set $\psi_1 = \varphi_1$, $\psi_n = \varphi_n - \varphi_{n-1}$ for $n > 1$. Then $f = \sum_{\nu=1}^{\infty} \psi_\nu$, and

$$\begin{aligned} I(f) &= \lim I(\varphi_n) \\ &= \lim I\left(\sum_{\nu=1}^{n} \psi_\nu\right) \\ &= \lim \sum_{\nu=1}^{n} I(\psi_\nu) \\ &= \sum_{\nu=1}^{\infty} I(\psi_\nu). \ ∎ \end{aligned}$$

3. Lemma: *Let $\langle f_n\rangle$ be a sequence of nonnegative functions in L_u. Then the function $f = \sum_{n=1}^{\infty} f_n$ is in L_u and $I(f) = \sum_{n=1}^{\infty} I(f_n)$.*

Proof: For each n there is a sequence $\langle\psi_{n,\nu}\rangle$ of nonnegative functions in L such that $f_n = \sum_{n=1}^{\infty} \psi_{n,\nu}$. Hence $f = \sum_{\nu,n} \psi_{n,\nu}$. Since the set of pairs of integers is countable, f is the sum of a sequence of nonnegative functions in L and so must be in L_u. Also

$$I(f) = \sum_{\nu,n} I(\varphi_{n,\nu})$$

$$= \sum_{n=1}^{\infty} I(f_n). \quad \blacksquare$$

For an arbitrary function f on X we define the upper integral $\bar{I}(f)$ by setting

$$\bar{I}(f) = \inf_{\substack{g \geq f \\ g \in L_u}} I(g),$$

where we adopt the convention that the infimum of the empty set is $+\infty$. We define the lower integral $\underline{I}$ by setting $\underline{I}(f) = -\bar{I}(-f)$. Elementary properties of these upper and lower integrals are given by the following lemmas. The properties in Lemma 4 follow directly from the definition of $\bar{I}$.

4. Lemma: *We have* $\bar{I}(f + g) \leq \bar{I}(f) + \bar{I}(g)$. If $c \geq 0$, $\bar{I}(cf) = c\bar{I}(f)$. *If* $f \leq g$, *then* $\bar{I}(f) \leq \bar{I}(g)$ *and* $\underline{I}(f) \leq \underline{I}(g)$.

5. Lemma: *We have* $\underline{I}(f) \leq \bar{I}(f)$. *If* $f \in L_u$, *then* $\underline{I}(f) = \bar{I}(f) = I(f)$.

Proof: We have $0 = I(0) = I(f - f) \leq \bar{I}(f) + \bar{I}(-f)$. Hence $\underline{I}(f) = -\bar{I}(-f) \leq \bar{I}(f)$.

To prove the second statement, we note that if $f \in L_u$ then $\bar{I}(f) \leq I(f)$ by the definition of $\bar{I}$. If $g \in L_u$ and $f \leq g$, then $I(f) \leq I(g)$ and so $I(f) \leq \bar{I}(f)$, whence $\bar{I}(f) = I(f)$. If $\varphi \in L$, then $-\varphi \in L \subset L_u$, and so $\bar{I}(-\varphi) = I(-\varphi) = -I(\varphi)$, and hence $\underline{I}(\varphi) = I(\varphi)$. But each $f \in L_u$ is the limit of an increasing sequence $\langle \varphi_\nu \rangle$ of functions in L. Since $f \geq \varphi_\nu$, we have $\underline{I}(f) \geq \underline{I}(\varphi_\nu) = I(\varphi_\nu)$.
Hence

$$I(f) \geq \lim I(\varphi_\nu) = I(f).$$

Since $\underline{I}(f) \leq \bar{I}(f) = I(f)$, we have $\underline{I}(f) = I(f)$. $\blacksquare$

6. Lemma: *Let* $\langle f_\nu \rangle$ *be a sequence of nonnegative functions, and let* $f = \sum_{\nu=1}^{\infty} f_\nu$. *Then* $\bar{I}(f) \leq \sum_{\nu=1}^{\infty} \bar{I}(f_\nu)$.

Proof: If $\bar{I}(f_\nu) = \infty$ for some ν, we are done. If not, given $\epsilon > 0$, there is a function $g_\nu \in L_u$ such that $f_\nu \leq g_\nu$ and $I(g_\nu) \leq \bar{I}(f_\nu) + \epsilon \cdot 2^{-\nu}$. Since each g_ν is nonnegative, Lemma 3 implies that the function $g = \Sigma g_\nu$ is in L_u and that $I(g) = \Sigma I(g_\nu) \le \Sigma \bar{I}(f_\nu) + \epsilon$. Since $g \ge f$, we have

$$\bar{I}(f) \le \sum_{\nu=1}^{\infty} \bar{I}(f_\nu) + \epsilon,$$

and the lemma follows since ϵ was an arbitrary positive number. ❚

We shall call a function f on X **integrable** with respect to I (or I-integrable) if $\bar{I}(f) = \underline{I}(f)$ and this value is finite. We denote the class of functions integrable with respect to I by L_1. For f in L_1 we shall write $I(f)$ for $\bar{I}(f)$. Thus we have an extension of our original I to all of L_1. Properties of L_1 and this extended I are given by the following proposition:

7. Proposition: *The set L_1 is a vector lattice of functions containing L, and I is a positive linear functional on L_1, which extends the functional I on L.*

Proof: If f is in L_1, so is cf, since $\bar{I}(cf) = c\bar{I}(f) = c\underline{I}(f) = \underline{I}(cf)$ for $c \ge 0$, and $\bar{I}(cf) = c\underline{I}(f) = c\bar{I}(f) = \underline{I}(cf)$ for $c \le 0$. If f and g are in L_1, then

$$\bar{I}(f + g) \le I(f) + I(g),$$

and

$$-\underline{I}(f + g) = \bar{I}(-f - g) \le -I(f) - I(g)$$

or

$$\underline{I}(f + g) \ge I(f) + I(g).$$

Thus

$$\underline{I}(f + g) = \bar{I}(f + g) = I(f) + I(g),$$

and so $f + g$ is in L_1. Consequently, L_1 is a linear space, and I is a linear functional on L_1. Lemma 5 implies that $L_1 \supset L$ and that our definition of I on L_1 gives us a positive linear functional which agrees with our original I on L_1.

To prove that L_1 is a lattice, it suffices to show that if $f \in L_1$, then $f^+ \in L_1$. Let $f \in L_1$. Then for each $\epsilon > 0$ there are functions g and h in L_u such that $-h \le f \le g$ while $I(g) < I(f) + \epsilon < \infty$ and $I(h) \le -I(f) + \epsilon < \infty$. Since $g = (g \vee 0) + (g \wedge 0)$ and $(g \wedge 0) \in L_u$, we have $I(g \wedge 0) > -\infty$ and $I(g \vee 0) \le I(g) - I(g \wedge 0) < \infty$. Thus the function $g_1 = g \vee 0$ is in L_u and $I(g_1) < \infty$. Let $h_1 = h \wedge 0$. Then $h_1 \in L_u$, and $-h_1 \le f^+ \le g_1$. Since $g \ge -h$, $g_1 + h_1 \le g + h$.

Consequently, $I(g_1) + I(h_1) \leq I(g) + I(h) < 2\epsilon$. Since $-I(h_1) \leq \underline{I}(f_1) \leq \bar{I}(f_1) \leq I(g_1)$, we have $\bar{I}(f_1) - \underline{I}(f_1) < 2\epsilon$, and so $\bar{I}(f) = \underline{I}(f)$, since ϵ was an arbitrary positive number. Since $0 < \bar{I}(f_1) \leq I(g_1) < \infty$, we have $f \in L_1$. Thus L_1 is a lattice. ❙

The following proposition is the analogue for L_1 of the monotone convergence theorem. It also shows that L_1 and I satisfy the same conditions (D) and (D′).

8. Proposition: *Let $\langle f_n \rangle$ be an increasing sequence of functions in L_1, and let $f = \lim f_n$. Then $f \in L_1$ if and only if $\lim I(f_n) < \infty$. In this case $I(f) = \lim I(f_n)$.*

Proof: Since $f \geq f_n$, $\bar{I}(f) \geq I(f_n)$. Thus if $\lim I(f_n) = \infty$, then $\bar{I}(f) = \infty$, and $f \notin L_1$.

Suppose $\lim I(f_n) < \infty$. Set $g = f - f_1$. Then $g \geq 0$, and $g = \sum_{n=1}^{\infty} (f_{n+1} - f_n)$. Hence by Lemma 6,

$$\begin{aligned}\bar{I}(g) &\leq \sum_{n=1}^{\infty} I(f_{n+1} - f_n)\\ &= \sum_{n=1}^{\infty} I(f_{n+1}) - I(f_n)\\ &= \lim I(f_n) - I(f_1).\end{aligned}$$

Thus

$$\begin{aligned}\bar{I}(f) &= \bar{I}(f_1 + g)\\ &\leq I(f_1) + \bar{I}(g) \leq \lim I(f_n).\end{aligned}$$

Since $f_n \leq f$, we have $\underline{I}(f) \geq I(f_n)$, and so

$$\underline{I}(f) \geq \lim I(f_n).$$

Thus $\underline{I}(f) = \bar{I}(f) = \lim I(f_n)$. ❙

The following two propositions are the analogues for the integral I of Fatou's lemma and the Lebesgue convergence theorem.

9. Proposition: *Let $\langle f_\nu \rangle$ be a sequence of nonnegative functions in L_1. Then the function $\inf f_\nu$ is in L_1, and the function $\underline{\lim}\, f_\nu$ is in L_1 if $\underline{\lim}\, I(f_\nu) < \infty$. In this case*

$$I(\underline{\lim}\, f_\nu) \leq \underline{\lim}\, I(f_\nu).$$

Proof: Let $g_n = f_1 \wedge f_2 \wedge \cdots \wedge f_n$. Then $\langle g_n \rangle$ is a sequence of nonnegative functions in L_1, which decrease to $g = \inf f_\nu$. Thus $-g_n \uparrow -g$, and since $I(-g_n) \leq 0$, we must have $g \in L_1$ by Proposition 8.

To prove the rest of the proposition, let $h_n = \inf_{\nu \geq n} f_\nu$. Then $\langle h_n \rangle$ is a sequence of nonnegative functions in L_1 which increases to $\underline{\lim}\, f_\nu$. Since $h_n \leq f_\nu$ for $n \leq \nu$, $\lim I(h_n) \leq \underline{\lim}\ I(f_\nu) < \infty$. Hence $\underline{\lim}\, f_\nu \in L_1$ and $I(\underline{\lim}\, f_\nu) \leq \underline{\lim}\, I(f_\nu)$ by Proposition 8. ▌

10. Proposition: *Let $\langle f_n \rangle$ be a sequence of functions in L_1 and suppose that there is a function g in L_1 such that for all n we have $|f_n| \leq g$. Then if $f = \lim f_n$, we have*

$$I(f) = \lim I(f_n).$$

Proof: The functions $f_n + g$ are nonnegative, and $I(f_n + g) \leq 2I(g)$. Hence by Proposition 9 we have $f + g$ in L_1 and

$$I(f + g) \leq \underline{\lim}\, I(f_n + g) = I(g) + \underline{\lim}\, I(f_n).$$

Hence

$$I(f) \leq \underline{\lim}\, I(f_n).$$

Since the functions $g - f_n$ are also nonnegative, we have

$$I(g - f) \leq \underline{\lim}\, I(g - f_n) = I(g) - \overline{\lim}\, I(f_n).$$

Hence

$$\overline{\lim}\, I(f_n) \leq I(f),$$

and so $\lim I(f_n)$ exists and is equal to $I(f)$. ▌

11. Corollary: *The functional I is a Daniell integral on the vector lattice L_1.*

3 MEASURABILITY

We say that a nonnegative function f on X is measurable (with respect to I) if $g \wedge f$ is in L_1 for each g in L_1.

12. Lemma: *If f and g are nonnegative measurable functions so are $f \wedge g$ and $f \vee g$. If $\langle f_n \rangle$ is a sequence of nonnegative measurable functions which converge pointwise to a function f, then f is measurable.*

Proof: If f and g are nonnegative measurable functions and h is in L_1 then $h \wedge (f \wedge g) = (h \wedge f) \wedge (h \wedge g)$ and $h \wedge (f \vee g) = (h \wedge f) \vee (h \wedge g)$. Hence the measurability of $f \wedge g$ and $f \vee g$ follows from the fact that L_1 is a lattice. If $\langle f_n \rangle$ is a sequence of nonnegative measurable functions converging to f and g a function in L_1, then $\langle f_n \wedge g \rangle$ is a sequence of functions in L_1 converging to $f \wedge g$. Since $|f_n \wedge g| \leq |g|$, we have $f \wedge g$ in L_1 by Proposition 10. ∎

We say that a set A in X is **measurable** with respect to I if its characteristic function χ_A is measurable. We say that A is **integrable** if its characteristic function χ_A is integrable. Note that a measurable subset of an integrable set is itself integrable.

13. Lemma: *If A and B are measurable sets so are the sets $A \cup B$, $A \cap B$, and $A \sim B$. If $\langle A_n \rangle$ is a sequence of measurable sets, then the sets $\bigcap A_n$ and $\bigcup A_n$ are measurable. If the function 1 is measurable, then the class $\mathcal{A}$ of measurable sets is a σ-algebra.*

Proof: The measurability of $A \cap B$ and $A \cup B$ follows from the fact that $\chi_{A \cap B} = \chi_A \wedge \chi_B$ and $\chi_{A \cup B} = \chi_A \vee \chi_B$. If g is in L_1, we have $g \wedge \chi_{A \sim B} = g \wedge \chi_A - g \wedge \chi_{A \cap B} + g \wedge 0$, and the measurability of $A \sim B$ follows from that of A and B. If $A = \bigcup A_n$, then

$$\chi_A = \lim (\chi_{A_1} \vee \cdots \vee \chi_{A_n})$$

and the measurability of A follows from Lemma 12. A similar argument holds for $\bigcap A_n$. If 1 is a measurable function, then the set X is a measurable set, and the complement of a measurable set is measurable. ∎

14. Lemma: *If 1 is a measurable function and f a nonnegative integrable function, then for each real number α the set*

$$E = \{x : f(x) > \alpha\}$$

is measurable.

Proof: If α is negative, $E = X$ and is measurable since $\chi_E = 1$ and 1 is measurable. Hence we assume $\alpha \geq 0$. If $\alpha = 0$, set $g = f$, while if $\alpha > 0$, let $g = (\alpha^{-1}f) - [(\alpha^{-1}f) \wedge 1]$. Since g is the difference of two functions in L_1, g is in L_1. In either case we have $g(x) > 0$ for $x \in E$, and $g(x) = 0$ for $x \in \tilde{E}$. Let $\varphi_n = 1 \wedge (ng)$. Then $\varphi_n \in L_1$, and $\varphi_n \uparrow \chi_E$. Hence χ_E is measurable, and so E is measurable. ∎

15. Lemma: *Let the function 1 be measurable, and define a set function μ on the class $\mathcal{A}$ of measurable sets by*

$$\mu E = I(\chi_E)$$

if χ_E is integrable, and $\mu E = \infty$ otherwise. Then μ is a measure.

Proof: We have $\mu\varnothing = I(0) = 0$. If A and B are integrable sets with $A \subset B$, we have $\chi_A \leq \chi_B$, and so $\mu A \leq \mu B$. Thus μ is monotone for integrable sets and consequently for measurable sets.

Let $\langle E_i \rangle$ be a disjoint sequence of measurable sets, and let $E = \bigcup E_i$. If one of the E_i is not integrable, then E is not integrable, and

$$\mu E = \infty = \sum \mu E_i.$$

If each E_i is integrable, E will be integrable if and only if $\Sigma \mu E_i < \infty$ by Proposition 8, since $\chi_E = \Sigma \chi_{E_i}$. In either case $\mu E = \Sigma \mu E_i$, and the measure μ is countably additive. ∎

This measure μ has the property that the integrable sets are precisely the measurable sets of finite measure. The following theorem tells us that the Daniell integral I on L_i is equivalent to the integral with respect to this measure μ.

16. Theorem (Stone): *Let L be a vector lattice of functions on X with the property that if $f \in L$ then $1 \wedge f \in L$, and let I be a Daniell integral on L. Then there is a σ-algebra $\mathcal{A}$ of subsets of X and a measure μ on $\mathcal{A}$ such that each function f on X is integrable with respect to I if and only if it is also integrable with respect to μ. Moreover,*

$$I(f) = \int f \, d\mu.$$

Proof: Let $\mathcal{A}$ be the class of sets which are measurable with respect to I. Lemma 13 asserts that $\mathcal{A}$ is a σ-algebra, and Lemma 14 asserts that each nonnegative I-integrable function is measurable with respect to $\mathcal{A}$. Since each I-integrable function is the difference of two nonnegative I-integrable functions, every I-integrable function must be measurable with respect to $\mathcal{A}$.

Let μ be the measure given in Lemma 15, and let f be a nonnegative function which is integrable with respect to I. For each pair $\langle k, n \rangle$ of positive integers let

$$E_{k,n} = \{x \colon f(x) > k/n\}.$$

Then $E_{k,n}$ is measurable, and since

$$\chi_{E_{k,n}} = \chi_{E_{k,n}} \wedge \left(\frac{n}{k} f\right),$$

we have $\chi_{E_{k,n}} \in L_1$, and $\mu(E_{k,n}) < \infty$. Set

$$\varphi_n = \frac{1}{n} \sum_{k=1}^{n^2} \chi_{E_{k,n}}.$$

Then $\varphi_n \in L_1$ and $\varphi_n \uparrow f$. Hence $I(f) = \lim I(\varphi_n)$. But

$$\begin{aligned} I(\varphi_n) &= \frac{1}{n} \sum_{k=1}^{n^2} I(\chi_{E_{k,n}}) \\ &= \frac{1}{n} \sum_{k=1}^{n^2} \mu(E_{k,n}) \\ &= \int \varphi_n \, d\mu. \end{aligned}$$

Since

$$\int f \, d\mu = \lim \int \varphi_n \, d\mu$$

by the monotone convergence theorem, we have

$$I(f) = \int f \, d\mu,$$

and f is integrable with respect to μ. Since an arbitrary f which is I-integrable is the difference of two nonnegative I-integrable functions, it follows that such an f must also be integrable with respect to μ and that

$$I(f) = \int f \, d\mu.$$

If f is a nonnegative function on X which is integrable with respect to μ, we construct $E_{n,k}$ and φ_n as before. Since $\int f \, d\mu < \infty$, each $E_{n,k}$ has finite measure, and so $\chi_{E_{n,k}}$ and hence φ_n belong to L_1. Since $\varphi_n \uparrow f$ and $\lim I(\varphi_n) = \int f \, d\mu < \infty$, we have $f \in L_1$ by Proposition 8. Thus each f which is integrable with respect to μ is also integrable with respect to I. ❙

4 UNIQUENESS

In the present section we show that the extension to L_1 of a Daniell integral I on L is unique, and that under suitable hypotheses there is only one measure μ such that $I(f) = \int f \, d\mu$ for each $f \in L$. We begin by proving a proposition of some interest in its own right which describes the structure of functions in L_1. It is the analogue for I of Proposition 12.9.

Let us denote by L_{ul} the class of those functions on X which are the limit of a decreasing sequence $\langle f_n \rangle$ of functions in L_u with $I(f_n) < \infty$ and $\lim I(f_n) > -\infty$. It follows from Proposition 8 applied to $\langle -f_n \rangle$ that $L_{ul} \subset L_1$. If f is any function on X such that $\bar{I}(f)$ is finite, then given n we can find $h_n \in L_u$ such that

$$f \leq h_n \quad \text{and} \quad I(h_n) \leq \bar{I}(f) + \frac{1}{n}.$$

Setting $g_n = h_1 \wedge h_2 \wedge \cdots \wedge h_n$, we have $f \leq g_n \leq h_n$, and so $\langle g_n \rangle$ is a decreasing sequence of functions in L_u with $\bar{I}(f) \leq I(g_n) \leq \bar{I}(f) + \frac{1}{n}$. Hence the function $g = \lim g_n$ is in L_{ul}, while $f \leq g$ and $\bar{I}(f) = I(g)$. We have thus established the following lemma:

17. Lemma: *If f is any function on X with $\bar{I}(f)$ finite. Then there is a $g \in L_{ul}$ such that $f \leq g$ and $\bar{I}(f) = I(g)$.*

A function f on X is called a **null function** if $f \in L_1$ and $I(|f|) = 0$. If f is a null function and $|g| \leq f$, then $0 \leq \underline{I}(|g|) \leq \bar{I}(|g|) \leq I(f) = 0$. Hence $g \in L_1$, and g is a null function.

18. Proposition: *A function f on X is in L_1 if and only if f is the difference $g - h$ of a function g in L_{ul} and a null function h. A function h is a null function if and only if there is a null function k in L_{ul} such that $|h| \leq k$.*

Proof: If $f = g - h$, then f is the difference of two functions in L_1 and so must itself be in L_1. If $|h| \leq k$ with k null, then h is a null function.

If f is in L_1, then Lemma 17 asserts the existence of $g \in L_{ul}$ such that $f \leq g$ and $I(f) = I(g)$. Hence $h = g - f$ is a nonnegative function and $I(h) = 0$, making h a null function. If h is a null function, then by Lemma 17 there is a function $k \in L_{ul}$ with $|h| \leq k$ and $I(k) = I(|h|) = 0$. ▌

19. Proposition: *Let I be a Daniell integral on a vector lattice L of functions on X and let J be a Daniell integral on a vector lattice $\Lambda \supset L$. If $I(f) = J(f)$ for all $f \in L$, then $\Lambda_1 \supset L_1$ and $I(f) = J(f)$ for all $f \in L_1$.*

Proof: By applying Proposition 8 twice we see that $L_{ul} \subset \Lambda_1$ and that $I(f) = J(f)$ for $f \in L_{ul}$. Hence by the second part of Proposition 18 each function which is null with respect to I must also be null with respect to J. By the first part of Proposition 18 every function f in L_1 must be in Λ_1, and $I(f) = J(f)$. ▌

20. Proposition: *Let L be a vector lattice of functions on a set X, and suppose that* $1 \in L$. *Let* $\mathcal{B}$ *be the smallest σ-algebra of subsets of X such that each function in L is measurable with respect to* $\mathcal{B}$. *Then for each Daniell integral I there is a unique measure* μ *on* $\mathcal{B}$ *such that for every* $f \in L$

$$I(f) = \int f\,d\mu.$$

Proof: The existence of μ is a special case of Theorem 16 and we have only to prove the uniqueness of μ on $\mathcal{B}$. Let $\mathcal{A}$ be the σ-algebra of measurable sets given by Lemma 13. Lemma 14 asserts that each f in L is measurable with respect to $\mathcal{A}$, and so we must have $\mathcal{B} \subset \mathcal{A}$. Since $1 \in L$, the functions χ_B are in L_1 for each B in $\mathcal{A}$ and hence for each B in $\mathcal{B}$. The uniqueness of μ on $\mathcal{B}$ will be established if we can show that $\mu(B) = I(\chi_B)$ for each B in $\mathcal{B}$.

If we let Λ be the set of functions on X which are measurable with respect to $\mathcal{B}$ and integrable with respect to μ and set

$$J(f) = \int f\,d\mu$$

for $f \in \Lambda$, then Proposition 19 implies that $J(f) = I(f)$ for $f \in L_1 \cap \Lambda$. But if $B \in \mathcal{B}$, then $\chi_B \in L_1 \cap \Lambda$, and so

$$\begin{aligned} \mu B &= J(\chi_B) \\ &= I(\chi_B). \end{aligned}$$

Thus μ is uniquely determined on $\mathcal{B}$ by I. ▌

We can still establish the uniqueness of the measure μ in this proposition if instead of assuming $1 \in L$, we make the weaker assumption that there is an everywhere positive function in L_1 (Problem 3). Without some such assumption the measure μ need not be unique on $\mathcal{B}$ (Problem 4).

Problems

1. Let μ be a measure on an algebra $\mathcal{A}$ of sets, and let L be the family consisting of those functions which are finite linear combinations of characteristic functions of sets in $\mathcal{A}$ with finite measure. Show that L is a vector lattice, and that we can define I on L to be integration with respect to μ. Show that I is a Daniell integral on L and discuss its extension. What is the relation of this to Theorem 12.6?

2. Prove directly from the definition in Section 3 that if f_1 and f_2 are two nonnegative measurable functions, then $f_1 + f_2$ is measurable.

3. Prove that the conclusion of Proposition 20 still holds when the hypothesis that $1 \in L$ is replaced by the hypothesis that there is an everywhere positive function e in L_1. (Hint: $X = \bigcup_{n=1}^{\infty} \{x\colon e(x) > 1/n\}$, and the proof given can be modified to show that μ is unique on sets of $\mathcal{B}$ which are contained in $\{x\colon e(x) > 1/n\}$.)

4. Let $X = (-\infty, \infty) \cup \{\omega\}$, and let L consist of all functions on X which are Lebesgue integrable on $(-\infty, \infty)$ and vanish at ω. Then L is a vector lattice, and the smallest σ-algebra with respect to which each function in L is measurable is the family $\mathcal{B}$ consisting of all sets B such that $B \cap (-\infty, \infty)$ is Lebesgue measurable. Let I be defined on L by $I(f) = \int f(x)\,dx$. Then I is a Daniell integral on L. What is the measure μ constructed in Theorem 16? Show that there is another measure ν defined on $\mathcal{B}$ such that for each f in L, $I(f) = \int f\,d\nu$.

5. **a.** Define a measure μ on the I-measurable sets by $\mu E = I(\chi_E)$ if E integrable, and $I(\chi_E) = \sup \{I(\chi_A) : A \subset E,\ A \text{ integrable}\}$ otherwise. Show that μ is a measure and is the smallest measure such that $I(f) = \int f\,d\mu$.

b. Show that for this measure $\mu(X) = \|I\| = \sup \{I(f)\colon f \in L, f \leq 1\}$.

c. Show that if $\|I\| < \infty$, then this measure μ is the unique measure such that $I(f) = \int f\,d\mu$ and $\mu(X) = \|I\|$.

5 MEASURE AND TOPOLOGY

We are often concerned with measures on a set X which is also a topological space, and it is natural to consider conditions on the measure so that it is connected with the topological structure. One way of approaching this is by the use of outer measures which are Carathéodory outer measures with respect to certain families of continuous functions on X. A simpler approach is to consider Daniell integrals on suitable vector lattices of continuous functions on X, and this is the approach we shall follow in the next two sections.

Let X be a locally compact Hausdorff space. From the point of view of integration theory the most useful family of functions on X is the family $C_0(X)$ consisting of all continuous real-valued functions which vanish outside a compact subset of X. If f is a real-valued function, we define the **support** of f to be the closure of the set $\{x: f(x) \neq 0\}$. Thus $C_0(X)$ is the class of all continuous real-valued functions on X which have compact support. The class of **Baire sets** is defined to be the smallest σ-algebra $\mathcal{B}$ of subsets of X such that each function in $C_0(X)$ is measurable with respect to $\mathcal{B}$. Thus $\mathcal{B}$ is the σ-algebra generated by the sets $\{x: f(x) \geq \alpha\}$ with $f \in C_0(X)$. A measure μ is called a **Baire measure** on X if its domain of definition is the σ-algebra $\mathcal{B}$ of Baire sets and if $\mu(K) < \infty$ for each compact set K in $\mathcal{B}$. The following proposition relates the positive linear functionals on the space $C_0(X)$ to the Baire measures on X.

21. Proposition: *Let X be a locally compact Hausdorff space, and let I be a positive linear functional on the space $C_0(X)$ consisting of all real-valued continuous functions on X with compact support. Then there is a Baire measure μ such that for each f in $C_0(X)$ we have*

$$I(f) = \int f\, d\mu.$$

Proof: The space $C_0(X)$ is a vector lattice, and I will be a Daniell integral on $C_0(X)$, provided it satisfies condition (D). To see this, let $\varphi \in C_0(X)$, and suppose that $\langle \varphi_n \rangle$ is an increasing sequence of functions in $C_0(X)$ such that $\varphi \leq \lim \varphi_n(x)$. We may assume, by subtracting $(\varphi \wedge \varphi_1)$ if necessary, that φ and the φ_n are nonnegative. Let K be the support of φ, and let ψ be a non-negative function in $C_0(X)$ which is positive on K. For a given $\epsilon > O$, the set K is covered by the open sets $O_n = \{x: \varphi(x) - \epsilon\psi(x) < \varphi_n(x)\}$. Since K is compact and the sets O_n are increasing, we must have $K \subset O_N$ for some N. Hence $\varphi - \epsilon\psi < \varphi_N$ on K. Since $\varphi \equiv O$ off K, this inequality holds everywhere, and so

$$I(\varphi) - \epsilon I(\psi) \leq I(\varphi_N) \leq \lim I(\varphi_n).$$

Since ϵ was arbitrary and $I(\varphi) < \infty$,

$$I(\varphi) \le \lim I(\varphi_n).$$

Thus I is a Daniell integral.

It follows from Theorem 16 that there is a measure μ defined on the class $\mathfrak{B}$ of Baire sets such that for each f in $C_0(X)$

$$I(f) = \int f\, d\mu.$$

It remains only to show that, if K is a compact set in $\mathfrak{B}$, then $\mu(K) < \infty$. But if K is any compact subset of X, there is a non-negative function f in $C_0(X)$ such that $f(x) = 1$ for $x \in K$. Then

$$\mu(K) \le \int f\, d\mu = I(f) < \infty. \quad \blacksquare$$

If X is compact, then $C_0(X)$ is just the space $C(X)$ of all continuous real-valued functions on X. If I is a positive linear functional on $C(X)$, then as before I is a Daniell integral. Proposition 20 implies that in this case the measure μ given by Proposition 21 is unique. Hence we have the following proposition:

22. Proposition: *Let X be a compact space, and let I be a positive linear functional on the space $C(X)$ consisting of all continuous real-valued functions on X. Then there is a unique Baire measure μ on X such that for each f in $C(X)$*

$$I(f) = \int f\, d\mu.$$

Since $I(1)$ is finite, the measure μ must be finite. Thus the proposition shows that there is natural one-to-one correspondence between Baire measures on X and positive linear functionals on $C(X)$.

Problems

6. Let X be a separable locally compact metric space. Show that the class of Baire sets is the same as the class of Borel sets (= smallest σ-algebra containing the open sets).

7. Let X be a locally compact Hausdorff space, and let $\bar{C}_0(X)$ be the space of all uniform limits of functions in $C_0(X)$.

a. Show that a continuous real-valued function on X belongs to $\bar{C}_0(X)$ if and only if for each $\alpha > 0$ the set $\{x\colon |f(x)| \ge \alpha\}$ is compact.

b. Let X^* be the one-point compactification of X. Then $\bar{C}_0(X)$ consists precisely of the restrictions to X of those functions in $C(X^*)$ which vanish at ∞.

c. If B is a Baire set in X^*, then $B \cap X$ is a Baire set in X.

8. Let X be an uncountable set with the discrete topology.

a. What are $C_0(X)$ and $\bar{C}_0(X)$?

b. What are the Baire sets in X?

c. Let X^* be the one-point compactification of X. What is $C(X^*)$?

d. What are the Baire subsets of $C(X^*)$? Show that X^* has a compact subset which is not a Baire set.

e. Show that there is a Baire measure μ on X such that $\mu(X) = 1$ and $\int f\,d\mu = 0$ for each f in $C_0(X)$.

9. a. A locally compact space is called **σ-compact** if it is the union of a countable collection of compact sets. Use Problem 3 to show that the Baire measure in Proposition 21 is unique if X is σ-compact.

b. A set E is called **σ-bounded** if it is contained in a σ-compact set. Prove that if E is a Baire set, then E or $\tilde{E}$ is σ-bounded. (Hint: The family of Baire sets with this property is a σ-algebra with respect to which each function in $C_0(X)$ is measurable.)

c. Show that the measure μ in Proposition 21 is unique on each σ-bounded Baire set.

d. If $\|I\| = \sup\{I(f): f \in C_0(X), f \leq 1\}$ is finite, the measure μ in Proposition 21 can be chosen so that $\mu(X) = \|I\|$, and there is a unique Baire measure with this property. (See Problem 5.)

10. a. Let X be a locally compact Hausdorff space, μ a Baire measure on X, and I the integral on $C_0(X)$ defined by μ. If E is an integrable set with respect to I, then μE is the infimum of $I(\varphi)$ over all functions φ with $\varphi \geq \chi_E$ and $\varphi = \sum_{n=1}^{\infty} \varphi_n$ where $\varphi_n \in C_0(X)$.

b. If E is integrable, then $\mu E = \inf\{\mu O: O \supset E, O \text{ a Baire set}\}$.

c. If K is compact, then $\mu(K) = \inf\{I(\varphi): \varphi \in C_0(X), \varphi \geq \chi_K\}$.

d. Show that the conclusion of (*b*) remains true if E is any σ-bounded Baire set.

e. Let X be compact, and μ a Baire measure on X. Then for any Baire set E and any $\epsilon > 0$ there is an open set O and a closed set K such that

$$K \subset E, \qquad \mu E < \mu K + \epsilon$$

$$E \subset O, \qquad \mu E > \mu O - \epsilon.$$

11. Let μ be a Baire measure on a locally compact space X. Let U be the union of all open Baire sets O with $\mu O = 0$. The complement $F = \tilde{U}$ of U is a closed set called the **support** (or carrier) of μ.

a. If O is an open Baire set with $O \cap F \neq \varnothing$, then $\mu O > 0$.

b. If K is a compact Baire set with $K \cap F = \varnothing$, then $\mu K = 0$. (Each point of K is contained in an open set of measure zero. Thus by compactness K is contained in an open set of measure zero.)

c. If E is a σ-bounded Baire set with $E \cap F = \varnothing$, then $\mu E = 0$.

d. If $f \in C_0(X)$ and $f \geq 0$, then $\int f\,d\mu = 0$ if and only if $f \equiv 0$ on F. (Hint: The set $\{x: f(x) > 0\}$ is a σ-bounded Baire set.)

e. Give an example to show that F need not be a Baire set.

f. It follows from (*c*) that if X is compact (or σ-compact) then $\mu E = 0$ for each Baire set with $E \cap F = \varnothing$. Construct an example to show that this need not be true if X is not σ-compact. [See Problem 8(e).]

6 BOUNDED LINEAR FUNCTIONALS ON C(X)

Let X be a compact Hausdorff space and $C(X)$ the space of real-valued continuous functions on X. In the last section we described the positive linear functionals on $C(X)$, and in this section we consider the bounded linear functionals on $C(X)$. We first note that if F is a positive linear functional on $C(X)$ and if $|f| \leq 1$, then

$$|F(f)| \leq F(|f|) \leq F(1).$$

Hence it follows that

$$\|F\| = F(1).$$

The next proposition shows that every bounded linear functional on $C(X)$ is the difference of two positive ones. Since the proof makes no use of particular properties of $C(X)$ other than that it is a vector lattice of bounded functions containing 1, we state the proposition in this generality. If L is a vector lattice of bounded real-valued function on a set X, L becomes a normed linear space when we define $\|f\| = \sup |f(x)|$. A linear functional is bounded if there is an M such that

$$|F(f)| \leq M\|f\|,$$

and we define as usual

$$\|F\| = \sup_{\|f\| \leq 1} F(f).$$

23. Proposition: *Let L be a vector lattice of bounded functions on a set X, and suppose $1 \in L$. Then for each bounded linear functional F on L, there are two positive linear functionals F_+ and F_- such that $F = F_+ - F_-$ and $\|F\| = F_+(1) + F_-(1)$.*

Proof: For each nonnegative f in L define

$$F_+(f) = \sup_{0 \le \varphi \le f} F(\varphi).$$

Then $F_+(f) \ge 0$, and $F_+(f) \ge F(f)$. Moreover, $F_+(cf) = cF_+(f)$ for $c \ge 0$. Let f and g be two nonnegative functions in L. If $0 \le \varphi \le f$ and $0 \le \psi \le g$, then $0 \le \varphi + \psi \le f + g$, and so

$$F_+(f + g) \ge F(\varphi) + F(\psi).$$

Taking suprema over all such φ and ψ, we obtain

$$F_+(f + g) \ge F_+(f) + F_+(g).$$

On the other hand if $0 \le \psi \le f + g$, then $0 \le \psi \wedge f \le f$ and $0 \le \psi - (\psi \wedge f) \le g$, and so

$$\begin{aligned} F(\psi) &= F(\psi \wedge f) + F(\psi - [\psi \wedge f]) \\ &\le F_+(f) + F_+(g). \end{aligned}$$

Taking the supremum over all such ψ, we get

$$F_+(f + g) \le F_+(f) + F_+(g),$$

and so

$$F_+(f + g) = F_+(f) + F_+(g).$$

Let f be an arbitrary function in L, and let M and N be two nonnegative constants such that $f + M$ and $f + N$ are nonnegative. Then

$$\begin{aligned} F_+(f + M + N) &= F_+(f + M) + F_+(N) \\ &= F_+(f + N) + F_+(M). \end{aligned}$$

Hence

$$F_+(f + M) - F_+(M) = F_+(f + N) - F_+(N).$$

Thus the value of $F_+(f + M) - F_+(M)$ is independent of the choice of M, and we define $F_+(f)$ to be this value. The functional F_+ is now defined on all of L, and we have easily $F_+(f + g) = F_+(f) + F_+(g)$ and $F_+(cf) = cF_+(f)$ for $c \ge 0$. Since $F_+(-f) + F_+(f) = F_+(0) = 0$, we have $F_+(-f) = -F_+(f)$ and F_+ is a linear functional on L.

Since $0 \leq F_+(f)$ and $F(f) \leq F_+(f)$ for $f \geq 0$, both F_+ and the linear functional $F_- = F_+ - F$ are positive linear functionals, and $F = F_+ - F_-$.

We always have $\|F\| \leq \|F_+\| + \|F_-\| = F_+(1) + F_-(1)$. To establish the inequality in the opposite direction, let φ be any function in L such that $0 \leq \varphi \leq 1$. Then $|2\varphi - 1| \leq 1$, and

$$\|F\| \geq F(2\varphi - 1) = 2F(\varphi) - F(1).$$

Taking the supremum over all such φ, we have

$$\begin{aligned} \|F\| &\geq 2F_+(1) - F(1) \\ &= F_+(1) + F_-(1). \end{aligned}$$

Hence $\|F\| = F_+(1) + F_-(1)$. ∎

24. Theorem: *Let X be a compact Hausdorff space and $C(X)$ the space of continuous real-valued functions on X. Then to each bounded linear functional F on $C(X)$ there corresponds a unique finite signed Baire measure ν on X such that*

$$F(f) = \int f\,d\nu$$

for each f in $C(X)$. Moreover, $\|F\| = |\nu|(X)$.

Proof: Let $F = F_+ - F_-$ as in Proposition 23. Then by Proposition 22 there are finite Baire measures μ_1 and μ_2 such that

$$F_+(f) = \int f\,d\mu_1$$

and

$$F_-(f) = \int f\,d\mu_2.$$

If we set $\nu = \mu_1 - \mu_2$, then ν is a finite signed Baire measure, and

$$F(f) = \int f\,d\nu.$$

Now

$$\begin{aligned} |F(f)| &\leq \int |f|\,d|\nu| \\ &\leq \|f\|\,|\nu|(X). \end{aligned}$$

Hence $\|F\| \leq |\nu|(X)$. But

$$\begin{aligned} |\nu|(X) &\leq \mu_1(X) + \mu_2(X) \\ &= F_+(1) + F_-(1) = \|F\|. \end{aligned}$$

Thus $\|F\| = |\nu|(X)$.

To show the uniqueness of ν, we note that if ν_1 and ν_2 were both finite signed Baire measures such that

$$\int f\,d\nu_i = F(f)$$

for $i = 1, 2$ and $f \in C(X)$, then $\lambda = \nu_1 - \nu_2$ would be a finite signed Baire measure such that

$$\int f\,d\lambda = 0$$

for all $f \in C(X)$. Let $\lambda = \lambda^+ - \lambda^-$ be the Jordan decomposition of λ. Then integration with respect to λ^+ gives the same positive linear functional on $C(X)$, as that given by λ^- and so by Proposition 22 we must have $\lambda^+ = \lambda^-$. Hence $\lambda = 0$, and $\nu_1 = \nu_2$. ∎

25. Corollary: *Let X be a compact Hausdorff space. Then the dual of C(X) is (isometrically isomorphic to) the space of all finite signed Baire measures on X with norm defined by* $\|\nu\| = |\nu|\,(X)$.

The fact that the space of finite signed Baire measures on X is the dual of $C(X)$ enables us to conclude a number of things about this space. For example, it follows from Proposition 10.3 that the space of Baire measures is complete, and it follows from Theorem 10.15 that the set of Baire measures with $|\nu|\,(X) \leq 1$ is compact in the weak* topology. Some consequences of this are explored in the problems.

Problems

12. Let L and F be as in Proposition 23. Show that if G and H are two positive linear functionals on L such that $F = G - H$ and $G(1) + H(1) \leq \|F\|$, then $G = F^+$ and $H = F^-$. (Hint: Use the definition of F^+ to show that $G - F^+$ is a positive linear functional.)

13. Let X be a compact Hausdorff space $\mathcal{F} = \{f_\alpha\}$ a family of continuous real-valued functions on X and $\{c_\alpha\}$ a corresponding family of constants. Suppose that for each finite set $\{f_{\alpha_1}, \ldots, f_{\alpha_n}\}$ there is a signed Baire measure ν with $|\nu|\,(X) \leq 1$ such that

$$\int f_{\alpha_i}\,d\nu = c_{\alpha_i}.$$

Then there is a finite signed Baire measure ν with $|\nu|\,(X) \leq 1$ such that for every f_α,

$$\int f_\alpha\,d\nu = c_\alpha.$$

14. a. Let X be a compact Hausdorff space and $g, f_1, \ldots, f_n$ continuous real-valued functions on X. Suppose that there is a signed Baire measure ν with $|\nu|(X) \le 1$ on X such that for each i we have $\int f_i \, d\nu = c_i$. Then there is a signed Baire measure μ on X with $|\mu|(X) \le 1$ such that

$$\int f_i \, d\mu = c_i$$

and

$$\int g \, d\mu \le \int g \, d\lambda$$

for any signed Baire measure λ with $|\lambda|(X) \le 1$ and such that $\int f_i \, d\lambda = c_i$.

b. Suppose that there is a Baire measure ν on X with $\nu(X) = 1$ and $\int f_i \, d\nu = c_i$. Then there is a Baire measure μ on X with $\mu(X) = 1$ and $\int f_i \, d\mu = c_i$ which minimizes $\int g \, d\mu$ among all Baire measures which satisfy these conditions.

c. Let $G, F_1, \ldots, F_n$ be continuous functions on $\mathbf{R}^m$ (= Euclidean m-dimensional space), and let $f_1, \ldots, f_m$ be continuous functions on X. Show that if there is a Baire measure ν with $\nu(X) = 1$ such that

$$F_i\left(\int f_1 \, d\nu, \ldots, \int f_m \, d\nu\right) = c_i,$$

then there is a Baire measure on X which minimizes

$$G\left(\int f_1 \, d\nu, \ldots, \int f_m \, d\nu\right)$$

under these restrictions.

15. Let B be the Banach space of signed Baire measures on a compact Hausdorff space X. What are the extreme points of the unit sphere of B?

16. ***Alternate proof of the Stone-Weierstrass Theorem.*** We can use the techniques of this section, together with results of Chapter 10, to give a proof of the Stone-Weierstrass theorem which does not depend on Lemma 9.24. This proof is due to deBranges.

Let $\mathcal{A}$ be an algebra of real-valued continuous functions on a compact space X which separates points and contains the constants. Let $\mathcal{A}^\perp$ be the set of signed Baire measures on X such that $|\mu|(X) \le 1$ and $\int f \, d\mu = 0$ for all $f \in \mathcal{A}$.

a. Use the Hahn-Banach Theorem and Corollary 25 to show that if $\mathcal{A}^\perp$ contains only the zero measure, then $\bar{\mathcal{A}} = C(X)$.

b. Use the Krein-Milman Theorem and the compactness of the unit ball in $C^*(X)$ to show that if the zero measure is the only extreme point of $\mathcal{A}^\perp$, then $\mathcal{A}^\perp$ contains only the zero measure.

c. Let μ be an extreme point of $\mathcal{A}^\perp$. Then if $f \in \mathcal{A}$, $\|f\| \leq 1$, the measures $f\,d\mu$ and $(1 - f)\,d\mu$ are in $\mathcal{A}^\perp$. Hence $f\,d\mu = c\,d\mu$ for some constant c.

d. Then $f - c \equiv 0$ on the support of μ [See Problem 11(d)].

e. Since f separates points, the support of μ can contain at most one point. Since $\int 1\,d\mu = 0$, the support of μ is empty, and μ is the zero measure.

14 *Mappings of Measure Spaces*

1 POINT MAPPINGS AND SET MAPPINGS

Let X and Y be any two spaces and φ a mapping of X into Y. Then associated with φ are several mappings of objects associated with Y into corresponding objects associated with X. For example the set mapping Φ defined by $\Phi(E) = \varphi^{-1}[E]$ is a mapping of the subsets of Y into the subsets of X. This mapping preserves unions, intersections, and complements. It is called the set mapping induced by or adjoint to φ. We refer to φ as a point mapping. If $\langle X, \mathcal{A}\rangle$ and $\langle Y, \mathcal{B}\rangle$ are measurable spaces, the point mapping φ of X into Y is called **measurable** if $\varphi^{-1}[E] \in \mathcal{A}$ for each $E \in \mathcal{B}$. Thus φ is measurable iff Φ maps $\mathcal{B}$ into $\mathcal{A}$.

Also associated with φ is the mapping φ^* of the space of real-valued functions on Y into the space of real-valued functions on X defined by $\varphi^*(f) = f \circ \varphi$. The mapping φ^* is often called the adjoint of φ, and it preserves sums, products, maxima, etc. If φ is measurable, then φ^* takes measurable functions into measurable functions.

Let $\mathcal{A}$ be an algebra of subsets of X and $\mathcal{B}$ an algebra of subsets of Y. Then a mapping Φ of $\mathcal{B}$ into $\mathcal{A}$ such that $\Phi(Y) = X$, $\Phi(\tilde{E}) = \sim\Phi(E)$, and $\Phi(A \cup B) = \Phi(A) \cup \Phi(B)$ is called a (lattice) **homomorphism**. If $\mathcal{A}$ and $\mathcal{B}$ are σ-algebras and Φ has the property that $\Phi\left(\bigcup_{i=1}^{\infty} E_i\right) = \bigcup_{i=1}^{\infty} \Phi(E_i)$, then Φ is called a **σ-homomorphism**. Every set mapping induced by a point mapping of X into Y is a σ-homomorphism, but we can have σ-homomorphisms which are not induced by any point mapping (Problem 2).

Let $\langle X, \mathcal{A}\rangle$ and $\langle Y, \mathcal{B}\rangle$ be measurable spaces and Φ a σ-homomorphism of $\mathcal{B}$ into $\mathcal{A}$. Then Φ induces a mapping Φ^* of measures on $\langle X, \mathcal{A}\rangle$ into measures on $\langle Y, \mathcal{B}\rangle$ if we define $\Phi^*\mu$ by $(\Phi^*\mu)(E) = \mu(\Phi(E))$. We have the following proposition which may be thought of as a change of variable formula.

1. Proposition: *Let φ be a measurable point mapping of the measure space $\langle X, \mathcal{A}, \mu\rangle$ into the measurable space $\langle Y, \mathcal{B}\rangle$. Let Φ be the induced set mapping of $\mathcal{B}$ into $\mathcal{A}$. Then for each nonnegative measurable function f on Y we have.*

$$\int_Y f\, d\Phi^*\mu = \int_X (f \circ \varphi)\, d\mu.$$

Proof: The proposition is clearly true if f is a characteristic function. From this it follows for f a simple function. Since $\int f$ is the supremum of the integrals of all nonnegative simple functions less than f, thc proposition follows. ▌

Problems

1. Let $\mathcal{B}$ be a family of subsets of Y which contains Y, $\varnothing$ and each set $\{y\}$ consisting of a single element. Then each mapping Φ of $\mathcal{B}$ into the subsets of X which preserves finite intersections and arbitrary unions, and for which $\Phi(Y) = X$ and $\Phi(\varnothing) = \varnothing$, is induced by a point mapping. (The sets $E_y = \Phi(\{y\})$ are disjoint and their union is X. Let $\varphi(x) = y$ for x in E_y.)

2. Let $X = Y = [0, 1]$, and let $\mathcal{A}$ be thc collection of all subsets of $[0, 1]$ which are either countable or the complements of countable sets. Then $\mathcal{A}$ is a σ-algebra. Let $\mathcal{B} = \{Y, \varnothing\}$. For $E \in \mathcal{A}$, define $\Phi(E) = \varnothing$ if E is countable, $\Phi(E) = Y$ if E is the complement of a countable set. Then Φ is a σ-homomorphism and it is not induced by any point mapping of Y into X.

3. Prove that $\Phi^*\mu$ is a measure.

4. Show that the adjoint mapping φ^* can be extended to map the extended real-valued functions on Y into the space of such functions on X. Generalize Proposition 1 to this case.

5. a. Let φ be a measurable point mapping of $\langle X, \mathcal{A}, \mu\rangle$ into $\langle Y, \mathcal{B}, \nu\rangle$ and Φ the induced set mapping of $\mathcal{B}$ into $\mathcal{A}$. Suppose $\Phi^*\mu$ is absolutely continuous with respect to ν and that ν is a finite (or σ-finite) measure. Define $\left[\dfrac{d\mu}{d\nu}\right]$ to be the Radon-Nikodym derivative of $\Phi^*\mu$ with respect to ν. Then for each nonnegative measurable function f on Y we have

$$\int_X (f \circ \varphi)\, d\mu = \int_Y f \left[\frac{d\mu}{d\nu}\right] d\nu.$$

b. Let f be a nonnegative measurable function on $[0, 1]$ and g a monotone absolutely continuous function on $[0, 1]$ with $g(0) = 0$, $g(1) = 1$. Then

$$\int_0^1 f[g(t)]g'(t)\, dt = \int_0^1 f(t)\, dt.$$

6. a. Let $\langle X, \mathcal{A}\rangle$ and $\langle Y, \mathcal{B}\rangle$ be measurable spaces and Φ a σ-homomorphism from $\mathcal{B}$ to $\mathcal{A}$. Show that there is a unique linear mapping T_Φ of the measurable real-valued functions on Y into the measurable real-valued functions on X, which takes nonnegative functions into nonnegative functions, such that for characteristic functions χ_E we have

$$T_\Phi(\chi_E) = \chi_{\Phi(E)}.$$

b. Let μ be a measure on $\langle X, \mathcal{A}\rangle$ and f a nonnegative measurable function on Y. Then

$$\int_X T_\Phi(f)\, d\mu = \int_Y f\, d\Phi^*(\mu).$$

2 MEASURE ALGEBRAS

By a Boolean algebra we mean a set of elements on which two binary operations $\vee$ and $\wedge$ and a unary operation $'$ are defined subject to the following rules:

i. $A \vee A = A$ $\qquad A \wedge A = A$
ii. $A \vee B = B \vee A$ $\qquad A \wedge B = B \wedge A$
iii. $(A \vee B) \vee C = A \vee (B \vee C)$ $\qquad (A \wedge B) \wedge C = A \wedge (B \wedge C)$
iv. $A \vee (B \wedge C) = (A \vee B) \wedge (A \vee C)$
iv′. $A \wedge (B \vee C) = (A \wedge B) \vee (A \wedge C)$
v. $(A \wedge B)' = A' \vee B'$
vi. $(A')' = A$
vii. $\exists 0$ such that $A \wedge 0 = 0$ and $A \vee 0 = A$
viii. $A' \wedge A = 0$.

One example of a Boolean algebra is an algebra $\mathcal{A}$ of subsets of some set X with $\vee$, $\wedge$, $'$ interpreted to mean $\cup$, $\cap$, $\sim$. We shall sometimes call $\vee$, $\wedge$, $'$, 'union', 'intersection', and 'complementation'.

A Boolean algebra $\mathcal{A}$ becomes partially ordered if we define $A \leq B$ to mean $A \wedge B = A$. Then 0 is the smallest element, while $X = 0'$ is the largest element. Moreover, $A \vee B$ is the smallest element of $\mathcal{A}$ which is larger than both A and B.

A Boolean algebra $\mathcal{A}$ is called a Boolean σ-algebra if for each sequence $\langle A_n \rangle$ of elements of $\mathcal{A}$ there is a smallest element B such that $A_n \leq B$ for all n. This element B is denoted by $\bigvee_{n=1}^{\infty} A_n$. In a Boolean σ-algebra the element $C = \left(\bigvee_{n=1}^{\infty} A_n'\right)'$ is the largest element such that $C \leq A_n$ for all n. We write $C = \bigwedge_{n=1}^{\infty} A_n$. One example of a Boolean σ-algebra is given by a σ-algebra of subsets of a set X. Another is the following: Let $\langle X, \mathcal{A}, \mu \rangle$ be a measure space and $\mathcal{N}$ the family of sets of measure zero. We call two sets of $\mathcal{A}$ equivalent modulo $\mathcal{N}$ if their symmetric difference is in $\mathcal{N}$. Then finite or countable unions and intersections of equivalent sets are equivalent, and so the class of equivalent sets is a Boolean σ-algebra which we denote by $\mathcal{A}/\mathcal{N}$. In fact the only properties we need of $\mathcal{N}$ are (i) if $A \in \mathcal{N}$ and $B \in \mathcal{A}$ with $B \subseteq A$ then $B \in \mathcal{N}$, and (ii) if $A_n \in \mathcal{N}$, then $\bigcup_{n=1}^{\infty} A_n \in \mathcal{N}$. A subset of a Boolean σ-algebra $\mathcal{A}$ with the corresponding properties is called a **σ-ideal**, and we may define the Boolean σ-algebra $\mathcal{A}/\mathcal{N}$ of equivalence classes of $\mathcal{A}$ mod $\mathcal{N}$.

By a **measure algebra**, we mean a Boolean σ-algebra $\mathcal{A}$ together with a nonnegative real-valued function μ defined on $\mathcal{A}$ such that $\mu(A) = 0$ iff $A = 0$ and $\mu\left(\bigvee_{i=1}^{\infty} A_i\right) = \sum_{i=1}^{\infty} \mu A_i$ if $A_i \wedge A_j = 0$ for $i \neq j$. We call μ a measure on $\mathcal{A}$. If $\langle X, \mathcal{B}, \mu \rangle$ is a finite measure space and $\mathcal{N}$ is the collection of sets of measure zero, then we obtain a measure algebra when we look at μ on the Boolean σ-algebra $\mathcal{A} = \mathcal{B}/\mathcal{N}$, that is when we fail to distinguish between sets of $\mathcal{B}$ which differ by a set of measure zero.

In a Boolean algebra we define the symmetric difference $A \vartriangle B$ of two elements by $A \vartriangle B = (A \wedge B') \vee (A' \wedge B)$. A measure algebra becomes a metric space if we define $\rho(A, B) = \mu(A \vartriangle B)$. This metric space is always complete, and the mappings $A \to A'$, $\langle A, B\rangle \to A \vee B$ and $\langle A, B\rangle \to A \wedge B$ are continuous. A measure algebra is called **separable** if it is separable as a metric space.

A mapping Φ of a measure algebra $\langle \mathcal{A}, \mu\rangle$ into a measure algebra $\langle \mathcal{B}, \nu\rangle$ is called an **isomorphism into** if $\Phi(A') = [\Phi(A)]'$, $\Phi(A_1 \vee A_2) = \Phi(A_1) \vee \Phi(A_2)$ and $\mu(A) = \nu(\Phi(A))$. The mapping Φ is called an isomorphism if it is onto. Considering the measure algebras as metric spaces, an isomorphism is an isometry which preserves complements and finite unions. It follows that an isomorphism also preserves countable unions and intersections (Problem 9).

A set $A \neq 0$ in a measure algebra $\mathcal{A}$ is called an **atom** if $B \leq A$ can occur only for $B = A$ and $B = 0$. Let $\mathcal{M}$ be the class of measurable subsets of $[0, 1]$, $\mathcal{N}$ the class of subsets of measure zero, and m Lebesgue measure. Then $\langle \mathcal{M}/\mathcal{N}, m\rangle$ is a separable measure algebra without atoms. The following theorem (which is due to Carathéodory) asserts that, apart from isomorphism, it is the only such measure algebra.

2. Theorem: *Let $\langle \mathcal{A}, \mu\rangle$ be a separable measure algebra with $\mu(X) = 1$. Then there is an isomorphism Φ of $\langle \mathcal{A}, \mu\rangle$ into the measure algebra $\langle \mathcal{M}/\mathcal{N}, m\rangle$ induced by Lebesgue measure m on $[0, 1]$. The isomorphism Φ is onto iff $\mathcal{A}$ has no atoms.*

Proof: Since $\langle \mathcal{A}, \mu\rangle$ is separable, there is a sequence $\langle A_n\rangle$ of elements which are dense in $\mathcal{A}$. Let $\mathcal{A}_n$ be the Boolean algebra obtained by taking all unions of intersections of the sets $A_1, \ldots, A_n$ and their complements. Let $\mathcal{A}_\infty = \bigcup_{n=1}^{\infty} \mathcal{A}_n$. Then $\mathcal{A}_\infty$ is again a Boolean algebra. For, given any A and B in $\mathcal{A}_\infty$, they belong to $\mathcal{A}_n$ and $\mathcal{A}_m$, respectively. But if $m \leq n$, we have $\mathcal{A}_m \subset \mathcal{A}_n$, and so A', $A \vee B$ and $A \wedge B$ are all contained in $\mathcal{A}_n \subset \mathcal{A}_\infty$.

We shall define by induction a mapping Φ of $\mathcal{A}_\infty$ into the algebra $\mathcal{I}$ of all finite unions of half open subintervals of $[0, 1)$. The algebra $\mathcal{A}_1$ consists of the four sets $0, A_1, A_1', X$, and we have $\mu A_1 + \mu A_1' = \mu X = 1$. Let $\Phi(A_1) = [0, \mu A_1)$, $\Phi(A_1') = [\mu A_1, 1)$, $\Phi(0) = \varnothing$, $\Phi(X) = [0, 1)$. Then Φ preserves unions, intersections, complements and measure. Suppose now that Φ has been defined on $\mathcal{A}_{n-1}$ so that it maps $\mathcal{A}_{n-1}$ onto the algebra generated by half open intervals $[0, x_1)$, $[x_1, x_2) \ldots [x_k, 1)$, and suppose that Φ is measure preserving and preserves unions and complements. We wish to extend the mapping Φ to $\mathcal{A}_n$. Let $B_0, \ldots, B_k$ be the sets in $\mathcal{A}_{n-1}$ which are mapped onto the intervals $[0, x_1), \ldots, [x_k, 1)$. Then $\mathcal{A}_{n-1}$ consists of all finite unions of the sets $B_0, \ldots, B_k$, and $\mathcal{A}_n$ consists of all finite unions of $A_n \wedge B_0, \ldots, A_n \wedge B_k, A'_n \wedge B_0, \ldots, A'_n \wedge B_k$. For those intersections which are 0, set Φ equal to $\varnothing$. For those which are not 0, let $\Phi(A_n \wedge B_j) = [x_j, x_j + \mu(A_n \wedge B_j))$ and $\Phi(A'_n \wedge B_j) = [x_j + \mu(A_n \wedge B_j), x_{j+1})$. Since $\mu(A_n \vee B_j) + \mu(A'_n \vee B_j) = \mu(B_j) = x_{j+1} - x_j$, we see that these are properly defined intervals, Φ is measure preserving, and $\Phi(A_n \wedge B_j) \cup \Phi(A'_n \wedge B_j) = [x_j, x_{j+1}) = \Phi(B_j)$. From this it follows that we can extend Φ to all of $\mathcal{A}_n$ so that it preserves unions, complements and measures.

Thus we have defined by induction the mapping Φ from $\mathcal{A}_\infty$ to $\mathcal{M}/\mathcal{N}$ so that it is measure preserving. Hence it is an isometry. Since $\mathcal{A}_\infty$ is dense in $\mathcal{A}$ and the metric space $\mathcal{M}/\mathcal{N}$ is complete, we can extend Φ to be an isometry from $\mathcal{A}$ into $\mathcal{M}/\mathcal{N}$.

To see that Φ preserves complements, let E be any element in $\mathcal{A}$ and choose $A \in \mathcal{A}_\infty$ so that $\mu(E \triangle A) < \epsilon$. Then $A' \in \mathcal{A}_\infty$, and $\mu(E' \triangle A') = \mu(E \triangle A) < \epsilon$. Since Φ is an isometry and $\Phi(A') = \sim\Phi(A)$, we have $m(\Phi(E') \triangle \widetilde{\Phi(A)}) < \epsilon$ and $m(\widetilde{\Phi(E)} \triangle \widetilde{\Phi(A)}) = m(\Phi(E) \triangle \Phi(A)) < \epsilon$. Hence $m(\Phi(E') \triangle \widetilde{\Phi(E)}) < 2\epsilon$ for all $\epsilon > 0$. Thus $\Phi(E') = \sim\Phi(E)$ in the algebra $\mathcal{M}/\mathcal{N}$. A similar argument shows $\Phi(E \vee F) = \Phi(E) \cup \Phi(F)$.

Since Φ is an isometry, it is one-to-one into. To identify the range of Φ, let E be the set of endpoints of those intervals which were used in defining the mapping Φ on the algebras $\mathcal{A}_n$. Then Φ maps $\mathcal{A}_\infty$ onto the algebra of finite unions of half-open intervals with endpoints in E. Suppose that $\bar{E}$ is not all of $[0, 1]$, and let I be one of the open intervals of which $[0, 1) \sim \bar{E}$ is composed, that is, an interval contained in $\sim\bar{E}$ whose endpoints lie in $\bar{E}$. Since the endpoints of I lie in $\bar{E}$, I is a limit of intervals in $\Phi[\mathcal{A}_\infty]$, and so lies in $\Phi[\mathcal{A}]$. Let $A \in \mathcal{A}$ be such that $\Phi(A) = I$, and let B be an element of $\mathcal{A}$ with $B \leq A$. Then $\Phi(B) \subset I$. Since B can be approximated by elements in $\mathcal{A}_\infty$, $\Phi(B)$ can be approximated by elements in $\Phi[\mathcal{A}_\infty]$. But these latter are sets which either contain I or do not meet I. Hence

$\Phi(B) = I$ or $\Phi(B) = \varnothing$, and we have $B = A$ or $B = \varnothing$, since Φ is one-to-one. Consequently, A is an atom.

We have thus proved that if $\mathcal{A}$ has no atoms, then $\bar{E} = [0, 1]$. But if $\bar{E} = [0, 1]$, then every half-open interval is in $\Phi[\mathcal{A}]$, and hence $\Phi[\mathcal{A}]$ contains every Borel set. Since every measurable subset of $[0, 1]$ is the union of a Borel set and a set of measure zero, we have in this case $\Phi[\mathcal{A}] = \mathcal{M}/\mathcal{N}$. ▮

This theorem states that, if $\langle X, \mathcal{B}, \mu\rangle$ is a separable measure space without atoms for which $\mu(X) = 1$, then the corresponding measure algebra is isomorphic to the measure algebra induced by Lebesgue measure on [0, 1]. It does not assert the existence of a point mapping between [0, 1] and X, or even of a set mapping of $\mathcal{B}$ into the measurable sets of [0, 1], but only of a correspondence of sets of $\mathcal{B}$ modulo null sets with measurable sets modulo sets of measure zero. Thus if we have a set $B \in \mathcal{B}$, we do not assign to it a particular measurable set, but only an equivalence class of measurable sets in [0, 1]. In the next sections we shall develop criteria for asserting the existence of point mappings which induce given mappings of measure algebras.

Problems

7. Prove that in a Boolean σ-algebra we have $B \wedge \left(\bigvee_{n=1}^{\infty} A_n\right) = \bigvee_{n=1}^{\infty} (B \wedge A_n)$.

8. Let $\mathcal{A}$ be a Boolean σ-algebra and $\mathcal{N}$ a Boolean σ-ideal. Show that if $A \triangle B \in \mathcal{N}$, then $A' \triangle B' \in \mathcal{N}$, and that if $(A_n \triangle B_n) \in \mathcal{N}$ then $(\bigvee A_n) \triangle (\bigvee B_n) \in \mathcal{N}$. (Here $A \triangle B$ is the symmetric difference $(A \wedge B') \vee (A' \wedge B)$.)

9. a. Let $\langle \mathcal{A}, \mu\rangle$ be a measure algebra and $\langle A_n\rangle$ a sequence of elements such that $A_n \wedge A_m = 0$ for $n \neq m$. Then $\bigvee_{n=1}^{\infty} A_n = \lim_{k\to\infty} \bigvee_{n=1}^{k} A_n$. [Here lim means limit in the metric space defined by μ].

b. Let $\langle \mathcal{A}, \mu\rangle$ be a measure algebra and $\langle A_n\rangle$ any sequence of elements in $\mathcal{A}$. Then $\bigvee_{n=1}^{\infty} A_n = \lim_{k\to\infty} \bigvee_{n=1}^{k} A_n$.

c. Show that if Φ is an isomorphism of a measure algebra $\langle \mathcal{A}, \mu\rangle$ into a measure algebra $\langle \mathcal{B}, \nu\rangle$, then $\Phi\left(\bigvee_{n=1}^{\infty} A_n\right) = \bigvee_{n=1}^{\infty} \Phi(A_n)$.

10. Prove that a measure algebra is complete as a metric space. (If

$\langle A_n \rangle$ is a Cauchy sequence we may assume that $\mu(A_n \vartriangle A_m) < 2^{-N}$ for $n, m \geq N$. Then if $B_n = \bigvee_{\nu=n}^{\infty} A_\nu$, we have $\mu(A_n \vartriangle B_n) < 2^{-n+1}$. Now $\bigwedge_{n=1}^{\infty} B_n = \lim B_n = \lim A_n$.)

11. Show that in a measure algebra the operations $'$, $\wedge$, and $\vee$ are continuous.

12. Show that a measure algebra (as we have defined it with $\mu(X) < \infty$) can have only a countable number of atoms. Hence any complete separable measure algebra is isomorphic either to an interval (with Lebesgue measure), to a measure space consisting of a countable number of atoms (discrete measure space) or to a measure space which is the union of the preceding two.

13. Discuss measure algebras in which we allow μ to be an extended real-valued function.

3 BOREL EQUIVALENCES

If $\langle X, \mathcal{A} \rangle$ and $\langle Y, \mathcal{B} \rangle$ are measurable spaces, we may ask for conditions under which they are equivalent in the sense that there is a one-to-one mapping φ of X onto Y such that φ and φ^{-1} are measurable, that is, such that $\varphi[A] \in \mathcal{B}$ for each $A \in \mathcal{A}$ and $\varphi^{-1}[B] \in \mathcal{A}$ for each $B \in \mathcal{B}$. In the present section we shall always assume that X and Y are metric spaces and that $\mathcal{A}$ and $\mathcal{B}$ are the algebras of Borel sets. A one-to-one mapping of X onto Y which takes Borel sets into Borel sets and whose inverse takes Borel sets into Borel sets will be called a **Borel equivalence**. Thus any homeomorphism is a Borel equivalence, but we may have Borel equivalences which are not homeomorphisms. If X is Borel equivalent to Y and Y Borel equivalent to Z, then X is Borel equivalent to Z. We begin by establishing some lemmas:

3. Lemma: *Let X be a metric space and E a Borel subset of X. Then the Borel subsets of E are those Borel subsets of X which are contained in E.*

Proof: Since E is a Borel subset of X, $O \cap E$ is a Borel subset of X for each open subset O of X. Hence the Borel subsets of X which are contained in E form a σ-algebra which contain the (relatively) open subsets of E and so must contain every Borel subset of E. On the other hand the collection of those subsets of X each of which is the union of a Borel subset of E and a Borel subset of $X \sim E$ is a

σ-algebra which contains the open subsets of X. Hence it must contain all Borel subsets of X, and we see that a Borel subset of X which is contained in E must be a Borel subset of E. ∎

4. Lemma: *Let X and Y be metric spaces, and let X_0 and Y_0 be countably infinite subsets of X and Y. Then each Borel equivalence between $X \sim X_0$ and $Y \sim Y_0$ can be extended to a Borel equivalence between X and Y.*

Proof: Since X_0 and Y_0 are countably infinite, we can extend the Borel equivalence between $X \sim X_0$ and $Y \sim Y_0$ to be a one-to-one correspondence between X and Y. Since any countable subset of a metric space is an F_σ, the union and difference of a Borel set and a countable set are again Borel sets. Thus a subset of X [or Y] is a Borel set if and only if its intersection with $X \sim X_0$ [or $Y \sim Y_0$] is a Borel set. Hence the extended correspondence between X and Y is a Borel equivalence. ∎

If X is a topological space and A any set, we use X^A to denote the product space $\bigtimes_{\alpha \varepsilon A} X_\alpha$ where each $X_\alpha = X$. The set X^A is the set of all mappings of A into X. If X is metric and A is countable, then X^A is metrizable (cf. Problem 8.15). We shall use ω to denote the set of integers. The following lemma is an immediate consequence of the fact that $\omega \times \omega$ is countable.

5. Lemma: *If X is a topological space, X^ω and $(X^\omega)^\omega$ are homeomorphic.*

One of the simplest topological spaces is the space whose elements are 0 and 1 and whose topology is discrete. We often denote this space by **2**. The product space $\mathbf{2}^\omega$ is a compact metric space.

6. Proposition: *The unit interval* [0, 1] *is Borel equivalent to* $\mathbf{2}^\omega$.

Proof: Let X_0 be that subset of $\mathbf{2}^\omega$ consisting of those elements which have only a finite number of coordinates equal to 0 and of those which have only a finite number of coordinates equal to 1. Then X_0 is countably infinite. On $\mathbf{2}^\omega \sim X_0$ define φ as that mapping which sends x into $\sum_{i=1}^{\infty} \xi_i 2^{-i}$, where ξ_i is the ith coordinate of x. Then φ maps $\mathbf{2}^\omega \sim X_0$ in a one-to-one manner onto those elements of [0, 1] which are not of the form $p \cdot 2^{-n}$ with p and n integral, and

φ is readily seen to be a homeomorphism between $\mathbf{2}^\omega \sim X_0$ and these elements of [0, 1]. Since the set of elements of [0, 1] of the form $p \cdot 2^{-n}$ is countably infinite, the proposition follows from Lemma 4. ▎

7. Proposition: *Let I be the interval* [0, 1]. *Then* I^ω *and I are Borel equivalent.*

Proof: By Lemma 5 the spaces $\mathbf{2}^\omega$ and $(\mathbf{2}^\omega)^\omega$ are homeomorphic. Thus by Proposition 6 we have I Borel equivalent to 2^ω which is Borel equivalent to $(\mathbf{2}^\omega)^\omega$ which in turn is Borel equivalent to I^ω. ▎

8. Theorem: *Each complete separable metric space is Borel equivalent to a Borel subset of* [0, 1].

Proof: Since $I = [0, 1]$ and I^ω are Borel equivalent, it suffices to show that each complete separable metric space $\langle X, \rho \rangle$ is homeomorphic to a Borel subset of I^ω. We may assume without loss of generality that ρ is bounded by one. Let $\langle r_n \rangle$ be a dense sequence of points, and let f be that mapping of X into I^ω which assigns to x the point whose ith coordinate is $\rho(x, x_i)$. Then f is a one-to-one mapping of X onto a subset E of I^ω, for if $x \neq y$, there is an r_i with $\rho(x, r_i) < \rho(y, r_i)$. Since X and I^ω are metric, the mapping f will be continuous if $x_n \to x$ implies $f(x_n) \to f(x)$. But if $x_n \to x$, then $\rho(x_n, r_i) \to \rho(x, r_i)$ for each i, and so each coordinate of $f(x_n)$ converges to the corresponding coordinate of $f(x)$. Thus $f(x_n) \to f(x)$ (cf. Problem 8.14). The mapping f^{-1} will be a continuous mapping of E onto X if $f(x_n) \to f(x)$ implies $x_n \to x$. But if $f(x_n) \to f(x)$, then $\rho(x_n, r_i) \to \rho(x, r_i)$ for each i. Given $\epsilon > 0$, choose r_i so that $\rho(x, r_i) < \epsilon/3$ and choose N so that $|\rho(x_n, r_i) - \rho(x, r_i)| < \epsilon/3$ for $n \geq N$. Then for $n \geq N$, we have $\rho(x_n, r_i) < 2\epsilon/3$, and so $\rho(x_n, x) < \epsilon$. Consequently, f is a homeomorphism of X onto E.

It remains only to show that E is a Borel set. But E is dense in $F = \bar{E}$. By Problem 17 the completeness of X implies that E is a $\mathcal{G}_\delta$ relative to F and hence a Borel set relative to F. Thus E is a Borel subset of I^ω. ▎

Actually, a somewhat stronger statement is true: Each complete separable metric space is Borel equivalent to [0, 1]. (See Kuratowski [12], p. 227.) We shall only make use of the weaker statement given in Theorem 8.

9. Theorem: *Let X be a complete separable metric space and μ a Borel measure on X such that $\mu X = 1$ and such that $\mu\{x\} = 0$ for each set $\{x\}$ consisting of a single point. Then there is a Borel set $X_0 \subset X$ with $\mu X_0 = 0$, and a subset Y_0 of $[0, 1]$ of Lebesgue measure zero, such that there is a Borel equivalence ψ of $X \sim X_0$ with $[0, 1] \sim Y_0$ having the property that $\mu(\psi^{-1}[A]) = mA$, where m is Lebesgue measure on* $[0, 1]$.

Proof: Let φ be a Borel equivalence of X with a Borel subset E of $[0, 1]$, and define the Borel measure ν on $[0, 1]$ by $\nu A = \mu(\varphi^{-1}[A])$. Let f be the cumulative distribution function of ν, i.e. $f(x) = \nu[0, x]$. Then f is a monotone nondecreasing function on $[0, 1]$ which is continuous on the right. Since $f(x) - \lim_{t \to x^-} f(t) = \nu\{x\} = \mu\{\varphi^{-1}[x]\} = 0$, we see that f is continuous. Since $f(0) = 0$ and $f(1) = \nu[0, 1] = \mu X = 1$, f is a continuous mapping of $[0, 1]$ onto $[0, 1]$. For each $y \in [0, 1]$, the set $f^{-1}[\{y\}]$ is a closed set, and since f is nondecreasing it is either a closed interval or a single point. Let M be the set of y such that $f^{-1}[\{y\}]$ is a nondegenerate interval. Since these intervals are disjoint, M is countable. Now $mE = \nu(f^{-1}[E])$ by Problem 12.11, and so the set $N = f^{-1}[M]$ has ν-measure zero. Now f is a homeomorphism of $[0, 1] \sim N$ onto $[0, 1] \sim M$. Since N is a Borel set, the set $X_0 = \varphi^{-1}[N]$ is a Borel set, and $\mu X_0 = \nu N = 0$. Thus the mapping $\psi = f \circ \varphi$ is a Borel equivalence of $X \sim X_0$ with $\psi[X \sim X_0]$. Since φ is a Borel equivalence of X onto a Borel subset of $[0, 1]$, $\varphi[X \sim X_0]$ is a Borel subset of $[0, 1]$ contained in $[0, 1] \sim N$ and hence a Borel subset of $[0, 1] \sim N$. Thus $\psi[X \sim X_0] = f[\varphi[X \sim X_0]]$ is a Borel subset of $[0, 1] \sim M$ and hence of $[0, 1]$. Thus ψ is a Borel equivalence of $X \sim X_0$ with a Borel subset of $[0, 1]$. Since $mA = \mu(\psi^{-1}[A])$, we have $m(\psi[X \sim X_0]) = \mu(X \sim X_0) = 1$, whence the set $Y_0 = [0, 1] \sim \psi[X \sim X_0]$ is a Borel subset of Lebesgue measure zero. ▌

Problems

14. Show that if X is Borel equivalent to Y then X^A is Borel equivalent to Y^A.

15. Let X be a complete separable metric space, and μ a Borel measure on X. Let E be a Borel subset of X with the property that if A is a Borel subset of E then $\mu A = 0$ or $\mu(E \sim A) = 0$. Then there is a point x contained in E such that $\mu(E \sim \{x\}) = 0$. (Use Theorem 9.)

16. Let μ be a Borel measure on a space X. Then $\mu = \mu_0 + \mu_1$ where $\mu_1\{x\} = 0$ for each $x \in X$ and $\mu_0 E = \sum_{x \in E} \mu\{x\}$.

17. Let E be a dense subset of a Hausdorff space F, and g a homeomorphism of E onto a complete metric space X. Then E is a $\mathcal{G}_\delta$. (For each positive integer n, let O_n be the subset consisting of all $y \in F$ such that some open set containing y has an image under g whose diameter is less than $1/n$. Then O_n is an open set, and the homeomorphism g can be extended to a continuous mapping h of $G = \bigcap_{n=1}^{\infty} O_n$ into X, since X is complete. But $g^{-1} \circ h$ must be the identity, whence $E = G$.)

4 SET MAPPINGS AND POINT MAPPINGS ON THE UNIT INTERVAL

We say that $\langle X, \mathcal{A}, \mathcal{N} \rangle$ is a measurable space with null sets if $\mathcal{A}$ is a σ-algebra of subsets of X and $\mathcal{N}$ is a σ-ideal in $\mathcal{A}$. Each measurable point mapping φ of X into [0, 1] induces a σ-homomorphism Φ of the Borel subsets of [0, 1] into the σ-algebra $\mathcal{A}/\mathcal{N}$ by letting $\Phi(A)$ be the equivalence class containing $\varphi^{-1}[A]$. The following theorem states that, conversely, every σ-homomorphism of the Borel subset of [0, 1] into $\mathcal{A}/\mathcal{N}$ is induced in this way by a point mapping φ of X into [0, 1]. This theorem is due to Sikorski.

10. Theorem: *Let $\langle X, \mathcal{A}, \mathcal{N} \rangle$ be a measurable space with null sets, and let Φ be a σ-homomorphism of the family $\mathcal{B}$ of Borel sets in* [0, 1] *into the σ-algebra $\mathcal{A}/\mathcal{N}$ with $\Phi([0, 1]) = X$. Then there is a measurable mapping φ of X into* [0, 1] *such that for each $B \in \mathcal{B}$ we have $\varphi^{-1}[B]$ in the equivalence class $\Phi(B)$. If ψ is any other point mapping with this property, then $\psi = \varphi$ except on a subset in $\mathcal{N}$.*

Proof: For each rational number α in [0, 1] let A_α be a set in the equivalence class $\Phi([0, \alpha])$. We may take $A_1 = X$. If $\alpha < \beta$, then $\Phi([0, \alpha]) \leq \Phi([0, \beta])$, and so the set $E_{\alpha\beta} = A_\alpha \sim A_\beta$ is in $\mathcal{N}$. Let $E = \bigcup_{\alpha < \beta} E_{\alpha\beta}$, where α and β run through the rationals. Since this is a countable union and $\mathcal{N}$ is a σ-ideal, we have $E \in \mathcal{N}$. Set $B_\alpha = A_\alpha \cup E$. Then B_α is in the equivalence class $\Phi([0, \alpha])$, and $B_\alpha \subset B_\beta$ for $\alpha < \beta$.

For each $x \in X$, let $\varphi(x) = \inf \{\alpha: x \in B_\alpha\}$. Since $B_1 = X$, $\varphi(x)$ is defined for each x, and $0 \leq \varphi(x) \leq 1$. Thus φ is a mapping of X into $[0, 1]$. For each t we have $\{x: \varphi(x) \leq t\} = \bigcup_{\alpha \leq t} B_\alpha$. Hence φ is measurable, and $\varphi^{-1}[[0, \alpha]] = B_\alpha$. Let Ψ be the σ-homomorphism of $\mathcal{B}$ into $\mathcal{A}/\mathcal{N}$ induced by φ. Then Ψ agrees with Φ on the closed intervals with rational endpoints. Since Ψ and Φ are σ-homomorphisms, the family of sets on which they agree is a σ-algebra and so must be the family $\mathcal{B}$ of Borel sets.

If ψ is any other mapping of X into $[0, 1]$ which induces the σ-homomorphism Φ, then for each pair α and β of rational numbers the set $\{x: \varphi(x) \leq \alpha < \beta < \psi(x)\} = \varphi^{-1}[[0, \alpha]] \sim \psi^{-1}[[0, \beta]]$ and so must be in $\mathcal{N}$. Thus we see that the set $\{x: \varphi(x) < \psi(x)] = \bigcup_{\alpha,\beta} \{x: \varphi(x) \leq \alpha < \beta < \psi(x)\}$ is in $\mathcal{N}$. Similarly, $\{x: \varphi(x) > \psi(x)\} \in \mathcal{N}$, and so $\{x: \varphi(x) \neq \psi(x)\} \in \mathcal{N}$. ▌

11. Corollary: *Let $\langle X, \mathcal{A}, \mathcal{N}\rangle$ be a measurable space with null sets, Y a complete separable metric space, and Φ a σ-homomorphism of the Borel sets $\mathcal{B}$ of Y into $\mathcal{A}/\mathcal{N}$ with $\Phi(Y) = X$. Then there is a set $X_0 \in \mathcal{N}$ and a point mapping φ of $X \sim X_0$ into Y such that for each $B \in \mathcal{B}$ we have $\varphi^{-1}[B]$ in the equivalence class $\Phi(B)$.*

Proof: By Theorem 8 there is a Borel equivalence χ of Y with a Borel subset E of $[0, 1]$. For each Borel subset B of $[0, 1]$ let $\Psi(B) = \Phi(\chi^{-1}[B \cap E])$. Then there is a mapping ψ of X into $[0, 1]$ which induces Ψ. Let $X_0 = \psi^{-1}[\tilde{E}]$. Since $\psi^{-1}[\tilde{E}] = \Phi(\varnothing)$, we have $X_0 \in \mathcal{N}$. On $X \sim X_0$, the mapping $\chi^{-1} \circ \psi$ is defined and induces the σ-homomorphism Φ. ▌

A σ-homomorphism Φ from a Boolean σ-algebra $\mathcal{A}$ to a Boolean σ-algebra $\mathcal{B}$ is called a **σ-isomorphism** if there is a σ-homomorphism Ψ from $\mathcal{B}$ to $\mathcal{A}$ such that $\Psi \circ \Phi$ and $\Phi \circ \Psi$ are the identity mappings on $\mathcal{A}$ and $\mathcal{B}$.

12. Corollary: *Let X and Y be complete separable metric spaces, $\mathcal{A}$ and $\mathcal{B}$ their Borel sets, and let $\mathcal{M}$ and $\mathcal{N}$ be σ-ideals in $\mathcal{A}$ and $\mathcal{B}$.*

If Φ is a σ-isomorphism of $\mathcal{A}/\mathcal{M}$ onto $\mathcal{B}/\mathcal{N}$ then there are sets $X_0 \in \mathcal{M}$ and $Y_0 \in \mathcal{N}$ and a one-to-one mapping φ of $Y \sim Y_0$ onto $X \sim X_0$ such that φ and φ^{-1} are measurable and $\Phi(A) = \varphi^{-1}[A]$ modulo $\mathcal{N}$.

Proof: By Corollary 11 there is a set $Y_1 \in \mathcal{N}$ and a mapping φ of $Y - Y_1$ into X such that $\Phi(A) = \varphi^{-1}[A]$ modulo $\mathcal{N}$. Similarly there is a set $X_1 \in \mathcal{M}$ and a mapping ψ of $X \sim X_1$ into Y such that $\Psi(A) = \psi^{-1}[A]$. Since $\Phi \circ \Psi$ is the identity on $\mathcal{B}/\mathcal{N}$, the mapping $\psi \circ \varphi$ can differ from the identity mapping on $Y \sim Y_1$ only on a subset $Y_2 \in \mathcal{N}$. Let $Y_0 = Y_1 \cup Y_2$. Then φ is one-to-one on $Y \sim Y_0$, and $\varphi^{-1}[A] = \Phi(A)$ modulo $\mathcal{N}$, $\varphi[B] = \Psi(B)$ modulo $\mathcal{M}$. Thus $\varphi[Y \sim Y_0]$ differs from X by a set $X_0 \in \mathcal{M}$. ∎

Problems

18. a. Show that the exceptional set X_0 in Corollary 11 may be unavoidable. (Let Y be a countable space with the discrete topology, X the unit interval with $\mathcal{N}$ the family of all sets which contain no rational numbers.)

b. Show that the exceptional sets X_0 and Y_0 in Corollary 12 may be unavoidable.

19. Let X, Y, $\mathcal{A}$, $\mathcal{B}$, $\mathcal{M}$, $\mathcal{N}$ be as in Corollary 12, Φ a σ-homomorphism of $\mathcal{A}/\mathcal{M}$ into $\mathcal{B}/\mathcal{N}$, and let φ be the mapping given by Corollary 11.

a. The mapping φ is one-to-one except on a set $Y_0 \in \mathcal{N}$ if and only if there is a σ-homomorphism Ψ of $\mathcal{B}/\mathcal{N}$ into $\mathcal{A}/\mathcal{M}$ with $\Phi \circ \Psi$ the identity on $\mathcal{B}/\mathcal{N}$.

b. The mapping φ is onto all of X except for a set in $\mathcal{M}$ if and only if $\Phi(A) = 0$ implies $A = 0$.

5 THE ISOMETRIES OF L^p

We illustrate the use of the theorems in the preceding sections to derive a characterization of the isometries of $L^p[0, 1]$ into itself, that is of those linear mappings U of $L^p[0, 1]$ into itself such that $\|Uf\| = \|f\|$. We begin by establishing two inequalities, the first concerning real (or complex) numbers and the second elements in L^p.

13. Lemma: *Let ξ and η be real numbers. Then if $2 \le p < \infty$,*

$$|\xi + \eta|^p + |\xi - \eta|^p \ge 2(|\xi|^p + |\eta|^p),$$

while if $0 < p \le 2$,

$$|\xi + \eta|^p + |\xi - \eta|^p \le 2(|\xi|^p + |\eta|^p).$$

If $p \ne 2$, *equality can only hold if* ξ *or* η *is zero.*

Proof: If $p = 2$, we have equality for all ξ and η. If $2 < p < \infty$, then $1 \le p/2$, and applying the Hölder inequality with exponents $p/2$ and $p/(p-2)$ to $\alpha^2 + \beta^2$ we obtain

$$\alpha^2 + \beta^2 \le (\alpha^p + \beta^p)^{2/p}(1 + 1)^{(p-2)/p}$$

or

$$\alpha^p + \beta^p \ge 2^{(2-p)/2}(\alpha^2 + \beta^2)^{p/2}. \tag{1}$$

If $0 < p < 2$, replace p by $4/p$. Then (1) becomes

$$\alpha^{4/p} + \beta^{4/p} \ge 2^{(p-2)/p}(\alpha^2 + \beta^2)^{2/p}.$$

If we replace α by $\alpha^{p/2}$ and β by $\beta^{p/2}$, this becomes

$$\alpha^2 + \beta^2 \ge 2^{(p-2)/p}(\alpha^p + \beta^p)^{2/p},$$

or

$$\alpha^p + \beta^p \le 2^{(2-p)/2}(\alpha^2 + \beta^2)^{p/2}. \tag{2}$$

Since

$$0 \le \frac{\xi^2}{\xi^2 + \eta^2} \le 1,$$

we have

$$\frac{|\xi|^p}{(\xi^2 + \eta^2)^{p/2}} \le \frac{\xi^2}{\xi^2 + \eta^2} \qquad 2 < p \tag{3}$$

and

$$\frac{|\xi|^p}{(\xi^2 + \eta^2)^{p/2}} \ge \frac{\xi^2}{\xi^2 + \eta^2} \qquad p < 2. \tag{4}$$

Forming similar inequalities for η and adding, we get

$$|\xi|^p + |\eta|^p \le (\xi^2 + \eta^2)^{p/2} \qquad 2 < p \tag{5}$$

and

$$|\xi|^p + |\eta|^p \ge (\xi^2 + \eta^2)^{p/2} \qquad p < 2. \tag{6}$$

We verify that equality can hold in (3) or (4) and hence in (5) or (6) only if $\xi = 0$ or $\eta = 0$.

Assume $p > 2$, and replace α and β in (1) by $|\xi + \eta|$ and $|\xi - \eta|$, we get

$$\begin{aligned}|\xi + \eta|^p + |\xi - \eta|^p &\ge 2^{(2-p)/2}(|\xi + \eta|^2 + |\xi - \eta|^2)^{p/2}\\ &= 2(\xi^2 + \eta^2)^{p/2}\\ &\ge 2(|\xi|^p + |\eta|^p)\end{aligned}$$

by (5). This establishes the first inequality in the lemma, and the second follows similarly using (2) and (6). We see that in either case for $p \neq 2$ equality can occur in (3) and (4) only if $\xi = 0$ or $\eta = 0$. ∎

By integration we have the following lemma as a consequence of Lemma 13.

14. Lemma: *Let $1 \leq p < \infty$, $p \neq 2$, and suppose that f and g are in L^p. Then*

$$\|f + g\|^p + \|f - g\|^p = 2(\|f\|^p + \|g\|^p)$$

if and only if $f \cdot g = 0$ almost everywhere.

15. Theorem (Lamperti): *Let $1 \leq p < \infty$, $p \neq 2$, and let U be a linear transformation of $L^p[0, 1]$ into itself such that $\|Uf\|_p = \|f\|_p$. Then there is a Borel measurable mapping φ of $[0, 1]$ onto (almost all of) $[0, 1]$ and an $h \in L^p$ such that*

$$Uf = h \cdot (f \circ \varphi).$$

The function h is uniquely determined (to within a.e. *equivalence) and φ is uniquely determined (to within* a.e. *equivalence) on the set where $h \neq 0$. For any Borel set E we have*

$$\int_{\varphi^{-1}[E]} |h|^p \, dt = \int_E dt.$$

Proof: We define the support of a function f to be the set $\{t : f(t) \neq 0\}$. If $f \in L^p$, then the support of f is only defined modulo null sets. Thus for $f \in L^p$ the support of f is an element in the σ-algebra $\mathcal{B}/\mathcal{N}$ of Borel sets modulo sets of measure zero. We define a mapping Φ of the Borel sets of $[0, 1]$ into Borel sets modulo null sets by setting $\Phi(A)$ cqual to the support of $U\chi_A$. If A and B are disjoint, we have by Lemma 14 that

$$\|\chi_A + \chi_B\|^p + \|\chi_A - \chi_B\|^p = 2(\|\chi_A\|^p + \|\chi_B\|^p).$$

Since U is linear and preserves norms, we have, again using Lemma 14,

$$(U\chi_A) \cdot (U\chi_B) = 0 \qquad \text{a.e.}$$

Thus Φ takes disjoint sets into disjoint sets. If A and B are disjoint, $\chi_{A \cup B} = \chi_A + \chi_B$, and so $U\chi_{A \cup B} = U\chi_A + U\chi_B$. Since the two functions on the right have disjoint support, we see that $\Phi(A \cup B) = \Phi(A) \cup \Phi(B)$ for disjoint sets and hence for any pair for Borel sets.

If $\Phi[[0, 1]] = E$, we have $\Phi(\tilde{A}) = E \sim \Phi(A)$. Thus Φ is a homomorphism of $\mathcal{B}$ into the algebra of Borel subsets of E. If $A = \bigcup_{i=1}^{\infty} A_i$ with the A_i disjoint, we have

$$\chi_A = \lim \sum_{i=1}^{n} \chi_{A_i}$$

in L_p, and so by the continuity of U

$$U\chi_A = \lim \sum_{i=1}^{n} U\chi_{A_i}.$$

Hence $\Phi(A) = \bigcup \Phi(A_i)$, and Φ is a σ-homomorphism.

By Theorem 10 there is a Borel measurable mapping φ of E into $[0, 1]$ such that $\Phi(A) = \varphi^{-1}[A]$. Since Φ can only take sets of measure zero into sets of measure zero, the mapping φ must be onto all of $[0, 1]$ expect possibly for a set of measure zero. Extend φ to be defined on all of $[0, 1]$ by setting $\varphi(t) = 0$ for $t \notin E$.

The function $1 = \chi_{[0,1]}$ is in L^p. Let $h = U(1)$. The $h \in L^p$ and the support of h is E. If A is any Borel set in $[0, 1]$, we have $1 = \chi_A + \chi_{\tilde{A}}$. Hence $h = U\chi_A + U\chi_{\tilde{A}}$. But the functions on the right have disjoint support, and so $U\chi_A$ must equal h on the support of $U\chi_A$. Thus $U\chi_A = h \cdot \chi_{\Phi(A)} = h \cdot (\chi_A \circ \varphi)$. Hence, if ψ is any simple function, we must have $U\psi = h \cdot [\psi \circ \varphi]$. Since every function in L^p can be approximated in norm by a simple function and U is norm preserving, we have $Uf = h \cdot (f \circ \varphi)$ for all $f \in L^p$.

The remaining statements in the theorem now follow easily. ∎

Problems

20. **a.** Show that if the linear transformation U is onto $L^p[0, 1]$, then $X \sim E$ has measure zero.

b. Show in this case that φ is essentially one-to-one (that is, one-to-one except on a set of measure zero), that φ^{-1} is measurable, and that φ and φ^{-1} take sets of measure zero into sets of measure zero. (Hint: Apply Theorem 15 also to the transformation U^{-1}, and the uniqueness part of the theorem to $I = UU^{-1}$ and $I = U^{-1}U$.)

c. Show in this case that if we define a measure μ by $\mu A = m[\varphi(A)]$, then $|h|^p = \dfrac{d\mu}{dm}$.

21. What can you say about the isometries of $L^p(X, \mu)$ for general finite measure spaces? (Here you can not get a point mapping, but must be content with the set mapping Φ.)

22. Show that the characterization given in Theorem 15 is false for $L^2[0, 1]$.

Epilogue to Part III

In this part we have given a reasonably comprehensive discussion of abstract measure and integration. The central theorems are: the convergence theorems, the Radon-Nikodym theorem, the extension theorem for measures on an algebra, product measures and the Fubini-Tonelli theorems, the equivalence of abstract integration with that based on a measure, and the representation of bounded linear functionals on $C(X)$.

Several generalizations and refinements are possible: One is to consider rings and σ-rings of sets rather than algebras, that is, to assume the collection of sets on which a measure is defined is closed under union and relative complements, rather than union and complements. Little change occurs in the results obtained, but the proofs become somewhat more cumbersome. Another generalization is to consider infinite products of measure spaces rather than finite products. Our treatment of measures in topological spaces has been limited to Baire measures in locally compact spaces except for Proposition 12.24 which deals with metric spaces, but it is possible to consider also Borel measures in locally compact spaces. For a discussion of these three topics the reader should consult Halmos [4], which gives a very readable and thorough treatment of measure theory. For systematic treatment of the Daniell theory of integration in locally compact spaces the book by Loomis [13] is a good reference.

An important branch of measure theory which we have not touched upon is the theory of Haar measure, which is the theory of measure invariant under a group of transformations on the measure space. A nice introduction is given in Banach's appendix to Saks [15]. A full treatment is given in Halmos [4], and a treatment in terms of the Daniell integral in Loomis [13].

Another important aspect of measure theory is ergodic theory, which is the study of the properties of a measure preserving transformation and its iterates. The reader will find readable treatments in Hopf [10] and Halmos [6].

Bibliography

[*1*] G. Birkhoff and S. Mac Lane, *A Survey of Modern Algebra* (rev. ed.), New York, Macmillan, 1953.

[*2*] M. M. Day, "Normed Linear Space," *Ergebnisse der Mathematik und ihrer Grenzgebiete,* No. 21, Berlin, Julius Springer, 1958.

[*3*] N. Dunford and J. Schwartz, *Linear Operators,* New York, Interscience, 1958.

[*4*] P. R. Halmos, *Measure Theory,* New York, Van Nostrand, 1950.

[*5*] P. R. Halmos, *Naïve Set Theory,* Princeton, Van Nostrand, 1960.

[*6*] P. R. Halmos, *Entropy in Ergodic Theory,* Chicago, Univ. of Chicago Press, 1959.

[*7*] E. Hille and R. Phillips, *Functional Analysis and Semi-Groups,* "American Mathematical Society Colloquium Publications," Vol. 31, Providence, 1957.

[*8*] E. W. Hobson, *The Theory of Functions of a Real Variable and the Theory of Fourier's Series* (3rd ed.) Vol. 1, Cambridge, 1927.

[*9*] J. G. Hocking and G. S. Young, *Topology,* Reading, Mass., Addison-Wesley, 1961.

[*10*] E. Hopf, "Ergodentheorie," *Ergebnisse der Mathematik und ihrer Geheite,* Vol. 5, Berlin, Julius Springer, 1937.

[*11*] J. L. Kelley, *General Topology,* New York, Van Nostrand, 1955.

[*12*] C. Kuratowski, *Topologie I* (Monografje Matematyczne, Vol. 3), Warsaw, 1933.

[*13*] L. H. Loomis, *An Introduction to Abstract Harmonic Analysis,* New York, Van Nostrand, 1953.

[*14*] F. Riesz and B. Nagy, *Functional Analysis* (English ed.), New York, Ungar, 1956.

[*15*] S. Saks, *Theory of the Integral* (Monografie Matematyczne, Vol. 7), Warsaw, 1937.

[*16*] P. C. Suppes, *Introduction to Logic,* Princeton, Van Nostrand, 1957.

[*17*] P. C. Suppes, *Axiomatic Set Theory,* Princeton, Van Nostrand, 1960.

[*18*] A. E. Taylor, *Introduction to Functional Analysis,* New York, Wiley, 1958.

Index of Symbols

Subject Index